CAT
FIVE

CAT FIVE

by **ROBERT P. DAVIS**

*William Morrow
and Company,
Inc.*
New York
1977

MRS. LEE OLSEN is a contemporary
Palm Beach resident and she appears
in this book by special permission.
All the other characters are fictitious.

Printed in the United States of America.

1 2 3 4 5 6 7 8 9 10

Library of Congress Cataloging in Publication Data

Davis, Robert P
    Cat five.

    I. Title.
PZ4.D26433Cat [PS3554.A9377] 813'.5'4   77-9446
ISBN 0-688-03223-0

BOOK DESIGN   CARL WEISS

FOR

ELOISE,

WITHOUT WHOSE UNSELFISH

AND UNTIRING ASSISTANCE

THIS BOOK MIGHT NEVER

HAVE BEEN WRITTEN

CONTENTS

((7))

A NOTE FROM THE AUTHOR

CAT FIVE IS ABOUT A VICIOUS HURRICANE THAT TOTALLY DESTROYS THE glamorous old resort of Palm Beach, Florida, my hometown. There is always a danger in writing about the place where one lives; and, too, novelists have never fared very well in small towns, for some people feel they are eristic types who might whip out their pens for some caustic hometown reporting. This was the case of Thomas Wolfe. After he wrote about his fellow Ashevillians, he claimed he couldn't go home again.

In *Cat Five* I have tried to obviate the old mistake of placing people I know in the novel. To me that's the easy way out. Instead, I talked to quite a few Palm Beachers who have known the town for generations, and my characters, and some of their social war dances and bursts of humor, are based, to a degree, on persons no longer living. A few observations about the old resort are inevitably my own and they are subjective by definition. For an outside viewpoint I have used by permission a few impressions of a prominent sociologist who is preparing his own work on the textures of Palm Beach social life.

Some Palm Beachers, of course, will take exception to incidents in this novel; one already has, and after she read the manuscript she said, "How dare you destroy Palm Beach!" as if the whole place had been pulverized and dropped from the map. This is only a novel and I am happy to say that Palm Beach still stands, just as beautiful and manicured as ever, just as interesting, just as generous, just as dichotomous, just as delightfully whacky as it has been since the late nineteenth century when that magical sodbuster, Henry Flagler, looped over the first shovel of sandy earth to create his very special place, or dream, as the case may be.

I wish to thank those at the National Hurricane Center, especially Paul Hebert, for their assistance in preparing *Cat Five*. The hurricane forecasters in this novel are *not* based upon actual people, and the workings of the "center," while hinged to a few facts, are generally fictitious. Certain non-meteorological facts concerning hurricane Camille are also fictionalized.

People who read the book might ask if a storm of this intensity could hit Palm Beach and, if so, would there be such overall destruction with an appalling loss of life. The answers to these questions are, quite tragically, "Yes." Claudine has *already* happened. My fictional storm was based upon the parameters of the 1935 Key West hurricane, and as Florida hurricane experts are saying, she might come again, smashing a coastline which, because of overpopulation and lassitude, is totally unprepared. This, combined with flood-control inadequacies and various topographical deficiencies, could create the greatest natural disaster in the history of the United States. The experts claim that while Claudine is unlikely, it *could* happen just as I have described in *Cat Five*. I have written, then, about the improbable in hopes that people will always consider and prepare for the possible.

Palm Beach, Florida
March 1977

"CAT FIVE" IS HURRICANE SLANG.

The National Hurricane Center, Coral Gables, Florida, has devised a tropical storm intensity scale from one to five. A category five hurricane, the worst storm, is defined as having wind speeds in excess of 155 miles per hour, among other criteria. Some meteorologists refer to this extreme hurricane as a "Cat Five." There have been only two such storms of this intensity to hit the U.S. mainland in the twentieth century: the Labor Day hurricane that landfalled in the Florida Keys in 1935, and Camille, which struck the Gulf Coast on August 17, 1969.

PART ONE

IGNORANCE

Better to be unborn than untaught,
for ignorance is the root of
misfortune.

PLATO

CHAPTER

1

STEVE MITCHELL NOT ONLY SURVIVED THE DERANGED WAR IN SOUTH-east Asia but also prevailed for a time. Since Annapolis he had been embalmed in military ideals, but by the middle of 1969, as he flew his Phantom missions over Hanoi, Steve's spirit had become un-moored. He was a man of deep feelings, some complex, and what he did was a faultless assertion of his intelligence and moral char-acter, for one day he walked into the office of the squadron com-mander, more of a bard than a leader, and said, "Gipper, draw up the papers. I'm splitting."

They called the old man the "Gipper" because he had gone to Notre Dame and being mad, he used to teach baffled Asian kids two-hand touch, and when he wasn't doing that, he would crawl in and out of parked jets on Saturday and Sunday afternoons just for relaxation.

That June Steve was celebrating his twentieth anniversary since "plebe summer": full pension benefits, and he was only thirty-eight, young enough, he figured, to find a corporate connection; it came without too much difficulty. He learned that American Aircraft was developing the ultimate carrier-based fighter, the F-6 Bobcat, a sophisticated piece of flying weaponry that was designed to take on all comers until the year 2000. He sent in a truthful application, and one day an A.A. rep showed up at the Thailand base asking for a Commander Mitchell.

"So you see yourself as an American Aircraft man?" the executive started.

"I think I could help on the F-6 program, yes," Steve said with slight diffidence, revealing his ingrained modesty.

"How?"

"Well," Steve began slowly, "I have the experience . . . graduated from Annapolis in the top tenth . . . took an M.A. at Stanford . . . aeronautical engineering."

"Airframe or power plant?"

"Both, but I majored in systems."

"Good . . . good. We like systems people. Planes are systems today, not flying machines."

"Then I worked as a coordinator on the C-11 project . . . put in some time with manufacturers on armament refits. I saw active service while carrier based."

"How many missions?"

". . . Forty-one."

"How's your folio? Any ghosts in the drawer?"

"None."

There was more talk about the F-6 program, compensation, responsibility, benefits, and other corporate goulash, and then the executive said, "You might be hearing from us."

In the language of the airframe manufacturers with government contracts tucked away, Mitchell was an "inside straight," meaning that he knew carrier-based equipment, systems engineering, and having acted as a Navy advocate, he could easily become a corporate adversary, a government handle, a valuable patsy.

The telegram arrived within a week:

WE ARE HAPPY TO INFORM YOU THAT YOUR APPLICATION AT AMERICAN HAS BEEN FAVORABLY APPROVED. YOU WILL BE SERVING AS

ASSISTANT PROJECT MANAGER, SYSTEMS, F-6 PROGRAM, AT A START-
ING SALARY OF $38,000 PLUS BENEFITS TO BE DISCUSSED. YOU SHALL
REPORT, IF POSSIBLE, TO BETHPAGE, LONG ISLAND, AFTER HONOR-
ABLE SEPARATION SOMETIME BETWEEN JUNE AND AUGUST THIS YEAR.
CONGRATULATIONS.

> BRYAN MAC MASTERS
> VICE-PRESIDENT
> PROJECT MANAGER

The "Gipper" sputtered when Steve showed him the telegram,
but there was still dirty work to be done over Hanoi, and one night
when the ground-to-air missiles were crackling hotter than usual,
Steve's squadron buddy, Kit Henry, who wasn't too good in the air,
caught a dose of flak in the belly of his Phantom.

When they scrambled for home, Steve knew he couldn't leave
Kit. The ground-to-air gooks would surely pop him out of the sky
without an escort. Steve flew side by side with Kit, talking to him,
joking with him, encouraging him, and threading the kerosene-
leaking attack fighter in and out of darkened hills, until finally the
high intensities of the Thailand field emerged out of the morning
vapor like a vibrating golden thread. Kit laid his jet on the hard
surface with Steve following. Then, the rescue soufflé collapsed: Kit
lost the machine just as it kissed the concrete, causing an aggravated
ground loop, shattering the plane into a spray of flying pieces, which
suddenly glowed with the rich orange of a JP-4 kerosene blaze. Committed for the landing, Steve's jet crashed into the hot litter of the
other Phantom. There was a ball of fire and a grinding of crushed
metal and wires and tubes and spars and turbine parts sailing
through the air as eighteen million dollars' worth of sophisticated
hardware broke apart.

It was probably the most insidious crash of the Vietnam War.

Steve received a serious concussion, but the rescue crews had the
flames foamed in a matter of seconds, and both men were dragged
out with only minor burns and bumps. When Steve woke up in the
base hospital, he was looking into the green eyes of the most beautiful girl he had ever seen; she was not the *Cosmopolitan* type, but
rather the kind of exquisite all-American bronzed female one used
to see on the cover of *Calling All Girls*.

"Do you know where you are?" the nurse said in a deep mellow voice like Lauren Bacall's. She had a slight smile spread across her perfect face.

"In heaven?"

Her smile widened. "You're in a lousy part, but it's still earth."

"Are you married?" he asked her quickly.

"No, are you?"

He didn't remember answering the apparition, for he slipped away again and when his eyes opened the beautiful texture of his dream had been totally abraded; gazing down at him now was another nurse who looked like Fanny Farmer. "How do you feel, Commander Mitchell?"

"I don't know. Was there another girl here or did I imagine it?"

"There have been quite a few looking in on you. You were injured, Commander, but you're going to be fine."

"She had green eyes . . . a beautiful, unmarried girl. What's her name?"

"That was First Lieutenant Alice Hendricks."

"Tell her I need her."

"Please rest, Commander. You're still not well . . . it would be very dangerous for you to become excited."

"Who cares, dear . . . I want to go to Him with her."

The old nurse snapped straight. "I suppose you think that's funny."

"Hilarious."

The untoward event of crashing into a plane of one's own air force provided the climactic irony of Steve Mitchell's military career; they awarded him the Navy Cross for conspicuous gallantry, and he had to bite his tongue to halt the burps of laughter. During his weeks of recovery he swam and sailed with Alice Hendricks, and they loved each other more than heaven and earth. The "Gipper" cried at their wedding in the base chapel.

They left the Navy, flew home and at North Island, San Diego, they were separated from the military, taking with them wads of combat pay. On August 10 they departed from San Diego in a slightly used Chevrolet bound for Brunswick, Georgia, to meet Alice's parents. It was their honeymoon and they gaily tore through national parks and stayed at three- and four-star places. In New Orleans Steve and Alice made love almost continuously for three days; in between they ate and drank and listened to the hot jazz and the blaring trumpets of Bourbon Street. One hangover fused with the next, until finally they asked the manager of the Royal Orleans where they could go for sun and quiet.

"There's a nice beach place east of here 'bout forty miles . . . Pass Christian. I can book y'all into a motel if yuh want."

They left the next morning, turning east out of New Orleans on route 90 toward the island resort.

2

THE CRUEL SUN WAS RINGED WITH A HALO. THE FIRE WAS SO BLISTER-
ing that it turned the top of their car into a griddle, and the heat
burned through the roof making the air-conditioner useless; it
sucked in one gulp of candent air and expelled it almost as hot and
steamy.

"Damn this heat!" Steve blasted.

"We're almost there, darling," Alice said, as she slipped a quick
kiss on his handsome, bony face.

"I've just figured out who you look like," she said.

"Who?"

"A Marlboro man who always seems to lose the chuck wagon.
You ought to eat more."

As the car approached the drawbridge separating the long, thin
beach community of Pass Christian from mainland Mississippi, a
shot of raw, blinding light struck Steve's eyes and he slammed his

lids shut in defense. When he opened them as thin slits, the car was on the brow of the two-lane bridge; Steve could see the slick, motionless Gulf of Mexico before him, looking as if it had been baked into a shiny piece of polished chrome. The water was so white and piercing that Steve felt he had suddenly been dumped inside a steelmaker's furnace.

Strange, he thought.

Nothing moved. Bleached flags hung limply; the glazed Gulf was void of shrimpers, boaters, birds, swimmers, and there didn't seem to be any life behind the clapboard facades of the jerry-built beach houses perched on tarred stilts.

Like all pilots, Steve had a feel, a sense of atmosphere, the air in which he worked, and he wondered if the weather machine had suddenly gone crazy or broken down as things were missing: the usual slant of a gentle breeze darkening the water, a wave from some far-off place, summer cumulus sailing by, anything that suggested that weather was motion, energy.

Steve turned down the beach road and finally they came to the place where the private houses ended and the motels started. On the right side of Dune Road were squads of one-story models that looked like flattened-out cinderblocks—about all they were—and on the opposite side, or across the street, the motels came in higher varieties: two and three stories girded by balconies, designed so most of the guests had a view of the Gulf. The lower motels that fronted the beach were wedged together so tightly that it would have been difficult to slide a playing card between their drooping, leaking window air-conditioners.

The couple arrived at the Surf and Sand, which was the same as the other one-story pillboxes except that it was painted a hideous pink and before each front window were old, cracked tubs holding clusters of unwatered geraniums. The sun was so fierce that it made door handles bristle with heat. But the honeymooners didn't mind; all they wanted to do was flop on the sand and recover from the French Quarter.

Inside it was cool and the air was choked with the usual mélange of beach fumes: lingering traces of spilled beer, baby diapers, ancient cigar smoke, slightly decayed food, and the foul currents of one motel were sucked into the next by the back-to-back air-conditioners in an exchange of rank odors. Mr. Chasen, the proprietor, was fat, sweaty, and very old, and he waggled his thick finger at them.

"Howdy, folks. You must be the Mitchells," the old man said in his thick Mississippi twang. "I know y'all are tired. Can I offer yuh somethin' . . . a diet Dr. Pepper and a Moon Pie, mebbe?"

Without waiting for an answer, he waddled back of the counter and returned with two cans, which he popped open. Alice shook her head.

"Wish they wuz colder, but the old box is gettin' cranky."

Steve took one gulp of the warm, sweet drink as he signed the register; he crunched the stale chocolate cake and quickly asked for a bucket of ice and the room. Their bags were unloaded and they walked through the motel.

"How do y'all like that view?" Mr. Chasen said, partly covering his eyes from the glare, as he swung open the door to their room. "Can see the Gulf right out yuh windows."

"Is it always this hot?" Alice asked.

"No, ma'am . . . just the last couple of days. Things will cool off."

"Is that the forecast?" Steve asked.

"Sort of." Chasen hesitated. "There's a hurricane down by Cuba . . . calling this one Camille. . . . That ought to get some wind in here. We need it bad."

"What's the forecast for tomorrow?" Steve asked.

"Same's today."

"Will the hurricane hit here?" Alice asked mechanically.

"We're on a watch now. But look at the weather . . . calm as a sleepin' catfish, even the horseflies ain't flyin' . . . and they take a napper when the wind stops. We git hurricane watches all summer long. Nobody takes 'em seriously. That's life here . . . just part of bein' a Gulfer."

The yawning man wallowed in lassitude; his face was crinkled and it said he had lived a long time around these parts. Steve and Alice didn't worry about the storm far to the south of them. After the fat man had shuffled down the hall, the couple filled their plastic bathroom cups with the ice and poured in some vodka. They drank quickly, watching the lifeless Gulf, glad to be someplace cool. Steve came up behind Alice as she stood at the mirror and put his arms around her, his hands clasping her breasts, and soon she turned so that he could unbutton her blouse, and they climbed into the damp, coarse sheets. He slid inside her and their love was so complete that it washed away such brazen realities as a squalid beach motel, the heat, the time, the day, the hour, and who they were.

They did not leave the room until the whiteness was out of the Gulf and then everything turned coppery and cool as the sun lost its potency. The owner told them where to find the best shrimp and Creole stew, and by ten that night Steve and Alice were back at the Surf and Sand, pleased with the local food and the new noises. Katydids were singing and somewhere Steve heard a yapping gull. There were soft giggles and wisps of voices in other places, little filaments of sound that reassured them of life at Pass Christian. They walked to the beach, arm in arm, and dipped their toes in the warm water, and kissed each other passionately.

At the rear entrance of the cinderblock motel, Steve happened to glance upward: Where the sun had been, there was a filmy moon and around it the same halo with its big, blurry edges. Steve thought it was odd. Just then Alice took Steve's hand and guided him inside. It had been a long day.

The following dawn glowed amber, not the usual gray. Steve and Alice were up early, figuring that this was the best time of day to enjoy the beach. At seven in the morning there were a few others out swimming. Far off a shrimper was cutting a clean furrow through the sea, and gulls were crusing in and out of the cumulus clouds. As the sun lifted, the attack became brutal and by eight o'clock the beach was vacant and the shrimper with its pounding one-lung diesel had disappeared along with the clouds. The same calm and eerie silence of the previous day fell upon Pass Christian, and there was nothing left to hear but the hum of the air-conditioners trading their fetid, dampish air.

Mississippi remained motionless. But three hundred miles to the south there was heaving violence: Great masses of foam were being tossed about, and the fast-moving wave hills had gray beards that were flopping and curling one over another. Camille was growing up quickly. She had turned the slick, oily Gulf into raging masses of boiling water created by the friction of the hard chattering wind that, according to readings from the sondes dropped by the hurricane reconnaissance planes, was nipping along at 90 miles per hour sustained and 110 in periodic gusts.

What perplexed the batteries of tropical storm specialists watching Camille was her vitaminized growth. It had only been two days earlier that she was identified as a suspicious cloud cluster off the southwest coast of Cuba, but within five hours, after a second airborne penetration, she was a hurricane: The girl had been christened and she eclipsed her youth and moved into maturity with horrifying audacity. At ten o'clock that morning the hurricane unit of the New Orleans Weather Service alerted the local stations to the west, for they remembered the classic case: In 1900, six thousand residents near Galveston died in the greatest single disaster in United States history when another hurricane pounced upon a thin strip of Texas beach, snatching almost everything there. Five dogs and one cat survived, along with a few humans.

There is a subtle psychology to hurricane warning: If everyone over a wide area is alerted, warned, and chided, no one takes it seriously; thus, the Weather Service must particularize a landfall, placing the emphasis on a certain area. That's why the eastern region, from New Orleans to Apalachicola, Florida, flew gale warnings at this time, while stations to the west hung out the blood-red hurricane flags. The girl was going west of the Delta; that's what the track told them.

When Steve and Alice came out on the beach at three o'clock that day, it was "heavenly": The high cirro-stratus, telltales of a tropical storm, had drawn a curtain across the sun, shielding its sting and, too, the Gulf was no longer dazzling white and slick; now it was darker, rippled by cat's-paws, and the light breeze, the forewinds belonging to Camille, felt good. Even a few shrimpers were out dragging. The swimmers were back and so was the man who rented the Hobie Cats down by the next motel.

"Come on, darling . . . let's rent one of the catamarans," Steve said.

They ran down the beach, rented a boat, and twenty minutes later they were skimming over the darkening Gulf; the light cat's-paws had grown into ripples, then wavelets. A sea was developing. The waves were enlarging in proportion to the increased velocity of the wind, but they were still in their infancy and no regular formation was apparent. It was called a chop, but even as they tacked the Hobie back and forth, the confused water started to form a regular pattern; the crests and troughs of the two-foot waves were now moving in the direction of the rising wind.

Steve had an odd feeling that something treacherous was coming; any sea that turned from cat's-paws to regular cresting waves in forty minutes was a portent of extreme wind power. The scene at the Pass Christian beach mirrored joy, not timidity or caution. People pulled out their flags and they flapped gaily in the brisk new breeze; kites were bobbing, yanking at their taut strings, and someone had a giant helium air balloon on the end of a long cord that said, "Love, not War." The waiting in dank motel rooms was over. The beach was jammed and kids splashed and ran about, and even from the "cat," Steve and Alice could hear the chorus of laughter.

The sultriness was gone. Color came back. The Gulf was azure, sparkling, and the freshening wind, the new smells, the luminosity, the overturning of the heat wave were hopeful portents. The chilling of the water and the air seemed to say renewal.

But the waves continued to rise. Their height and length opened. Steve was not the only one who felt that the nimble wind was a warning; others sensed it, too; so, one by one, the "cats" tacked their way toward shore. The concessionaire took down the masts, pulled the twin hulls very far up on the beach, and chained his boats to anything strong.

In a way, everyone on the beach, even the vacationers, felt that something was going to happen, but there was no articulated fear. The foreboding at Pass Christian in the hours before the storm evoked a different kind of reaction. There was expectancy, restrained excitement, thankfulness that the weeks of heat had been sucked up by something called Camille. They knew, of course, that she was out there somewhere, but always someplace else, for everyone knew these "ladies" were fickle-brained, unpredictable. Nobody foresaw the possibility that, perhaps, they had been singled out, targeted, by the metaphysical attack drawing nearer and nearer.

Who believes the weather bureau anyway, the people reassured themselves. "If they say a storm's coming this way, it always goes the other way. There's plenty of time to get into your car and drive away." Escape was so close. You could look over from the sandy spit of Pass Christian and almost count the pine needles on the trees of the hearty mainland.

Safety was just a slingshot away.

"Should we eat at the same place?" Alice asked as she finished dressing just after seven.

"Why not?" Steve answered as he built his vodka martini in the plastic cup.

When they came from the front of the motel, Mr. Chasen, who was nibbling his Moon Pie, looked up and said, "Hear the news, Commander Mitchell?"

"What's that?"

"They say Camille is headin' toward New Orleans."

Steve stopped for a moment. He looked at the lethargic man who continued, "They'll get torn up over there, but we're safe. I've seen 'em hit twenty miles away, and there's nothin' much happens unless yuh right in the path."

"Where is it supposed to come ashore?" Steve asked.

"Waveland. Can yuh imagine a town called that? It's west of here."

There were four National Weather Service recording stations in the landfall area, each sending constant data on wind regime and tide rise to the specialists at the New Orleans Hurricane Center. Three recording stations were west of Pass Christian: Gulfport, Grand Isle, and Eugene Isle. At four o'clock on the afternoon of August 16 the western stations began to see a tide rise, or storm surge—water being piled up by Camille's wind friction. As the hurricane neared, John Scott, a New Orleans tropical storm specialist, began to restudy the tide rise charts of several hurricanes that had slammed ashore on the Gulf Coast: mainly, Hurricane No. 13 in 1947 (they didn't have names then); Flossy, 1956; Audrey, 1957; and Carla, 1961.

The data on these hurricanes was gathered not by the Weather Service, as clearly brought out in the Commerce Department's bulletin "Technical 48," but by the U.S. Army Corps of Engineers. The surge accuracy was secretly distrusted by the atmospheric scientists in the hurricane section. But Scott saw enough inputs, right or wrong, concerning tide rise to be deeply concerned. He predicted, merely by extrapolation, a tide rise of up to twelve feet along the low basin west of the Delta, and at 4:27 he notified the civil defense authorities of two Mississippi counties and four Louisiana parishes to evacuate the marshy lowlands and the hundreds of island bayous.

It went well.

State police cars joined with local officials and the Coast Guard, and around eighteen hundred residents, mostly small shrimping families and offshore oil well suppliers, were pulled out. They had the necessary time and daylight. Scott's evacuation orders also included Hancock County and the town of Waveland, but not Pass Christian, for historical hurricane data, the measured tide rises from past storms that affected lands east of the Delta, showed no indication of extreme high-water rises past the town of Waveland.

That evening Steve took Alice to the Shrimp Nest, and when they returned from dinner, he noticed that the wind regime had accelerated. They walked down to the beach to see the waves, along with hundreds of others. There were breakers slashing the shore, but they were only about three feet high, young, unformed particles of disturbed water bottoming out upon the gently shoaling sand. All who viewed the mini-spectacle were reassured because the combers didn't seem to be high or fulminating and, in fact, most of the old-timers recalled the Gulf in much more agitated fits before a hurricane.

This was a small hurricane in diameter. The fetch, or length a wave must travel to build up, was missing and so was the time needed to develop inordinately high seas. Those watching the breakers that night felt confident; they returned to their homes and motels relieved that Camille was going elsewhere. But the hurricane had a much more devastating weapon than wind and waves.

No one at Pass Christian could possibly have imagined what it was.

PASS CHRISTIAN COULD RECEIVE EIGHT RADIO STATIONS AND THREE TV stations, and each was interrupting its programming with hurricane information, advisories, and evacuation orders. Steve listened carefully and as he twisted the dials from one station to another, he became aware that there were various versions and contradictions in the hurricane statements; he was confused as the wind outside began to hiss with increased velocity.

Finally, at ten after eleven that night, he picked up the phone and called Mr. Chasen.

The old man, who seemed to be into his cups, drawled wearily, "Everybody's goin' across the street to Moore's Motel for a hurricane-watchin' party . . . plenty of booze, Commander."

"Shouldn't we leave the beach, Mr. Chasen?"

"Can if yuh want, but I don't see no cars movin' down Dune Road."

"Are we all right?" Alice asked, as Steve slowly placed the phone on the cradle.

"I guess so. No one seems worried."

"Then, darling, forget about it and let's make love."

Alice, in her shortie nightgown, sat on the edge of the bed and ran her hand lightly down Steve's chest. In a minute he was exploring her breasts and then her long, beautiful legs; it was not long before the crash of the hurricane waves and the peal of the wind were wiped from his mind as he experienced the warmth and excitement of a beautiful girl—one he loved with an intensity he had never known before.

John Scott at the New Orleans Hurricane Center had developed a sharp headache from being on duty sixteen hours. At four o'clock in the morning, August 17, he was handed a note from the communications section: Transocean drilling rig No. 60, a semisubmersible in the path of Camille, radioed the Weather Service that their anemometer had blown away after recording a wind gust of 158 miles an hour!

After the eye passed over the half-shattered rig, the central pressure was recorded at 27.80 inches of mercury. This stunned the weary-eyed Scott, for it told him two things: The hurricane had deepened and had changed her mind. If the center of the storm had passed over the rig, that meant she was moving to the east of the forecasted track and now she would landfall between Waveland and Pass Christian.

Scott's hand shook as he picked up the phone. Harrison County, which included Pass Christian, had to be evacuated and fast!

The message was received over the single-side-band radio at civil defense headquarters where an emergency staff had been called in that morning after the area was placed on "hurricane watch."

"Get to the goddamned Pass Christian beach and pull everyone out quick!" Scott shouted over the phone.

The log of the local radio station indicated that their all-night man made the announcement at 5:17 A.M. and repeated it every ten minutes, but the big country "P" did not have quite as many all-night listeners as their salesman claimed. Only eleven of the 763 beach residents and motel guests heard the message. Six of them stayed in their beds; three got up and went out and looked at the waves and, deciding that they were no bigger than the evening before, returned to their houses, thinking that someone was putting them on. Two families in the stilt houses packed their cars and left for the Harrison County high school gymnasium where the Red Cross evacuation center was being set up.

Pass Christian had five police cars, two of which were in the repair shop that night. The other three were on night patrol, one on Dune Road, two on the mainland. At 5:48 when Camille's wind regime had strengthened to seventy-nine knots over the beach and the rain had begun, there was a serious head-on collision on State Road 90 just to the north of the Pass Christian town line. Two of the local police cars responded to take the injured to the hospital at Gulfport, a town adjacent to Pass Christian.

The only police unit left moved up and down Dune Road instructing residents to "prepare" for evacuation.

At 6:10 that morning, the day of Camille, Officer Reeves radioed into dispatch.

"I need more help over here. We gotta go door poundin'."

The dispatcher, a Sergeant Esposito, who had a lot of other problems that night besides Camille (two robberies, a marital disagreement resulting in a five-inch laceration, the major car crash on 90), merely said, "Oh, shit! Over."

"Lookit," Reeves said, "I can't do this fuckin' thing alone."

"Joey, goddammit, we're on the tape. Cool it."

"But what do I do?"

"We'll get the fire department to help. They got a bunch of volunteers."

The fire department's three trucks, four paid men, and twenty-one volunteers responded at once, and as dawn came, two pumpers and one ladder truck went up and down Dune Road ringing their bells and sounding their sirens. But again, some people were stumped; they thought there was a fire and few associated the sirens with the order to evacuate.

At daybreak the wave spectrum and wind gusts appeared to be the same as the night before, and there was little alarm. Camille's surge was not yet overtopping the low dunes. People followed the old pattern: They dressed, had early breakfasts and, one after one, their cars were slowly loaded, and some of them began to creep down through the rain puddles of Dune Road toward the west bridge.

In the Surf and Sand Alice Mitchell awoke at 6:10 with a splitting headache. She had heard neither the radio message to "prepare" for evacuation nor the orders from the bullhorn. Alice looked out the window and, as so many others did, saw the small, curling waves. She went into the bathroom and took a Bromo-Seltzer; she then decided to do something about her hair. She washed and dried it and she carefully applied her makeup and returned to the bedroom forty minutes later looking and feeling better.

Alice paused, glancing down at the well-developed muscles of Steve's sunburned back and listening to his slow breathing. She felt the urge to be with him and for a moment she thought of slipping off her robe and burying her refreshed and perfumed body next to the man she loved, but he looked so contented in his deep sleep, and what better thing to do on a rainy, windy day?

She took out a pair of Pucci bikini panties she had brought back from an expensive shop in Thailand, and then slid back the squeaky folding door of the closet. Selecting a pale-blue shirtwaist dress, she carried it to the bathroom. She wanted to look great for Steve that day. A little later, as she was sitting in the chair putting on matching sandals, Alice noticed that the floor was wet around the back door. She went to the window and pulled up the blind.

The sea was up to the base of the motel. Its surface was bobbing with miniature white-capped crests and the confused water seemed to be marching like a whole regiment of feather-topped soldiers toward the motel. Alice was stunned and she let out a loud, panicky scream. "Steve!"

He bounded from the bed, half asleep, trying to separate his dream from what was happening in the real world.

"What's the matter?" he yelled, looking at her staring out the window, locked in horror.

She did not answer. Steve crossed to her. "Oh, my God!" He grabbed her. "Now you listen . . . go pack up everything we have . . . just throw the clothes in the suitcases."

He ran into the hall. Mr. Chasen and three young teen-agers met him.

"Commander Mitchell, I was just comin' down your way. The

lake's overflowed . . . backin' up. It happened so fast," the old man said in a halting voice.

"The water's up to our room!"

"I know . . . I know. It came up in ten minutes. I'm tellin' you, sir, I've never seen anything like this. We usually have time. Anyhow, the boys will carry your baggage across the street to Moore's Motel."

"I'm not interested in another motel. I want to get off this island!"

"You can't . . . the road by the bridge is flooded. That's what they say. All the cars are comin' back . . . some are stalled."

Steve pounded his fist into his hand. "I knew we should have left last night!"

"But we didn't hear the evacuation order until half an hour ago," the distressed motel man said. "By that time the water had risen three feet . . . three feet in half an hour. But everything's OK. We have breakfast ready and music at Moore's. Bloody Marys all set up."

When they reached the road in front of the Surf and Sand, the sight appalled them. A fast cataract of sandy water was dashing between the packed motels, forming a large plume as it shot high over the road, and from the lake came another raging current. The charging effusions collided in the middle of the two-lane street, forming a watery fence.

The storm tide was slobbering and swirling around almost up to their knees as Steve and Alice waded across from the Surf and Sand to Moore's, a stout-looking structure across the street. Strangely enough, there was no panic. A boy in a rowboat whirled in the froth, laughing, and several other youths on surfboards were paddling about, trying to stand up for a quick hurricane ride on the raging scud. Through the veil of rain, Steve could see other people making their way across Dune Road from the one-story motels to the two- and three-story motels. Music was playing and people were laughing as they hung over the higher balconies, watching.

The bellboys settled Steve and Alice into their new room, number 308, and being on the third floor about twenty-four feet above the road, the hazard seemed far below them, insignificant. Mr. Chasen came by and said there would be a "hurricane-watching breakfast" in the motel conference room on the third floor.

The man was slightly apprehensive now but had prepared well. There were eggs, biscuits, coffee, country ham, grits, sausage, Bloody Marys, and music in the conference room, plus a hurricane-tracking chart. The atmosphere was gay, spirited.

Outside the wind whistled at a higher pitch and rain slashed away like some bedeviling bombardment, but inside it was dry, warm, and apparently safe. There was no dread.

At least, not until the first explosion!

All the lower windows of the motel shattered from the wind and water pressure. It brought everyone, including Steve and Alice, to the door where they were met by a swift tongue of salty air. Some edged out onto the balcony leaning against the ninety-mile-an-hour wind, trying to see what was happening below them. For one thing, the water had risen dramatically; it was almost over the first floor, and across the street they could see the Surf and Sand about to be submerged.

"Alice, I want to speak to you alone . . . quickly!" Steve said.

They pulled their wet coats over them and excused themselves. He led her to their room where he said gravely, "This water is coming up very fast. I think we'll go under."

"What!" she said in a disbelieving cry. "Steve, we're three stories up!"

"I know where we are, but I think we should have a plan. Listen to me," he said in an analytical tone. "They said last night the water would rise six feet. It's already over eleven feet and the hurricane isn't even supposed to hit until eleven o'clock . . . three hours from now. Look at the Surf and Sand. You can't see it . . . and our car's under."

There was terror in Alice's green eyes but she was calm. "What do we do? There're no boats . . . we can't go any higher."

"We'll make our own boat. Those cheap doors are hollow . . . they'll float. Take the small tool packet in my bag and start knocking on the hinges. We'll have a couple of rafts ready, just in case. I'll be right back."

"Where are you going?"

"To warn the others." He forced himself out of the door as Alice went to work. Steve returned in a matter of minutes. "God, I pleaded with them . . . begged," he cried. "They said the water *never* comes above the second floor. Half of them are drunk already, Alice. They're about to die and don't know it!"

Another crash!

Explosions rattled the place as the windows careened inward and the glass in 308 popped; it didn't crack and collapse. It was more of a total shattering: The air was suddenly jammed with a million glittering arrows, which lodged in the wallboard, in the beds, in the dresser, but they had heard the initial crack and ducked to the floor.

The booming roar of the storm sucked up the seawater and carried it inside their room, which became darker and darker as the sea rose and the racing inky clouds lowered. A hard blow hit the side of the motel; the electric cable snapped and the crackles of spitting electricity could be heard over the clamor of wind and water. The vicious surge began to rise with more energy; one could see the killer inching up and up.

Time was short! They knew that the three-story motel would be overtopped.

"The water's up sixteen feet already," Steve bellowed over the whine of the hurricane. "I'm going to help the others. You keep pounding off the door hinges."

Steve crawled out along the wobbly balcony. He felt the growing pressure of the wind and saw the angry lather lapping up at him, gaining and gaining and gaining.

When he entered the conference room, it was not as noisy as before; the country western group still played, but where there had been laughter and smiles and confidence twenty minutes ago, there was now growing dread.

"Everyone! Be careful of the glass blowing in," Steve ordered. "Make rafts. Knock these door pins out!"

They were slow to respond, but then the glass erupted behind the curtain and a wave bounded in, drenching them. The whole structure began to groan deeply and sway a bit as seething, fast-exploding water crested against the facade, spraying its sheets high over the rocking building.

That evoked the final alarm.

People began to scream and those who had held their emotions in check, mostly teen-agers, started yanking off the doors; everyone finally realized what was happening.

Too late.

Steve edged back along the balcony and just as he reentered their room the first direct surge wave slopped inside 308; it was a gentle invasion at first, but within two or three minutes cresting water crashed into the opened motel room. The furniture was afloat.

He and Alice quickly tied the two rafts together by stretching a sheet from doorknob to doorknob. When the water was up to their knees, they launched their rig against the wall of wind and the jumping, thrusting waves, and they bobbed out in front of the motel. They saw a few chain rafts being pushed out of the conference room. Some people who had nothing to float on tried to swim but were ripped by the glass still wedged in the sills. Steve heard them screaming over the wind. They were trailing blood and innards, holding their bellies, their backs, their heads, their legs and arms. They came out in a crimson mass, but they were washed in again, only to be poured out of the gutted room, but this time there were fewer of them and their gasping screams had been reduced to defeated murmurs. They knew they were finished.

They were swept inside the big conference-room window and then there was another crash: The powerful water had demolished the rear windows. When the boiling crest came back for more energy, no bodies appeared, just a lot of blood and a few outstretched hands, wrinkled and chilly, not yet dragged down by the natural outrage. The two or three young people who had managed to escape on makeshift rafts were soon flipped off and they disappeared beneath the swirling gray surface.

Steve clamped his large hand around Alice's arm. He saw the grisly destruction of the beautiful girl: Her lips were coated with salt, and blood oozed from her mouth. He encircled her with powerful hands. He would never let her slip away; they had survived Vietnam and Camille wasn't going to get them, not now when they had everything to live for.

"Steve, I can't breathe," she whimpered.

"Hold on. You'll be all right. Just make sure you don't let go," he screamed.

Her eyes became encrusted with stinging salt and seawater lapped into her opened mouth, and he reached over and closed her lips.

"Breathe through your nose . . . your nose!" he yelled.

They were being transported someplace inland by the onrush. For a time things went well. The motel doors were handling the seas and Steve shot a smile and a "thumbs up" to his wife. She smiled back and said, "Breathing through my nose is better. I'm OK now."

"What happened to your mouth?"

"I bit my tongue," she laughed weakly.

Steve smiled back and he reached across and kissed her briny cheek. As they approached the lake, the waves began to settle down, but the battering wind kept its pitch. In front of them, coming out of the scud like stiff sentinels, was a line of Australian sea pines, bent and almost needleless; but at least their roots were deep enough to withstand Camille and it was something they could grasp onto until the storm passed inland. Steve and Alice had sailed across a body of water 1,100 yards wide in a matter of minutes, though the senses, the inner ears, the eyes, minds, the spirits were so abraded by a hurricane of Camille's intensity that their bodies seemed to have been hauled into another place without dimension or duration.

The shearing friction of the 190-mile-an-hour hurricane wind shredded the wave tops into horrifying valleys and, forming billions of angry, crisscrossed cuttings, sliced into the large combers.

The wind was the god.

It not only lathered the sea into total madness but also snatched the salt, which was churned to the surface. The air was clogged. It was a dreadful, painful mass of sodium chloride—salt—being whipped into tiny, hard-edged balls, briny pellets that, once shaped, were hurled by the piercing wind at a speed exceeding that of a shotgun blast.

Steve and Alice fought two devastating enemies: One was the barrage of the wind and waves; the other was the ingestion of sodium-contaminated air. Once the salt reached their lungs, it dissolved and began to build up on the warm juices of their windpipes, causing their quickly gulped breaths to become shorter and shorter, and their mouths opened wider to suck in the desperately needed air. But this compounded the deadly cycle. Their senses became dulled and their lungs vibrated and heaved, demanding more and more salt-free air that wasn't there.

They somehow wrestled and fought their way through the mass

of tangled roots and water until the trees grew larger, clearer. Alice smiled with renourished confidence. Her face was caked salt-white, but they were almost there. Salvation seemed very near, as it always does to the dying, and that renewed their determination to live.

From behind them, from out of the vapor, came a counterwave, a "rogue" the oceanographers call it, a sea that crosses the regular waves at a tangential angle for reasons that have not yet been totally explained by the experts. Their doors had been riding well, lifting, falling, bobbing slightly with the diminishing waves, which were bottoming out on the shallow sand. The rogue was high, steep; it snapped their easygoing motion, and the lip of the counterwave, or the curl, notched in under the leading edges of the doors.

Both rafts flipped up and over at the same time.

Salty, swishy darkness.

When Steve's head broke through the frothy wave spill, he saw Alice in front of him, sailing toward the pines, still aboard the door; she had caught the breaker's crest and was skillfully riding it. They waved at each other, smiling, signaling that all was OK. Alice began to paddle her door around to come back for Steve; just as she turned and faced him, another rogue, smaller than the first, dropped over his head. He was caught in the vortex. It spun him around and upside down crazily, and he surfaced, not knowing his direction or orientation. Steve paddled around and the sea pines slid into view. But Alice was gone. So was the door.

Steve thought she had been whisked into the tidal trees by the rogue wave, so he paddled with all his remaining strength, and after a furious splash and thrust, he reached the base of the slimy trees. "Alice!" he screamed. "Alice!"

Nothing. Only the roar of the wind.

He tried to climb the stripped branches to get a better view, but they were draped in seaweed and every bit of scum dragged from the bottom; it was impossible to pull himself up.

"Oh, God, nothing must happen to her! Not after coming so close!" Steve said to himself.

His heart thumping against his ribs, he circled in and out of the slashed pines, paddling the door, calling, calling, calling, calling, and his voice and strength gave way shortly after twelve o'clock.

His head spun, his body ached, and when he looked at his watch it was after two. He had been so exhausted he had fallen asleep holding onto the door.

Camille was inland.

The wind was down and the water level had dropped, but the rain was still heavy. Steve had to locate Alice; she was somewhere within the flooded sea pines, probably frightened, trying to find him. After all, she had been on the Stanford swimming team and she, obviously, was working her door around the tangle of debris searching for him. He paddled the raft around all that day. As the water receded, Steve continued to tramp along the soggy needles of the pine hammock looking for her body, for the door, for a piece of clothing, a shoe, anything.

He found nothing. Alice was gone.

Later that night Steve Mitchell was found on the far side of the pines, wandering around in delirium, on littered route 90. He was crying "Alice," and he was shaking. They took him to the hospital in Gulfport along with 780 others.

Camille had snatched about ninety lives at Pass Christian alone.

Alice Mitchell, the new bride, might have been one of them.

4

IT WAS LIKE THE VIOLENT BIRTH OF THE WORLD ALL OVER AGAIN; mother sea had erupted with such ferocity and temper that nothing was left of the ordinary little beach community of Pass Christian except for a few lightpoles that canted out of the mounded sand at weird angles just to prove that there had been a whole community before Camille's barbaric stripping.

She looted everything on the beach.

The mainland side was a sodden dump of seashells, soft sand pocked with litter: baby dolls, scraps of food, old tires dragged up from the ocean bottom, blankets and parts of beds sucked out of houses, dead fish, dead dogs, dead birds, dead cows, dead pigs, and dead people. And those who still walked around bloodied and stunned.

The day after Camille, when she was far up in the Blue Ridge Mountains dumping torrential rains in the coal valleys causing landslides and flash floods, the sun and sea at Pass Christian sparkled with more brilliance than anyone had ever seen. Perhaps the great weather machine was embarrassed for having declared war on an innocuous little place. There was a spreading anger on the mainland. Ninety people had died on the beach that day, and in Mississippi alone four thousand had been seriously injured by Camille's thrust; the property damage was estimated to run into the billions. Everyone wanted to know why the evacuation hadn't begun earlier when there was time to escape; why did the storm tide, forecasted to rise six to eight feet, rise to 26.2 feet at Pass Christian? It added up to a devastating collision of errors and misapprehensions and that was cold comfort to relatives who poked inside canvas bags at the high school morgue finding the withered dead faces of those they knew and loved.

Steve Mitchell lost his mind temporarily. He was convinced that his beloved Alice was still alive. She was looking for him someplace, wandering around, perhaps suffering from amnesia. As soon as he was able to leave the hospital, Steve, dazed and exhausted and coughing deeply embedded salt, returned to the pine hammock where he had last seen Alice. He walked over every foot of the soft needle bed searching for a scrap of her clothes, a piece of jewelry, the door, part of the door, a footprint, anything that would tell him she was there or had been there. But after hours of tramping through mire and wreckage, he had found nothing so he decided to seek help.

He went to the Harrison County executive, a real-estate man named Teddy Burke, and he asked for volunteers. There were none, but for a promise of five dollars an hour, Teddy rounded up a local army of people needing quick cash for food and rebuilding.

Not one inch of earth was left unturned in the pine hammock; the digging went down four feet, which everyone said was about the depth that someone would be buried if that were the case.

No Alice.

No door.

Then the search spread out along the high-tide line of rising soybean fields eighteen hundred yards north of route 90; still, no clues. By the third day, four more bodies had risen to the surface of the lake. Alice was not among them.

Then Steve made the most difficult phone call of his life. He had to call Alice's parents to tell them the terrible news. After a most painful conversation, fraught with horror and disbelief, they told Steve they would set out for Pass Christian immediately.

They arrived at Steve's motel on the mainland late that evening, plain people, distraught, with eyes puffy and red. Steve could imagine what they had talked about on the fast drive down from Georgia: "How could she come back from Vietnam safely and be killed by a storm? Why didn't her husband save her? How come he survived?"

"I can't tell you exactly what happened," Steve said, "because I saw her one moment, and the next moment she was gone."

"If she did walk away, Steve, would she carry this door you said she was using?"

That was the weakness in Steve's theory: Where was the door?

"I have two things in mind to do," he told her parents. "First, we'll continue the search here. If she is dead, which I doubt, her body will be in the vicinity someplace. Then, I'm offering a reward and the newspapers all over Mississippi are willing to run photos. We need a picture, though. Oh God, Mrs. Hendricks, I don't even have a picture of Alice."

"I've got one," Mrs. Hendricks said, reaching into her purse.

They combed the area for two weeks. The A.P. ran photographs all over the state, to no avail, and although Steve still clung fiercely to hope, Alice's parents' faith that their daughter was all right began to crumble.

They went back to Georgia and Steve's agonizing frustration turned to anger, mirroring opinion all along the Gulf Coast. The papers leveled criticism at almost every official body, for Camille's toll of 248 dead was almost unbelievable as all the facts and figures drifted in: In Mississippi and Louisiana alone, 144 persons were killed; 8,931 received serious injuries; the total property damage was pegged at $1.28 billion—one of the greatest natural disasters in the history of the United States.

Steve was a determined man, pigheaded sometimes, and being military-trained, he was used to exactitude, finding precisely what happened. In the beginning he took his wrath out on the wrong person, the Pass Christian police chief, who was a prickly man anyhow and didn't appreciate outside intimidation.

The chief said, "Listen here, Commander Mitchell, you better get hold of yourself. I know what happened. A lot of other people 'round here lost folks, too, but it wasn't our fault. Here's our police log . . . had it Xeroxed 'cause a lot of investigators been in sayin' what you're sayin'. See . . . there's the call from the civil defense. We took it at five-fifteen. That was the order to evacuate. Now, there just wasn't no way we were gonna get almost seven hundred people off that beach with one police car and three fire trucks. By seven-thirty that morning, the access roads to the bridges were underwater, so I had to pull my men out. That water came up so fast . . . we didn't have a chance."

The trail of blame next led to the civil defense people who, in turn, passed it on.

"We did what we were told to do, Commander Mitchell. Our advisories came over the single side band from the hurricane folks in New Orleans. Go see them."

Two days later Steve was sitting in the bare office of John Scott, the man who had had sense enough to yank the cord that morning when the Transworld drilling rig sent in their report. Most informed people said that if Scott hadn't acted as fast as he did, everyone on the Pass Christian beach would have died.

"Commander Mitchell, do you realize you're about the sixth person who's been in here shaking his finger at me?"

"How did it happen?"

"Very simple," the man sighed. "We don't know enough."

"But you knew that Camille was a category-five blow; why didn't you order everyone on the coast evacuated just as a precaution?"

"Everyone from Waveland to Galveston was ordered to evacuate, and we lost only a few there."

"What went wrong at Pass Christian?"

"We had no idea the surge would rise twenty-six feet. There was nothing in our historical data to indicate a tide rise of that magnitude . . . nothing, and we thought the storm was going westward. That was the track all night."

John Scott reached over and brought out "Technical 48." "Here's the best paper we have on storm surge written by a man named Harris, the leading expert on hurricane water levels. He says in the introduction . . . 'Accurate and detailed observations of abnormal water levels during hurricanes are difficult to acquire and few systematic collections of such data are available. Because of the lack of basic data, theoretical research has been largely restricted to calculations based upon unverified postulates.' He goes on to say . . . 'Although studies of this kind have led to a better understanding of the phenomena, they have not led to the development of any outstandingly successful prediction systems.' "

Scott slowly placed the paperbound document back on the shelf and turned to Steve, hunching his shoulders.

"You told me you're an Annapolis man . . . you've studied weather . . . you're a flier, an engineer. Do you know what that means?"

"Yeah, it means that you people don't know shit about storm tides."

"Bluntly put, but . . . yes. Even the expert says there is no way successfully to predict the surge from a killer storm like Camille. From past data, we estimated six to eight feet east of the Delta."

"Then how in hell did it reach twenty-six feet?"

He shrugged. "Something to do with the topography of the basin. Five miles from Pass Christian the high-water mark was only eleven feet. Why was that?"

"Jesus, we can navigate in space and every other damned thing, and we can't even predict a simple thing like a high tide. Tides have been around since the beginning of time, man."

"I'll even go you one better, Commander. We aren't really sure why hurricanes begin . . . why they grow like Camille did . . . why they peter out . . . where they will go. If we knew all those things, no one would ever die in a hurricane. We could save everybody. These tropical storms—hurricanes, typhoons, cyclones—they're all the same, have killed more people in the world than all the earthquakes, volcanoes, floods, tornadoes, tidal waves combined. Think of that. Someday, if we get sufficiently advanced in mathematics, physics, fluid mechanics, and controlled experiments in the atmosphere and on the oceans, we may be able to solve the great hurricane mystery. Until then, we're going to have tragedies like Camille. It's a real problem because people don't take these storms seriously. They have hurricane-watching parties. . . ."

"I know. I attended one recently," Steve said ruefully.

And then his thoughts shifted to Alice.

STEVE DID NOT REPORT FOR HIS JOB AT BETHPAGE. ALICE'S BODY AND the door were never found, although Steve continued to hunt for clues for almost three months after the tragedy at Pass Christian. As the weeks and months went by, his anguish, which had been tempered by the idea that Alice was still alive, became unbearable. He kept saying to himself that if she were dead, her body would have turned up. He ran small ads in papers all over the country and he employed two missing persons bureaus to find her, but nothing was ever discovered.

In his mind he refused to bury her.

He continued to love Alice just as much if not more. She was always in his thoughts and it propelled the man to take up the study of storm surge. He went to the University of Chicago, gained a Ph.D. in atmospheric sciences, and then joined the National Hurricane Center in 1972.

The center, headquarters for the entire research, tracking, and hurricane-warning systems for the United States and Puerto Rico, was located on the fourth and fifth floors of the Computer Building on the campus of the University of Miami at Coral Gables. The building was owned by the university and the upper floors were rented to the hurricane section of NOAA (National Oceanic and Atmospheric Administration) under the U.S. Department of Commerce—simply, the National Weather Service.

If one were to stand in the university parking lot and look up at the Computer Building, the most vital warning center in the United States after North American Defense Warning System, the importance of what went on there would not be visible. There were no outside hints except for antennas on the roof and a radar dome that was located on top of a higher building across the street. The Computer Building was entirely girded by great expanses of tinted green glass, lineated by scalloped cement columns running from the ground to the fifth floor where they fluted into curved arches to support the modern entablature and the overhanging roof.

It looked more like a small American embassy in some far-off land, certainly not the most consequential warning and tracking center in the country. It was so exposed that one would have thought the Computer Building would be the first to go in any sort of hurricane. Why wasn't the whole business buried in an underground bunker like the SAC headquarters outside Omaha, Nebraska?

There was nothing but offices on the fourth floor where twenty-two people concentrated on all aspects of hurricane formation, movement, and devastation. Some scientists were even exploring such airy subjects as tropical storm impact on awnings and wild orchids. But, by far, one of the most serious studies conducted on the fourth floor was that devoted to predicting hurricane surge; the tragedy of Camille had underlined the need to understand why the water had risen far over the estimated levels.

Working with Steve Mitchell on storm surge research was a beautiful young woman, Billy Haughton, who carried two Ph.D.'s, one from MIT and another from the Scripps Institute of Oceanography in La Jolla, California. She was sandy-haired and sharp-boned, unlike the delicate-featured Alice Hendricks who had been the essence of femininity. Billy wore Levi's most of the time and she detested the government bureaucratic structure. She played a loud stereo rock station during the day, which Steve, eventually, was able to turn off in his mind, and on the gray walls of their office Billy hung bright-colored posters. When Lou Ballantine, the aging director of the hurricane center, quipped that the blaze of metallic hues was ungovernment-looking, Billy went out and bought larger ones, so that the research office began to take on the air of a discotheque.

On the fifth floor of the center were the radar room and the satellite room where Automatic Picture Transmissions (APTs) came in from the "eyes" in the sky. Packed into the core of the building on the same floor was the hurricane-tracking center, the "war room," and from that place the killer storms were identified and plotted, and warnings were dispatched. Across from the war room was the communications section; it held rows upon rows of clicking Teletypes that were linked to all parts of the world and to every Weather Service station in the United States.

There was harmony on the fourth and fifth floors until 1974 when Dr. Keith Landon, thirty-three years old and straight from the Princeton computer center, started work as a forecaster. He had gone to MIT with Billy, and almost from his first day at the center, he was completely at odds with Steve Mitchell. Steve had suffered through a devastating hurricane; Keith had never seen one, and the younger man's approach to all hurricane problems was via the computer. He walked around the center in tailor-made suits and he wore a vest, even in the torrid summer months. Keith made no secret of the fact that he wished to become the next director of the center, and then, with that credential, he would leave and start a private forecasting company for far eastern countries who depended upon cyclonic rainfall for crop production. Steve said that was arrogant and self-serving.

While the kindly Lou Ballantine did not really understand what Keith was doing, the director had received laudatory reports on Keith's sophisticated modeling from the computer authorities up at NOAA's Maryland facility. Lou took it as fact. He had been in the hurricane business for forty years, beginning when all they had were two red flags and a barometer. Knowing that he was going to retire the following year, in 1976 Lou promoted both Keith and Steve to Deputy Director status at the center. Steve had been in government service all his life and he turned out to be an orderly manager and highly devoted to his discipline. Ballantine couldn't decide who should take over the center after he retired: Keith or Steve. Their attitudes toward the business were totally divergent, and the bitterness and rivalry between the two men burst out in September when Lou met with them to go over the next year's budget.

"Lou," Keith began, "I'm requesting five million for my program to digitize a typical hurricane."

"There are no typical hurricanes," Steve snapped. "Each one's different."

"Well, anyhow," Lou said, "that's a hell of a budget. How would you spend the money?"

"I have it all worked out."

"I'm sure you do," Steve said.

"If you're going to sit there and snipe at me, Mitchell, let's call this meeting off. The fact that you've been through a 'cat five' doesn't mean a damned thing. I don't have to get my tootsies burned by hot lava to understand a volcano."

"Stop acting like children, both of you," Ballantine interjected. "Go ahead, Keith."

"Here's my proposal: We drop millions of recording devices into the next hurricane. These devices, attached to parachutes, send back temperature, wind, pressure, and rainfall data. When they hit the water, they report surface conditions. The devices float and we pick them up after the storm. The information is digitized. We construct a third-dimensional model to provide the first true picture of a storm. By fully understanding the anatomy of the hurricane, we can predict its course from the upper air steering currents."

"May I comment, Lou?"

"Of course, Steve."

Keith took out a pipe and settled back in the standard government conference chair as if he were a director of a mammoth corporation. His chiseled features carried authority; they gave him an appearance half handsome and half serious, and when he talked, an earnest smile came through. One wanted to take Keith Landon seriously and most people around the center did, except Steve who thought he was bombastic.

"First of all, I know something about air drops. You couldn't pull this off for less than fifteen million," Steve said.

"The Air Force gave me the figures," Keith answered crisply.

"Those are the first figures. But the Pentagon always passes the hat again. I can't see Commerce awarding that kind of an appropriation to the Air Force. Another thing . . . your emphasis is wrong."

"Like hell it is!" Keith thundered.

"We should put our money into saving people's lives."

"What would you do?" Keith asked.

"We're looking at a possible disaster along the Gold Coast. What if another Camille came in here or a storm like the one that hit the Keys in 'thirty-five? Winds over two hundred miles an hour! Florida hasn't had a direct hurricane hit in years . . . people are cocky. Ninety percent of them have never been in a hurricane. There's not enough bridge escapes over the intracoastal waterway. I say we put our money in public awareness. No one believes the Weather Service. Our credibility has always been low and for the wrong reasons. We have to save their lives for them!"

"My program will save people. Once we get a handle on these storms and know where they're going we've got it made."

"It's not that easy. And there's no guarantee your idea will work."

"Well, I think it's far more sophisticated than hurricane posters and documentary films. You know, Steve, I think you believe Jeane Dixon."

"Who?"

"The soothsayer. She predicted that a terrible hurricane would hit Palm Beach."

"You know I don't listen to that sort of thing."

"But you *are* haunted because of your wife. The whole sad experience has distorted your thinking. And, also, you don't understand the computer tool."

"My friend, I was using computers when you played in the Little League."

"Stop this!" Lou said, wiping a handkerchief across his bald head. "Both of you have offered interesting proposals. I'll study them. In the meantime, cool it. We have enough difficulties around here without all these private wars."

Lou fiddled with the old slide ruler on his desk, knowing that these two men would never come to terms with each other. If that storm Steve was always predicting ever materialized, he hoped he wouldn't be around to see it.

Keith and Steve's dispute continued and one afternoon Billy looked across her desk at Steve. "Do you personally dislike Keith?"

"No. He just won't see my side of the hurricane problem."

"Maybe you don't see his."

"That might be true."

"Steve, you know the only thing I've learned about hurricanes is that nobody agrees with anyone else. There're thousands of storm theories floating around here. You and I don't agree . . . we argue half the time."

"But we're more or less down to earth. Keith's up there in computer heaven."

"Maybe he's onto something. He graduated first in his class at MIT."

"What was he like in school?"

"The same way he is here, though I didn't know him all that well; we never dated."

"Speaking of dates . . . are you busy tonight?"

"No."

"Let's go have a great dinner and not talk hurricanes."

"Deal."

When Steve knocked at her apartment door in Coconut Grove that night, he hardly recognized the woman with whom he worked. Billy always looked like a kid at the center: Now she was beautifully turned out, chic.

To her surprise, Steve was different, too. They ate in the Café of the Ambassadors in south Florida, and Steve told amusing stories; it was all very relaxed. Afterward they went over to the Fontainebleau on Miami Beach for the stage show and to dance—a skill Steve had finely developed. Billy was astounded that evening to see such a contrast from the man she knew at the hurricane center. Steve was charming, debonair, attentive—and he had not mentioned one thing about hurricanes, storm surge, Camille, or his lost wife.

The next morning they continued their work in room 404 of the hurricane center as if the evening before had never happened. His meter had switched totally; there were no trivial phrases or stealing of laughs, and the old ghosts that surrounded Steve drifted back.

She could not understand Steve Mitchell. Billy had seen two sides to him and there were obviously others that she had not discovered yet. Five miles away from the center he appeared to be a gay boulevardier without a kernel of substance in his brain, but place him in that green government office with data and computer terminals, and a steely glaze came over him.

One day after trying to digitize the Tampa basin, an agonizing job of numerically recording the big bay from hydrographic charts and blending the output into a computer program, Steve said, "This is boring. How about having lunch with me?"

Billy was surprised, but they left for the Flame, a popular, dark little steak house in nearby Coral Gables.

"Something's been bothering me, Steve," Billy said as soon as they were settled in the booth.

"Really? What's that?"

"You've never mentioned that great evening we had in Miami Beach."

"What was there to talk about?"

"I had a good time."

"So did I."

"But you got superserious again the next morning."

"That's the way I am."

"But your whole life can't be locked up in one little room."

He did not answer but merely looked down and stirred the olive about his martini as she continued. "I don't mind working hard. We both do, but you act as if it were . . . ah . . ."

"Life or death?"

"Yes, I guess I was about to say that. I'm sorry."

"Nothing to be sorry about, but it does have to do with death. If surge weren't so serious, I guess we'd be unemployed."

"Well, forget it . . . I shouldn't have brought the subject up."

"You're right, though, Billy. I know . . . once I'm in that room, I change."

"Tell me something . . . What were you like in the Navy? Did you have many dates . . . affairs? How come you waited so long to marry?"

"That's a lot of questions."

"And none of my business . . . right? Apology time again."

"I did go out with a hometown girl for a long time. Got a 'Dear John,' and after a while I forgot about her. I was kind of a swinger, I suppose, before I went to Vietnam. I was really too old to fly missions, but carrier-based pilots were scarce. It all soured up . . . and that's why I got out . . . and then came that goddamned hurricane, and I . . . well . . . went right back to where I was in Vietnam."

"What do you do for kicks? When you're not in 404?"

"Once in a while I date a gal at Mercy Hospital. She's an OB resident, and I keep a private plane over at the new Tamiami Airport. I fly it weekends, and sit around the hangar a lot . . . mostly gabbing with the guys."

"Why did you ask me out to lunch?"

"I like you. As a matter of fact, I was going to ask you to come with me to the Virgin Islands for about three weeks. We both are due a little vacation."

Billy's expression registered surprise.

"I'm serious. I've chartered this Hatteras-53 and I thought we could go from island to island. Swim . . . try a little scuba. Billy, forget about the way I am in the office . . . give me a chance. It'll be fun, I promise."

"You know, Steve, there's a lot I like about you."

She suddenly felt sorry for the man sitting across from her; she had a desire to make him laugh, bring him around. She realized her reaction was impetuous, but she said, without hesitation, "I'll go, but no hurricane talk!"

Two weeks later they boarded a Pan American jet bound for St. Thomas, and booked into Bluebeard's Castle later that afternoon. The first night they went up on a high hill overlooking the city to have dinner; then they made the rounds of Charlotte Amalie drinking banana daiquiris, rum frappés, dancing to steel drums, and when their spirits were lifted totally and their bodies were satiated with odd-colored "rip-off" drinks, they took the taxi back to Bluebeard's. The night was warm, but it was fanned by the constant trade winds that robbed every flower of a little bit of scent. From the hotel they could look over the idyllic little harbor with its drifts of moonlight and twinkling, white-hulled cruise ships dressed and lying beside the dock. They stood on the terrace of the cocktail lounge having good-night Stingers. Steve, leaning against the railing, looked at Billy and smiled. Gone were all the refractions of his mind, the outward mask of gloom.

"Nice."

"Very nice," she answered.

The kiss came fast and passionately.

Billy never remembered being so stirred by a first embrace with a man. Their tongues found each other in a flick of time. They pressed themselves together tightly, so tightly that the breath was almost wrenched out of her.

"Wow!" Billy said, backing away slightly.

He did not answer, but approached her again. They clung to each other for a few seconds before realizing that the people on the bar stools were gazing their way.

"This isn't the place," he whispered.

"I agree."

Hand in hand they moved along the terrace to the grass, down the steps, and along the corridor leading to the main part of the hotel. She did not pause before her door; they continued beyond to his room carrying their drinks. Out on the balcony they stood a moment looking far down the slope to the cruise ships, and in another instant they were embracing, quickly exploring each other, but this time their excitement and passion were more intense and they breathed heavily, straining against one another.

She moaned softly and pushed herself toward him. He pulled away her shoulder straps, exposing her full, white breasts. The nipples stood erect, rimmed by the soft light of the moon, and Steve lowered his lips and kissed her gently. She felt the warmth spreading between her legs and she couldn't imagine that this was the man with whom she had spatted day after day. How far away it all seemed. She felt the light dress being winged off her as if it didn't exist. Steve sat on the edge of the bed and he cupped her breasts and tilted them toward his mouth.

She was gliding her fingers over his lean, muscular body; then she realized her probes were going deeper, beyond his stomach, lower and lower, until she grasped his stiffening penis. Hard. Beautiful.

Suddenly his pants were off. She lowered her head into darkness, her long blonde hair providing a curtain. It was warm in there, and the scents of the male filled her nostrils; she found it in the dimness and she kissed him, burying her mouth all about him.

They lay back on the bed. She could feel her own warm juices dampen her upper thighs.

"Please . . . sit on me . . ."

She liked it that way so she could enjoy a longer look at the man who was inside of her. His body, his face were there to watch and experience. She made her movements coincide with his. Then she felt the first explosions deep inside, farther down than she had ever remembered. She felt herself being transported as the throbbing continued. She felt his glorious shaft deep within her begin to vibrate, slowly, then quickly, urgently. Each thrust was transmitted to her whole body. His movements accelerated. He was coming.

Billy moved her hips higher and fastened her legs around him tighter. They were almost one body now. Then all of a sudden he came. Before his juices had expired, she climaxed again and it was almost with him. It was the best experience she had ever had with a man.

SHE WENT WITH STEVE TO THE CHARLOTTE AMALIE MARINA; THE
yacht standing ready for charter was much bigger than she had
visualized.

"Are we going to have a crew?" Billy asked.

"Of course . . . you and I."

"Isn't that a big boat for only the two of us to handle?" she said.

"Honey, I didn't go through Annapolis for nothing."

She nodded, thinking back to her own summers in Newport
where her father kept the family yacht, a sixty-one footer, moored
near the Ida Lewis Yacht Club; there had been sailing lessons at Bar
Harbor, one-design races out of Marblehead: Billy believed she could
help manage this yacht with the gleaming letters on the transom,
Pleasure Pie. Maybe that was an appropriate name, she mused. Anyhow, her laboratory happened to be the oceans of the world, more
particularly the heated oceans; and she had been to sea on several

oceanographic research vessels, so why should a short island trip aboard a sleek Hatteras with big twin GM diesels call for caution?

But, somehow, it did. This was still hurricane season and they were poking their bows into the waters everyone feared. But she went to the store with the provision list and bought ninety-five dollars' worth of food and sixty-two dollars' worth of vodka and cognac. That would keep the vessel afloat, she thought.

When Billy returned, there was a stake truck parked on the dock and barrels of diesel oil were being loaded onto the rear deck.

"Why are we loading oil?"

"It's easier. I don't trust the diesel oil you pick up in these outer islands. Clogs the fuel filters."

She didn't think any more about it. He was the professional Navy man and at noon that day they slipped their lines. Steve skillfully backed the yacht away from the finger dock, spun her around, and in a matter of minutes they were slicing through the still waters of the Charlotte Amalie harbor, heading toward the open Caribbean.

They rounded the Point and the yacht dipped, and curtains of trade-wind water flew over the forward deck, spraying it with salt and occasional flying fish.

Billy and Steve made love twice that night, each time as fulfilling and tender as the night before. She could not get enough of Steve Mitchell; he was full of great strengths and sexual drives, and he experimented, and that's what excited her. And there was something else: He was such a strange man—arousing, moody, earnest, mystic, mournful, a little crazy; but yes, he could be gay and fanciful without the slightest hint of what went on far into his head. Who was this man, really? Each hour she learned something new about him— and he had yet to speak of his tour in Vietnam, his early life, his first and forgotten loves, if he had any, his family, if he had any, and what his real purpose in life was. It had to be more than the unattainable goal of finding out what actually killed his wife.

The next morning at dawn they pulled the hook, wound up the diesels, and headed out of Tortola.

"Where are we going?" Billy asked.

"East. Steer a course of ninety-four degrees on the compass."

"Are we heading for another island?"

"Yes, eventually," he answered without looking directly at her.

But by evening the island Billy expected to see push over the horizon hadn't appeared, and she went up to where Steve was lounging on the flybridge reading a mystery novel while the helm was on the auto-pilot.

"Steve, where's the island?"

"I have something to tell you. There is no island."

He had a spare look on his face. She drew back, not understanding; she thought he was a little spooked in that moment, just a little, and a needle of trepidation stung her. "Are you kidding?"

"I've lied to you," he said.

"What!"

"We're not heading for an island right now."

"Where the hell are we going then . . . Africa?"

"We're just moving out to a little patch of ocean . . . right here," he said, handing her a chart of the Atlantic. "Latitude nineteen north, sixty-two west longitude."

"Why? What's out there?"

"It's one of the prevalent hurricane-spawning grounds."

"Oh, that's beautiful!"

"There's no storm out there right now."

"I'm goddamned mad. You said we were going on a pleasure cruise, and here we are talking shop."

"You brought it up."

"I don't like being lied to, Steve."

"Hear me out."

"OK, but why are we heading way out there? We're miles from anything."

"A couple of years ago, you remember, eight nations began an investigation of the doldrum waters . . . a tropical experiment."

"I read the reports."

"All right. They picked out a place that had a high concentration of hurricane development, around nineteen north, sixty-two west. They ran ships back and forth, recording water temperatures, realizing that the heat of the sea has a direct relation to hurricane formation."

"We all know that. The warmer the sea, the more interaction of high heat exchange."

"Look, Billy, here's a thermograph print-out from the hurricane grounds. Lately, I've been looking at temperatures sent in by the synoptic ships that happened to cross that spot. They're not usually accurate because ship's officers record the data and half the time they read their gauges wrong even when the equipment is functioning. But the temperature synoptics tell me a warming trend is developing out there. I don't know if I can trust them, though, so I decided to combine a bit of pleasure and fact-finding. There's a good thermograph aboard. I want to run the exact pattern they did a couple of years ago, comparing the two print-outs."

"Steve, why the hell is this the private duty of one oceanographer? There's money for these experiments. Wood's Hole has oceanographic ships. So does the University of Miami, and a half-dozen others."

"I've been to all of them already. They all say sure, furnish us the funds, and we'll schedule it two years from now."

"Did you tell Lou Ballantine what you're planning to do?"

"No."

"Why not?"

"Because it's my own experiment."

"But why can't you work it through the center?"

"Commerce is a muddling bureaucracy and you know it. I can find out what I want by myself. I'm paying for this. It won't cost anybody anything."

"You're just at war with the system, aren't you?"

"I never thought you'd react this way. Are you scared out here?"

"I'm not scared. But I'm a scientist, and I thought you were too, and this is so goddamned unscientific."

"Scientific? I have to laugh at that. All you and Keith Landon know about hurricanes is what you've read in books and technical papers. Billy, I've been through it."

"Let's not get into that. I know."

"But you can never realize the horror of these storms—to think they're anything but computer numbers—until you've felt the water and salt rushing into every corner of your mouth and lungs."

"I don't need to feel it. Out here or anyplace else."

"That's the attitude I'm trying to fight. Hurricanes to you are simply a business . . . politics . . . you study while the storms go on someplace else."

"I don't need a hurricane to kick me around."

"All right, I'm not saying you do."

"Then what in God's name are we doing out here?"

"By comparing the new thermograph with the one taken a couple of years ago, we'll establish a temperature trend."

"So what?"

"If it's what I think it is, I believe we can predict that a great hurricane is about to be triggered unlike anything we've seen before. Worse than Camille."

"Oh, will you forget that bitch?"

"I studied the water temperatures off western Cuba where Camille was born. There were two ships that reported a two-degree surface heating beforehand. I interviewed each master. They assured me that their readings were correct. One was a tanker on charter to Sun Oil . . . the other was a reefer vessel inbound to Tampico. What happened just after that? Camille came alive. I think there's a correlation: An abnormal surface heating can precipitate a great storm."

"But you can't extrapolate and say that ocean temperature definitely kicks off these things."

"The hotter the surface, the more energy transference."

"That's only a theory. There's no direct evidence to support it. You know that, Steve."

"There was clearly an uplifting of surface heat the summer of Camille. I looked at the climatological reports for the area. There was a relationship."

"And now you figure you are going to make a hero of yourself. You brought me along for a few fast screws on this amateur research vessel. It sure beats the old tugs out of Wood's Hole, doesn't it? No fucking or drinking on those boats . . . just a lot of hard work with bearded men in cutoff blue jeans. Steve, after you pick up your data, just swing little *Pleasure Pie* around and head for the nearest island with a jet airport. I'm going back to Miami."

"Why the hell are you so sore? You're acting like a woman, not a scientist."

"Well, dammit, you got me here under false pretenses. Couldn't you just have said, Billy, I want you to help me with an experiment?"

"I didn't think you'd go along with it," he said simply.

"I'm not a climatologist. I'm interested in surge and that, by the way, is what you're paid to work on. All this other stuff isn't our bag. You're not a tropical climatologist, either."

"I've studied it."

"But you haven't worked one day in that field professionally."

"I have the basics."

"Oh, God, get me out of here. You are a freak!"

He turned and looked out at the ocean, leaving her comment unanswered.

"Steve . . . I'm sorry." She put her hand on his arm. "But I think you've become a little spaced out from Camille and losing your wife like that. I don't blame you, but forget all this. Let the others do the climatological bit."

"Billy, please. We can do something worthwhile out here. There's a damned fine thermograph aboard."

"Who paid for the installation?"

"I did. It's the best one made so our pickups will be accurate. I want to cut through all the BS in oceanography and just find out one thing: Is this patch of ocean heating up or not?"

"OK, but it's about the least conclusive experiment I've ever heard of. It might be five degrees colder in another part of the hurricane sea. Storms are born off the Canaries. What are you going to do? Run *Pleasure Pie* all over the Atlantic? If you do, and you pick up tons of temperature data, what then? Are you prepared to draw a direct relationship between surface heating and hurricanes?"

"Yes. I think I'll be on the right track."

"Then, what are you going to say?"

"That we're in for a killer storm."

"Where will it hit?"

"I don't know."

"Steve," she said gently, "I think I've had enough of this talk. How about getting me a double vodka on the rocks?"

That night the swell increased from the southeast and the yacht pitched her bows, throwing off higher and higher sheets of spray. They ate in silence and cut back the RPMs of the diesels to steady *Pleasure Pie*. He slept in the early hours of the evening and Billy took the helm, but the seas began to build, and by eleven o'clock that night a squall lashed at the yacht. When he came up to relieve her, the ocean was a network of crawling whitecaps and the RPMs were cut back once more.

"When are we getting out of here?" she asked, drenched, the water coursing down her face.

"The glass is holding."

"How do you know this stuff won't develop?"

"I don't."

"That's cold comfort."

"If it grows into a depression, we'll find out from San Juan radio. There's a long-range single side band aboard."

"Then what?"

"We'll outrun it."

"Christ, Steve!" She handed him the wheel and went below.

She dried off, gulped down a brandy, and was asleep in the aft cabin in a matter of minutes, but her rest didn't last very long. Billy was awakened by a fearful clanging on the deck. She knew immediately what it was: The oil drums had come loose and the sea was tossing the small yacht about as if it were a bathtub toy. She pulled on her Levi's, grabbed her foul-weather gear, and was just leaving the cabin, holding onto the grab rails, when Steve appeared.

"We have problems," he said.

"I heard them."

"It's more than that. Three of the drums burst. They must have been rusty. There's oil all over the place. Don't light a cigarette whatever you do."

When she reached the deck, Billy was shocked to find that the night sea was piling up; the whitecaps had grown into full combers twisting and curling over each other, pressing down the bow of the yacht.

Billy was nervous about the rising sea. The aft deck was being washed by slapping waves leaping aboard; this was a pleasure yacht designed for the short seas, the inland waterways, and shallow craft didn't belong out here. They both knew it.

Number two oil was everywhere. Streams of it poured out from the drums finding its way below, coating everything with a slippery, umber surface.

"We have to jettison these drums, Billy," Steve called over the wind and the bash of the battering seas.

"Dammit, you fool! Two people can't handle this!"

"The disturbance is local."

"How do you know?"

"I called our office in San Juan. The satellite doesn't give us a picture of prehurricane."

"Then what the hell are we going through?"

"A heavy squall concentration . . . that's all."

"It's too damned heavy to be a squall."

"No, no . . . I've seen things like this before. That's not our problem."

They worked almost all night, securing the rest of their oil drums. Every inch of the once pristine yacht was oil-coated; and there was not enough benzine aboard to wipe the disgusting slick off themselves and the yacht.

By dawn the seas were down. The sun broke through and they hove to for a few hours' sleep, their bodies still bearing the tawny color of the diesel oil.

They awoke to a calm, still sea.

"Steve, I've had it. You're nuts. Turn this thing around."

"I'm sorry, Billy, but we're only five hours from the experimental grounds. Hang in, please."

She was not in a position to do otherwise. Gradually they cleaned up the yacht. They barely spoke to each other during the next two days as the yacht ran the temperature course back and forth, back and forth. The thermograph began to record the temperatures in sequence, and when they were almost finished a smiling Steve came up to the flybridge with two print-outs.

"Look at this, Billy! Here's the print-out from two years ago . . . and here's our data. Notice the pattern. It *is* warming . . . the ocean out here is heating up for some reason."

"Fantastic. Let's go home."

"Don't you have any reaction?"

"It's getting warmer. That's fine, but it doesn't lead us to anything."

"Oh, yes, it does! A super storm is on the way and it's going to make Camille look like a baby!"

It was not his prediction that daunted Billy Haughton because she didn't believe the correlations between heating and the birth of great storms; it was the way Steve talked in emphatic terms. He seemed to be saying, "I'm telling you people . . . listen to me. I'm the prophet . . . I know." And, too, there wasn't a look of terror on his face; it was almost a satisfied expression as if he wanted the storm to prove his theory.

She had had enough. They were right. He *was* a hurricane freak.

"Take this goddamned yacht home!" she demanded. "I don't read you, Steve Mitchell, as an oceanographer . . . or as a person!"

She went below and thought of a saner man: Keith Landon.

If the voyage to the hurricane grounds had proved anything, it was that Keith had been right when he sized up Steve.

CHAPTER

MEL HANSEN WAS THE ARCHITECT FOR THE PALACE BEACH SYSTEM, headquartered in Palm Beach; the chain, started back in 1901, ran nine hotels in Florida and the Bahamas. Mel was a short, thick-lipped, bronzed, cigar-smoking man in his early forties. And he was beefy and flabby and played a poor game of tennis and golf. Previously, he had been a motion-picture art director, after having been fired by several architectural firms in Los Angeles for having too many Babylons and apocalyptic images on his mind.

Mel married Denise Dassault, a fortune-hunting French actress, a few years before coming to Palm Beach. Mel and Denise met when they worked together on the feature, *Lord Jim*. Denise had only a minor role in the film and she knew her career was going downhill from that point. She and the flashy, bombastic art director quickly realized they were kindred souls and the two of them made a pact: they both wanted money, lots of it, and Denise would be "bait" to attract the money if Mel provided her with a plausible cover. Marriage. They decided Palm Beach would be the best place to find a wealthy man.

Mel was broke when he arrived in the resort, but what hadn't worked in the normal channels of commercial design came together at the Palace Beach, and Mel served the firm as house architect and vice-president for development at a salary of sixty thousand dollars a year. Mel, however, wanted more and he wasn't waiting for Denise to find it. He was a man with an impairment of ethical conscience, unable to distinguish between right and wrong, and he started deal-making with a man named Glen Markum, a schemer who had arrived on the Gold Coast after ending a career as a shoe salesman in Dayton, Ohio. Glen had bought into a few shabby beach motels in the early sixties, and he had saved and leveraged his profits carefully until he was able to finance small condominiums himself. This led to other larger ones and when he met Mel Hansen, he was ready for the final move into important South Florida real estate. Glen had the money; Mel, the ideas. Their first project together was the imposing forty-story Century Towers located on the ocean at the southern end of Palm Beach. Mel conceptually designed the twin-tower complex, but he took full credit for all the architecture. The appearance of the mammoth, green-glass structure moved Mel along his magic route to Palm Beach fortune.

Glen was a tall, lanky, gray-haired man in his late fifties and he wore his wealth excellently. Unlike Mel, he had learned that style should accompany status. He was smooth-talking whereas Mel was not; he dressed impeccably while Mel went around with his shirttail hanging out; he was deeply devoted to his family; Mel was not a family man and he didn't want children. But where the two men were perfectly socketed was in their cunning plans.

Their next deal involved a purchase of property under a third-party name; Mel then recommended the area for a new hotel site, selling the land back to the Palace Beach System at a greatly inflated price. When that worked, they went further. They submitted plans for other Palace Beach Hotels on St. Paul's Island and El Lugar Cay in the Bahamas, but these establishments were never built to specifications. Mel and Glen "optimized" the designs; the original materials were paid for but not delivered, and Mel and Glen pocketed the difference.

One morning Mel called Glen Markum and said, "I've been working on something all night . . . have to see you right away."

Thirty minutes later Mel eased his Rolls Silver Shadow around the long, banyan-shaded drive leading to Century Towers: two tinted-glass cubes that seemed to challenge the pure skies of the Gold Coast. Glen's apartment was on the top floor of the condominium; it had three balconies, eleven rooms and on a clear day, mostly in winter when· the northerners blew, one could see a green dot on the horizon: Bimini, forty miles away.

"Come in, Mel," Gloria Markum said, giving him a light kiss. She was a plain midwestern woman, daughter of an Indiana corn farmer; she went to the Methodist Church, dressed modestly, and spent her days writing to her children in Ohio. She had not the slightest idea how her husband had risen from a simple shoe salesman to a millionaire real-estate promoter and, like so many others in Palm Beach, she thought Mel Hansen was a genius.

Around the Markum place, Mel Hansen was a god and a likable one, for he always wore a perky smile and had time for small talk. One of the secrets of Mel's success, learned from his father, was what he called "personal chatting," which made people feel good because it indicated that Mel cared.

"The first lesson, Mel," his father had told him, "is to memorize people's birthdays, those you want to impress. Then learn about their family and their problems and know who's sick . . . somebody's always sick . . . continually ask how they're doing."

"How's your mother, Gloria . . . is she out of the hospital?" Mel now inquired.

"Yes, she came home the other day and I just received a letter from my sister, Angie . . . she says Mom's better."

"Well, these things take time, you know," Mel said, looking toward her tall, slender husband who was approaching them with *The Wall Street Journal* in one hand and a Scotch in the other. (Glen was a light morning nipper.)

"What the hell is up? Never seen you so excited, Mel."

"I have the plan of plans."

"Come on into the office," Glen said, moving down the hall to the last room, which the promoter used for his business.

"Glen, what's South Florida's greatest realty problem?" Mel asked as soon as the door was closed.

Glen didn't have to think; he responded with a snap, "Not enough beach front."

"Exactly! There're eleven thousand new residents coming into the area each month. That's a constant invasion. They want the sun first, the water second, but we're forced to build inland and the developments are goddamed tough to unload . . . no beach front and there's all those mosquitoes from the Glades."

"Agreed."

"Now, the South Florida Building Code comes up for renewal soon."

"That's right . . . the twenty-five-year review."

"What if we could persuade the local towns to switch their bulkhead ordinances to a uniform code? Then we'd be able to build forty, maybe fifty feet closer to the high-tide line."

"How? The condos are already up."

Mel smiled and his face glowed like the proverbial cat who had swallowed the canary. He unrolled two drawings, spreading them on Glen's drafting table.

"With fifty feet of new space we can take Century Towers and add Siamese wings right up to the fortieth floor. We anchor them to the existing structure with cross I beams. In this building alone, we'd come up with seventy-four new units. At two hundred thousand dollars a throw, you can see the jackpot."

"But what about the people with existing ocean views?"

"No problem. We just dogleg the extension and lay in three wings, outshoots to the beach, like big old branches."

Mel unrolled another tissue, smoothed it out, and again a hearty smile bloomed on his face.

"Damned clever."

"Moving to a uniform code would mean three hundred thousand extra units on the beach between here and Miami! We'd be placing a billion dollars . . . *a billion dollars* . . . into the coast real estate."

"What do we get out of this?"

"If we promote the new setback line, you and I will get first crack at the prime development sites. That'll be the deal, my friend."

Glen sipped his drink and walked to the expansive window. He looked down the long row of condominiums crowding the beach, one after another, like so many white sugar cubes pushed into the sand, an endless line that bent down and formed its own vanishing point with the horizon. Then in Glen's mind he visualized each high-rise with wings jutting out toward the beach and he saw the profit, the boondoggle. But he waited a minute, thought, and then shook his head.

"What's the matter?" Mel asked swiftly.

"The idea is brilliant. But how could we push it through? The whole south coast here is full of sand dune nuts. Every time there's a proposal to cut through a dune for an access road or a variance, that Jayson Kendall mounts an ecology campaign. Then, there're the hurricane people . . . already screaming that the beaches are overcrowded."

"Those guys can all be convinced," Mel said. "I went to Grazio . . . he's business manager for the building unions. I told him I had a plan to promote five billion dollars' worth of new construction and he lit up like a hundred-watter. There's so much unemployment in the unions. Grazio has ways of putting pressure on the state senators and reps in Washington. They can speak to the building commissioners. Half of 'em are in real estate to begin with. If they see windfall profits, those boys will move and that uniform code will be passed."

"But, Mel, you'll have one hell of a campaign mounted against you."

"So what? We can mount a campaign, too. For instance, who knows the most about seawalls and water?"

"How would I know?"

"The Dutch. They've been fighting the seas and storms for hundreds of years."

"What has that got to do with us?"

"Plenty. I called the world's acknowledged expert on seawalls, a Dutchman named Dr. Van Betzig. I asked him about protecting and reshaping the beach and he told me that with proper seawall design the beach not only can be protected but also improved—widened."

"Can we get this Betzig?"

"He's already agreed to be our consultant. He'll draw up a set of plans, specs for a uniform seawall code."

"And what about the hurricane people?"

"I'll have to go down to the hurricane center with some plans from Betzig. I'll get across the idea that we're saving the beach, not destroying it. So when we combine the ecological advantage with the business and political viewpoints, who the hell will turn down this goodie bag?"

"What about water mains, telephones, electrical cables?" Glen probed.

"Southern Bell says their central office can take the extra customers. They want new business. All they have to do is lay in the cables. Florida P. and L. will furnish a position statement. They have enough generating equipment."

"Traffic and parking?"

"Well, traffic is always a problem, but we can design two- and three-story parking lots.

"It's goddamned exciting, Mel. I gotta hand it to you. You're a genius."

"Then you're with me?"

"I always have been."

He raised his glass. "Here's to the new setback line, partner."

Then they shared a huge wink.

No small town in the world has been the subject of more colorful copy, barbs, scandalous stories, social rumors and all their journalistic offshoots than Palm Beach, Florida. It could be classified as a unit of social organization because it has a fire department, a city hall, sanitation workers, a police force, town ordinances and taxes like every other small town in America.

But it is hardly Americana. And just plain folks don't usually live there.

Palm Beach is a place, but it's more of an idea or an ideal, like some fragment detached from the universe bobbing around on a very long string that doesn't break even under the most unimaginable pressures and consequences of modern life.

The town provides a landscape not only for the people who dream but for social engineers, liberal rights advocates, social reporters, botanists, small-town planners, historians, the National Society of Morticians, educators, among others, all of whom have discovered that Palm Beach, because of an odd succession of events, provides an excellent workshop for study and research. It is far from the common currency of other small towns in the United States, perhaps the world.

Of the three early resorts in the United States, Newport, Saratoga, and Palm Beach, only the latter has not been breached and messed by the encroaching hinterlands. Perhaps it's the geography of Palm Beach, an island whose surrounding waters—the ocean on one side, Lake Worth on the other—tend to prevent acute change and the growth of some of the normal structures and institutions of communal organization. Whatever, Palm Beach is, apparently, the only town of over ten thousand in the United States without a mortician, cemetery, a hospital or infirmary, a public library, a public high school, a used-car lot, neon signs, a dogcatcher, and a tax-paying black family. Newport and Saratoga have installed most of these things, but Palm Beach exists and prevails without the usual list of town imperatives.

How? First of all, the resort is a bridge away from West Palm Beach, a city of over seventy thousand that, fortunately, provides the services for dying and preparations for burial and interment, among other P.B. deficiencies. One would have to go back into the history of Palm Beach to understand why there is no hospital or cemetery.

In the beginning people repaired to Palm Beach with great bursts of optimism; certainly no one wished to be buried there, so there was no cemetery; interment was forever elsewhere. And, too, the sons and daughters were privately educated at places like Choate and Hotchkiss and if, indeed, the blue-blooded yearlings required a bit of academics in the resort, they were sent to a local private high school.

A public high school was just not in the scheme of things.

Palm Beach had never held a parade until the Bicentennial. And that was a most interesting assembly; the P.B. fire and police departments had no bands and the men didn't know how to march, so the parade to dedicate a fine bronze statue of an American eagle was made up of trooping townspeople: socialites, ex-ambassadors, and millionaires. Some claimed that, per capita, it was the richest parade ever held in the history of the United States.

The local government takes the form of the Town Council, and even here the difference between Palm Beach and other towns is clear. Although they are elected, the councilmen are not politicians and they are not paid. There has never been a serious political scandal in the community, for the usually rich councilmen don't need money; hence, political favoritism and patronage have never been a part of the resort. This represents a kind of democratic purity. While most towns of over ten thousand population pay their mayor, Palm Beach does not and, in fact, it costs the mayor about $20,000 in unreimbursed expenses to serve in the honorable post.

Even in 1902 the P.B. legend was well entrenched and a writer for the old *New York Herald* had this to say about Palm Beach:

"Not to go to Palm Beach is a serious thing from a social point of view. If you cannot go there, you should in any event say that you are going, and then retire from Society for a time." Little has changed in Palm Beach since then.

Some of Palm Beach's old Spanish-style palaces have come down to make way for smaller, modern counterparts costing sometimes well over a million, but generally, as Robert Frost said about P.B., "the shadows fall the way they fell." The present society succeeds in living up to its venerable reputation, although things have been altered by liberalism, civil rights, and progressive income tax. As a matter of fact, it was only about ten years ago that the blacks from West Palm Beach had to be off the island by nightfall. Even to work for the rich, they had to have identification cards.

Just to the west of Palm Beach is the last American frontier: the Everglades. By 1900, this country's wild west had been tamed. There were maps of the prairies, the mountains, and the rivers; the Indians had been either destroyed or shoved into reservations. In 1898, Florida's "outback" was still unmapped; the Seminoles continued to raid the coastal settlements. (They did not sign a final peace treaty with the federal government until well into the twentieth century.) During the last years of the 1800s it was safe to travel anywhere in the United States with the exception of central South Florida, the vast unknown below Ocala, which dropped off into the eerie swamp, not only concealing provoked Indians but also poisonous snakes—the highest concentration in the country—alligators, mosquitoes, quicksand, swamps, sloughs, and thousands of other barriers to civilization.

One man wasn't afraid of all this. His name was Henry Flagler, partner in Standard Oil with Rockefeller. He recognized that South Florida, at least along the coast, could be tamed and there were riches to be plucked from the state's one great resource: the sun. In the same way the West was opened by rails, Flagler built his Florida East Coast Railroad, which introduced the carriage trade to a new Lotus Land.

A "creamy legend" began. The most unique town in the world was created by Flagler. In the beginning it was a plush mattress for the "right" rich and, later on, some "wrong" rich, and when the strivers came to town, things changed a tiny bit. The foam endured and there was serenity, but in all this green galore there was a weave of submerged violence.

Palm Beach and the land to the west form, perhaps, the greatest geographical and social dichotomy on earth: on the coast, a verdant paradise of flushed people; on the other side of Lake Worth in and around the City of West Palm Beach, the well-groomed greenery begins to thin and pale. The residents here are plain folks, living like anyone else in America. Moving on, deeper into the Glades and margin lands of Lake Okeechobee, the filament of life and nature changes. The succulent palms and Ficus trees are gone. There is nothing but rich earth stripped of its slash pines and cabbage palms to make room for grazing cows and miles of waving sugarcane stalks.

Two types of people live in these margin lands no more than fifteen miles from the social resort: migrant and black field workers and the landowners who have nothing in common with the "Islanders," as the P.B.'ers are called.

The brittleness of the Glade lands also flows into Palm Beach. While the resort has at present a calm appearance it began with a history of violence and crime that still exists.

Initially, Palm Beach was a small haven for people with "names," private railroad cars, and yachts. In 1894 Flagler opened his wooden hotel, the Royal Poinciana, the largest guesthouse in the world. In those days there were three classes of people in Palm Beach: the guests or "regents"; hometown fellows, or the "good ole boys," who settled on the finger island in the 1880s; and the blacks who served the whites. Back in 1890 the island was only a swampy mangrove strand with risings of Anastasia rock, crisscrossed by bicycle trails called shell roads. (Interestingly enough, palms are not indigenous to the island. They were planted despite some evidence that they floated ashore when a ship carrying palm nuts was wrecked off the resort. The beach is puny and erosive except at the far north end of the island.) There were no cars in the early days and the approach was by ferry or a bridge that supported a footpath and a railroad track. The blacks and Indians walked across, or rode bikes, carrying outsized baskets of things for the well-heeled guests who traveled the same bridge in private railroad cars.

The barish, mushy shell island that was to become the most famous outpost for fancy madness in the world went through many changes of social habitation. Up to World War I the escapists were Flagler's hotel guests situated either in his Royal Poinciana or at the Palm Beach Inn, a dull, uninteresting wooden structure that had burned down twice and been rebuilt.

Around the time of the great war two prophets arrived: Paris Singer and Addison Mizner. Singer of sewing machines had the money. Mizner had a brazen, clumsy pencil; he called himself an architect, although he never had a day's training in his life. Since Palm Beach people seemed to have a hankering for the unreal or elusive fantasy, those two minstrels opened a great package of dreams.

Mel Hansen in many ways was akin to Mizner. They both were stage designers. With Paris Singer's money, Mizner was able to leave a considerable mark. First, he designed a rehabilitation center for veterans at the far end of the main street, Worth Avenue, simply called the "Avenue" by P.B.'ers and the "mink mile" by a lot of others. The "center" was a rambling, stuccoed, poorly designed, poorly constructed embarrassment because it went this way and that way with a tint of Moorish and Spanish eclecticism, and it never rehabilitated anyone. Still, it became a legend and the home of one of Palm Beach's premier clubs, the Everglades. Mizner went on to design other buildings along the Avenue. They were Spanish stage sets with towers and twisting alleys and slit windows, and these were occupied by shopkeepers.

Then came a change. Mizner was somehow given a private commission, and he twisted his flabby ideas into domestic architecture when Mrs. E. T. Stotesbury, a Philadelphia millionairess and social leader married to a gaunt little ex-Civil War drummer boy, gave the artist the job of designing her home. Like most of his works, the Stotesbury home, "El Mirasol," a forty-room Moorish fantasy with a private zoo, was almost unlivable. Stairs went nowhere; balconies could not be stood upon; closet doors opened unto each other and there was no plan or sense of cross-ventilation. (Most of the Palm Beach "cottages" smelled, even with air-conditioning. The rancid, damp air was trapped and the great interiors with their heavy old Spanish furniture and thick, lush rugs seemed to mirror a horrible, smelly decadence which some secretly said was appropriate.)

But the construction of El Mirasol started a trend. The incurable optimists in Palm Beach thought of Mizner as an uncontested genius; a few claimed he was a stylish fraud.

Palm Beach was now the place to build a winter cottage, as opposed to the summer cottages in places like Newport. The bigger the better, and Mizner was the man to contact if one wanted a theatrical effect. It didn't matter how much it cost or how clumsy the design; the resort people loved everything he did. Mizner made a lot of money along with his friend, Mr. Singer, and the inhabitants went from hotel living to Mizner Spanish palaces. Palms were planted to make it "Palm Beach," and the fourteen-mile-long island gradually filled in.

Not only did the look of the resort change, but the social classes became separated. After spending some time in the resort, a well-known sociologist felt that the town was composed of stratified levels, some social, some economic, and although he concluded that there was overlapping between the "coveys," as he called them, the Palm Beach people were basically divided into six divisions.

The first of the Palm Beach coveys was the most obvious. The real rich: old money, old names, big houses, quiet parties where the press was excluded, the right P.B. clubs, the right marriages, and a certain distinction of family heritage in Palm Beach which usually meant having been around before motorcars were allowed on the island. The first covey was by far the smallest. On the whole, according to the behavioral scientist, this division did not associate with those in other coveys unless the lower orders belonged to the right P.B. clubs. But at the same time, they were not judged snobbish.

(The sociologist found very little outward snobbery in the resort.)

The second covey was generally peopled by those with fresher money who entertained generously, appearing with frequency in the town's papers. They were the glamorous new rich who formed the core of Palm Beach's recent society; they had no hope of attaining what the sociologist termed the "tight first covey."

The third covey was perhaps the largest. They were the marginal sorts, some with fair amounts of money, some just with bills, who were desperately working to achieve the second covey.

The fourth covey was the Jewish one, and except in rare cases, they did not mix with the Gentile community, preferring their own club and society which some said were flusher and tighter than those of the first and second coveys.

The fifth covey formed a Palm Beach contradiction and it was the most rueful of all. It consisted of penny-watching retirement couples who sat on old rockers under the shade of partly collapsing hotels. They went to the local movie house to see second-run films for $1.25 a ticket and they lined up early at Palm Beach's Hamburger Heaven for budget meals, and sometimes they strolled down to Worth Avenue to look in the great windows that were filled with things they could never buy.

There was a sixth covey in the P.B. structure, which, in some ways, seeped into other social partitions: the bachelor covey. According to the wandering sociologist, it was one of the most outrageous divisions in the resort, tracing its foundations back to the last years of the nineteenth century, and it was an inevitable covey. In the shadows of billowy, white gowns worn by moneyed widows came the legions of male fortune hunters who realized from the start of Flagler's pursuits that Palm Beach was the place to set their traps. Some scored well; others did not, but the history of the resort was full of marriages between well-mannered, poor men and rich ladies.

The bachelor covey was made up of widowers, divorced and single men. There were a few rich bachelors in Palm Beach who were generous and paid their own way, but their ranks were much thinner than the unsuspecting ladies believed. The sixth covey was roughly divided between the "takers" and the "walkers." (Sometimes they were intermixed.) The "takers" were those bachelors on the free haul, invited to expensive charity balls as suitable escorts, and few of them ever paid their own way. It was said of one popular Palm

Beach bachelor that he had bought only three meals in two years and that was under duress. The "walkers" were slightly below the "takers." They were considered the available "pants" for Palm Beach ladies who needed escorts, and if they didn't get drunk, danced reasonably well, laughed at the right jokes, remembered the names of those they had met, they might be promoted to "takers," which meant that their journeys through Palm Beach art galleries were elevated to lusher trips along the best cocktail and dinner party circuits of the second covey and sometimes the highest ranks of the first covey.

The bachelors existed in Palm Beach almost on their own terms because of the historically uneven mixture of the sexes. And the surplus of rich women to poorer men in Palm Beach provided the polite hometown boys with a perch that was hard to evacuate, even with promises of golden marriages consummated with trust funds set up by the eager, old brides.

Though the P.B. coveys were all different, one common thread laced through all the subdivisions but the sixth: control by women. It was a woman's town.

Palm Beach was a town of women on the way up and down and competition for recognition was often vicious and, at the same time, ludicrous. P.B. social survival—outside the first covey—generally depended on two factors: A "high queen" had to like you and that gave rise to accolades: "Didn't she look marvelous!"; "Did you see what she was wearing!"; "What a job she did on the charity ball!" Such praise was aired at the ladies' luncheons that were scheduled weeks, sometimes months in advance, and were often backed up by morning telephone conversations. One striver ran up $940 in a single month on nothing but local calls to her friends.

The second factor was the P.B. press. One society leader had her picture in the town journals 191 times in a single year and there were over 391 separate mentions of her during that period. The same woman's photograph had appeared a total of 2,152 times over a five-year span in the P.B. press.

Historically, few towns in the world with ten thousand population have such a record of wild passions. There were many old rituals that secretly blotted P.B.'s past.

The lynching of blacks was one.

Some who have studied the history of black-white relationships in the United States claim that around Palm Beach County the blacks feared the whites like nowhere else. Whether or not this was true is difficult to prove. But there are hard pieces of evidence that seem to support the saying. For instance, the Baker boys were sheriffs of Palm Beach County for about forty years. First there was George Baker, the father; he had two sons, Richard and Bob. When George gave up his badge, Bob took over the office; when he was through, he passed the shield on to his brother. The Baker rule was tyrannical.

When a white had a dispute with a black, the right and natural thing to do was kill him, and not only that, the Baker boys would hand out to every white "nigger shooter" a free straw hat: a nugget for disposing of troublemakers without clogging the court calendar.

The punishment for blacks was hanging: not merely a stringing up behind the walls of a state prison, but a public hanging. Around World War I, when Florida decided to go "electric," Palm Beach was one of the last counties in the United States to hold scheduled black hangings open to all.

The last public hanging in Palm Beach came in 1924 when three blacks slaughtering turtles on the beach were caught by Dick Smith, one of the town's deputies. Dick was killed, accidentally some claimed, and the next morning one of the blacks was found hanging from a live oak tree on the site where they were breaking ground for the large Episcopal church, Bethesda-by-the-Sea. The second black was taken out to sea for a "skiff ride" and dumped overboard with a rock around his neck, and the third was maimed for life.

There was only a cursory investigation and no one was indicted.

But the practice of Palm Beach "skiff rides" continued almost up until World War II.

In the thirties a Palm Beach attorney, Joe Peel, was skirting the law and Judge Chillingsworth, a popular Palm Beacher, said, "Joe, if you don't come around, I'll have you disbarred."

"Like hell you will!" Peel threatened.

The judge was killed before he could disbar the lawyer.

Joe got hold of a local madman, "Horse Apple," and another constituent; they rowed down the shoreline and beached their skiff and broke into the judge's home. His wife was there, so they took her for the skiff ride, too. Rocks and ropes were attached and over the Chillingsworths went.

Peel and his boys were not hung because due process had arrived in Palm Beach. They were sent upstate to the Florida slammer.

Robberies, some unreported, occurred with frequency. The most dramatic happened in 1976 when a group of visiting bandits snatched about four million dollars from the Palm Beach Towers condominium. Around the same time a prominent resident, an oil executive, was killed in cold blood by a gun blast through his front door, and an elderly real estate woman was killed by an intruder in early 1977.

Mel Hansen knew all this. He was an avid Palm Beach history buff. He had the feeling that he could get away with anything and, too, he believed that the more grandiose his designs were and the more bombastic his descriptions, the better they would succeed. There was some validity in his assumption, for many saw the dumpy man as the second coming of Addison Mizner.

Aside from the mammoth seawall proposal that he was advocating, Mel had something in mind for his own coffers: a row of prestigious beach condominiums that would extend toward the ocean on the north side of the eight-hundred-room twin-towered Palace Beach Hotel. The new condominiums, to be called Regency Walk, would have many advantages over existing beach front real estate: The units would be magnificent in detail and design; the owners could use the complete facilities of the large hotel and its staff; a telephone call would bring instant room service; and there would be a laundry, a beauty parlor, two eighteen-hole championship golf courses, eleven tennis courts, lawn bowling, a large pool and cabana club, a health spa. All this would be shored up by the impeccable reputation and stamp of the Palace Beach System.

To move the condominium scheme to fruition, Mel needed his surplus of sand, the fifty feet that would be provided, he hoped, by the new setback ordinance, since, if they built inland they'd have to destroy the hotel's ninth green and tenth tee along with the north end of the croquet grass. An impossibility.

The regulation governing the zoning setback line in Palm Beach stated:

546A. Town of Palm Beach Zoning Ordinance
Structures adjacent to ocean bulkhead. No structure of any nature shall be constructed closer than 150 feet from the designated ocean

bulkhead line established under Chapter 8 of the town code of ordinances unless bulkhead exists or is constructed in conjunction with said structure at a location approved by the town manager.

But not all of the towns stretching from Palm Beach south to Miami had the same ordinances. They differed, ranging between fifty feet in high-density zoning and one hundred feet in residential beach areas. The covenants had been generated around 1951 when the South Florida Building Code people had asked the hurricane experts in Coral Gables for a twenty-five-year average of high-water marks. Mel secured several pieces of information that he knew would aid his cause:

After 1963, for reasons never explained by the meteorologists, hurricanes began to glide past Florida's east coast, preferring a course up through the Gulf of Mexico, landfalling in the states of Texas, Mississippi, and Louisiana, much as Camille did. The Gold Coast had only received two direct hurricane hits since then. If the historical-averaging system were to be employed, Mel believed the trend would show that the Florida east coast was becoming a safer place to live.

The other point in Mel's favor was Florida's practice of seawall construction. He had learned, almost from the first day that he arrived in Palm Beach, that a seawall was not always a seawall. While there were many hurricane statutes packed into the South Florida Building Code—rules for wind load, provisions for lateral and vertical stresses and shearing, the depth of pilings and foundations—there was not a uniform mention of seawall guidance in all the towns. Engineers or architects, many of whom knew nothing about seawall technology, could build anything they wanted in some cases: cheap corrugated metal with weak tiebacks costing $500 a foot; or sophisticated, heavily anchored cement slab units that ran up to $2,500 a foot. Mel and Glen always took the cheapest route and Century Towers had a jerry-rigged seawall that cost less than $400 a beach foot. Most South Florida engineers and promoters silently agreed that if one wanted to cut corners, the seawall was the element that might easily be slighted.

Dr. Van Betzig had told Mel over the phone from Holland that with the right seawall they would never lose sand during a hurricane. Armed with that knowledge, Mel could take the edge off the ecological argument and demand that the codes be upgraded to contain a uniform seawall ordinance. After all, he was a responsible architect, not some money-hungry promoter.

Mel's plans, then, amounted to a trade-off: He would get his extra feet of sand for a uniform seawall code, the first in Florida's history. Who would object to laying in a new seawall when they were getting perhaps fifty feet of glorious building space? (Mel had decided to ask for fifty feet but would settle for something less.)

In the weeks that passed after Mel's meeting with Glen Markum, Dr. Van Betzig, an old whiskered veteran of the Dutch underground, arrived from Europe and performed a scrupulous survey of existing Florida seawalls.

He then announced with certitude, "Some of these walls are useless! They can be undermined . . . scoured, we call it. A major storm will overtop them. As the hurricane water drains back to the sea, it attacks the base of the seawall and eats the whole thing away as if it didn't exist."

Dr. Van Betzig drew up a set of new seawall plans and Mel and Glen viewed two movies the Dutchman had brought with him, each establishing the fact that a beach could be reclaimed, protected. The Dutch had been doing it for three hundred years. Mel's strategy, before approaching the directors of the Palace Beach System with the condominium scheme, was to line up as many letters of support and position papers as possible. With Dr. Van Betzig in tow, Mel interviewed all the South Florida building commissioners and they agreed to support the setback proposition.

One of Mel's advocates in Palm Beach was John Baxter, president of the hotel chain. John had hired Mel and he believed in him; not only that, the fifty-one-year-old smooth-faced executive with all the correct rubbings of Choate and Yale and Harvard Law adored the squatty man, not so much on a personal basis (they socialized in different circles; John was second covey whereas Mel was third), but from a business point of view Mel had done well by John.

Mel's two big projects for the Palace Beach—St. Paul's Island and El Lugar—were working, for they were so Addison Miznerish that they satisfied the needs of the socially nervous. They succeeded despite the fact that the chairman of the Palace Beach System, an elderly man, Philip Guest, originally a partner in the private banking firm of Brown Brothers Harriman, despised Mel Hansen. And he said to John Baxter one time, "Can't we do better than that man? Also, can't he get some decent clothes? I think he *buys* his ties with gravy stains."

John Baxter was impressed with Mel Hansen's proposal for the highest-priced condominium in the history of Palm Beach and the far-ranging seawall development, but Philip Guest thought it was the most irresponsible program he had ever heard. He agreed, though, to assemble the board, all prominent South Florida businessmen and bankers, and abide by the consensus.

They met on a hot May morning in the stuffy crimson-carpeted boardroom located off one of the loggias in the Palace Beach Hotel. Mel was loaded with plans and models; Dr. Van Betzig brought a film showing what a properly designed seawall could accomplish in the area of beach restoration, and he blended definite credibility into Mel's plan.

The majority of the board was in favor of the proposal. But Philip Guest made one last effort; he pushed to his feet and the crinkle-faced Princetonian who once played five-goal polo said, "Gentlemen, this is absurd! How can we as responsible businessmen allot eight million dollars to build a condominium beyond the present bulkhead line? Mr. Hansen tells us that if his new line is not adopted, we have to tear down what we put up. That's outrageous and impractical, an unreasonable business risk."

"It's not risky, Philip."

(Mel always called the chairman "Philip" and the chairman called the architect "Mr. Hansen.")

"Why?"

"Because the proposal will go through. Who can turn down a plan to rehabilitate the beach?"

"Let's wait until October when the commission meets. Why rush? It's only six months away and what do the hurricane people think of this?"

"I spoke to Dr. Ballantine at the center and he's going to send up two of his people, doctors Haughton and Landon, to assist. So they're for it. We'll miss the buying season if we don't start now. Our realty brokers tell us we need that model apartment no later than November when the season opens."

"I must say I agree with Mel," John said. "I've spoken to several of the commissioners. They're falling in line and Mel is right. We must have units to show people by November."

The proposal was passed by the board and Philip Guest shuffled out of the conference room shaking his head.

"Good work, Mel," John said afterward. "How about lunch?"

The two men crossed the broad lawns to a separate building housing the inside pool loggia of the hotel which, in turn, overlooked an outside pool and the glassy sea beyond. They passed by the long, colorful buffet table where Mel stuffed himself after three "victory" martinis. John seldom drank and he only nibbled at a salad. He was thin and a fine tennis player. (To be thin and play tennis have always been two prerequisites in some coveys of Palm Beach.)

"What are we going to do about our wives?" John asked.

"I don't know. My mind isn't on female disputes. Tell Cynthia to get off the social ladder."

"Tell your wife the same thing," John said with a pleasant laugh, which exposed his perfectly capped white teeth.

The conversation drifted back to the Regency Walk project. But neither man realized how deep and serious was the rift between Cynthia Baxter and Denise Hansen.

Cynthia was an attractive, pleasant, forty-year-old woman from Atlanta. She had met John Baxter in New York and quickly realized that he represented the social status and prestige she was looking for. They married and moved to Palm Beach two years later. Then Cynthia wanted to be in the front ranks of the second covey; in Palm Beach it was a difficult road up, and it revolved around the social leader, or the "Queen," as some social reporters called her. She was the pivotal bee.

At the time it was Maggie Dunsmore. She was eighty but looked fifty, for in Palm Beach women work at preserving their youth with more determination and money than perhaps anywhere else.

Maggie was adored by everyone in the second covey, and a few in the first covey. She surrounded herself with a court of five ladies, one of whom was Cynthia Baxter who hoped to inherit the throne. Denise was outside the "court," in the third covey, and she thought that by being admitted to Maggie's graces she could move up to the next level of Palm Beach society.

The keen, azure-eyed Maggie, however, was not a typical Palm Beacher. She was the town's arch liberal, liking Jews, Indians, and blacks. She had come to the resort so many years ago that no one in the younger set could remember when Maggie wasn't around. In the twenties and thirties, among many world-famous names, women vied for the position of most important hostess. There were some powerful old names dotting Palm Beach: the Whitneys, the Paynes, the Dodges, the Du Ponts, the Vanderbilts, among others of the same weight.

Into this heavy social web came Margaret Burrows Redford, the "lovable Maggie." She arrived in the resort in the winter of 1932 as part social secretary and part guest to the Morris Levington Dunsmores. (He was an ambassador during the Harding Administration.) Margaret had met the ambassador and his wife in Newport, Rhode Island, in her twenty-eighth year.

Margaret's father was the squash and tennis pro at the exclusive Racquet Club in New York City beginning in 1905. During the season of 1922 Maggie was the third-seeded woman player in the United States. Then came a disastrous marriage to Bryant Baldwin, an Albany manufacturer and social butterfly, who lost his money, prestige, and finally shot himself.

Shortly afterward, Margaret joined the Dunsmores in Palm Beach. She was long-legged and beautiful and a popular guest on Palm Beach's private courts as well as the Everglades Club, but she was still a semioutsider until she married the widowed ambassador. Then her position changed.

Maggie's interest in human rights and social engineering began when she waged war against a hideous Palm Beach invention: the "Afrimobile," later called the "Afromobile," and then, the wheelchair, pumped by panting black men. This vassal rig was originated because Flagler did not allow motorcars on the island and the only way to move about was by walking under the hot sun and that seemed arduous, not resortlike. The solution was a large wicker chair attached to a bicycle.

In the beginning the Afromobile was a single-seater; then it grew into a side-by-side arrangement and in the roasting sun the black men had to push not only the heavy rig but often two plump people besides.

For this work the drivers received ten cents an hour. Often they dropped of heat prostration and if it happened more than twice, the black driver was fired forever. It had been said that many black men died at the handlebars of their Afromobiles from heart attacks, but this was unconfirmed. At one time there were four hundred Afromobiles in Palm Beach and the last one pumped by an old black was seen in the resort as late as 1977.

Maggie would never ride in the abominations and she tried several times to have the slavish rigs outlawed by the Town Council.

A long time ago there was a black community in Palm Beach, a shanty row called the Styx, located on Sunset Avenue where it joined North County Road. The blacks were allowed to set up slatboard houses there as a matter of convenience to the whites: To have them close at hand meant they would be at work on time, and they could always be fetched quickly should someone decide to give an impromptu party for a hundred or more. However, the sight of the shacks was regarded by many as untidy and in the thirties it was decided that the black shantytown should come down. The blacks disappeared from Palm Beach to live on the far side of the lake.

The Indians came to Palm Beach for another purpose. They grew fresh vegetables and huckleberries on their flat lands and sloughs, which spread out east of Lake Okeechobee. They were permitted to enter Palm Beach because their vegetables were cheaper, better than those that could be purchased at the greengrocers and, too, they sold wild ducks, a popular item relished by the early Palm Beachers.

Maggie often saw squads of Indians sitting in the shade of the great loggias, always under the heavy banyan trees, and sometimes the servants would allow the Seminole children in the swimming pools if the residents were away. Maggie herself invited them for dips in her own pool and this shocked many of the nearby cottagers who wouldn't swim in the Dunsmore pool then because mucky redmen had used the same water.

Some P.B.'ers were annoyed that the Indians seemed to have the run of their island and the local grocers complained about the outside competition; the solution was an ordinance, which halted all door-to-door selling and solicitations. In the beginning the Indians didn't understand this, and some were arrested and transported quickly to the far side of the bridge with a stiff warning never to come back.

Maggie made it a point to buy all her vegetables from the Indians, her way of retaliation. Once a week she drove out along State Road 80 which headed into the Glades, and filled the trunk of her 1928 Rolls with whatever she could purchase from the tribes who set up roadstands.

With her progressive tendencies Maggie would have been doomed in Palm Beach if it had not been that Mrs. Stotesbury liked the young tennis player and Mrs. Marjorie Merriweather Post liked Mrs. Stotesbury, and that delicate weaving brought Maggie into Queendom.

Mel and his wife were two prosy Machiavellians who deserved each other. But Denise had not forgotten her original goal and she was looking for a richer man than Mel, one with fine blue blood. Denise had the looks, the body, the sexiness to interest any man and she carefully concealed her slummy background and played down the fact that she was a former actress, shaky credentials in Palm Beach if your name wasn't Cloris Leachman or Dina Merrill.

Denise came to Maggie's attention because the actress had taken 560 tennis lessons, sometimes two a day, and she became the most improved player in Palm Beach. That interested the Queen.

Furthermore, a friend at the court—Maggie's court, that is—made a special effort in her behalf. She was a willowy, very tall, auburn-haired woman called Nicole Bouchart, a Belgian who was married to a very rich, very bedridden fellow. (Palm Beach, being a mecca for fortune hunters, attracted an inordinate group of foreign people.) Nicole and Denise had met on the tennis court and they lunched frequently at Petite Marmite and spoke French together. Denise worked at the friendship. She knew it was her only chance to get near Maggie, and Denise had to pass her inspection if she was to enter the court. That was the fastest way to break into the second covey.

It had started on a hot summer afternoon. The air was steamy along the Avenue, and the large buildings such as Saks, Cartier's, Gucci's choked off the gentle sea breeze.

"Why don't we go back to the boat for a salad?" Denise suggested. "It's air-conditioned."

"I just have to stop into Martha's," Nicole said, "to pick up a dress."

Both women wore white Jax pants and Dior blouses. They looked like sisters; Nicole was older: She was forty-two, but appeared thirty. They had the same deep-blue eyes and they both went to Arden's twice a week and had the same hairstyle.

Later the women sat in the enclosed saloon of the 53-foot Hatteras eating small salads—naturally they were very weight and figure conscious.

"What do you want out of Palm Beach?" Nicole asked.

"What everyone wants," Denise laughed. "A rich husband with lots of style and intelligence, who doesn't drink too much and who's a very good dancer."

"You don't love Mel?"

"Of course not. I married him just to get here. He knows that, too. The William Morris agency wasn't calling anymore and I had to do something."

"But you don't seem to be looking or snatching."

"I've kept it cool, as the Americans say, but that doesn't mean I'm not looking."

"I know quite a lot about your background," Nicole said with a mocking smile.

"From whom?"

"A woman in Paris. Things get around."

Denise sharpened her voice in self-defense. "I did what I had to do and it wasn't always easy."

"But you won't get anyplace in Palm Beach, my dear, no matter how many press agents you have. I can tell you that."

"And why not?"

"You're married to a slob and you're an actress without proper breeding or distinction."

Nicole moved over and sat next to Denise and placed her arm around the woman's shoulder.

"But I like you. You're very attractive. Maybe we can patch a few of your fences."

"How? According to you, it's hopeless."

"Are you aware that Cynthia Baxter despises you? She says you steal her dinner guests."

"Cynthia's a very nervous social climber and how could I steal her guests? She lives in that thirty-room Mizner mansion with a pool, two tennis courts, three in help, and all we have is a rather small yacht."

"That doesn't matter. Cynthia has talked you down to Maggie, but the old birdie listens to me also. Now if I were to make up a story about your reputation, pop a few lies around, I think Maggie would take a closer look at you. She's quite a liberal. She doesn't mind actresses, but she can't stand fortune hunters with bad manners."

"Is that what she thinks I am?"

"Yes, and it all came from Cynthia."

"That bitch! She's one to talk."

"As I said, I might be able to change things."

"Why would you do this for me?"

"Because I want something."

"What?"

"You."

"Do I understand this correctly?" Denise asked, stiffening, then rising to fill her glass with white Beaujolais from the ice bucket on the small bar.

"Are you shocked?"

"No," Denise said, returning to the sofa. "I'm just thinking."

"You've been with women before and I'm not unattractive, am I?"

"Just the opposite."

"I find you very stimulating, Denise. You didn't answer my question . . . you have been with women?"

"A couple of times, but there were always men around . . . directors mostly . . . you know how it goes."

"Well, how do you feel about it?"

"I've never really tuned into a one-to-one female relationship. Why didn't you say something about this before?"

"Guess I didn't have the nerve."

Nicole did not wait for Denise's response; she reached over and kissed her and whispered, "Can't we go below?"

Denise got up. The decision was made. The two women went below and in the aft stateroom Nicole gently slipped off Denise's clothes. They made passionate love, and when they had climaxed and rested in each other's arms, Nicole said:

"You were much better than I thought, Denise. I'll start work with Maggie right away. You'll see how much I can do for you."

CHAPTER

10

BILLY HAUGHTON NEVER FORGOT HER CRUISE TO THE HURRICANE grounds, and she never again dated Steve Mitchell, although they continued to work together trying to solve the problems of storm surge. Several months after Billy returned from the voyage of the *Pleasure Pie,* she started dating Keith Landon.

Steve continued on his single course, tracing the beginnings of his anticipated killer storm, and he began visiting private groups without the sanction of the hurricane center. At first Dr. Ballantine paid little attention to Steve's erratic behavior, thinking that no one was listening to Steve, but then word began leaking back to the director's desk. Commerce heard about it and wondered.

"Where does all this come from?" the administrator of NOAA, Dr. Marc Peterson, asked Lou one day over the phone. "Who is this Mitchell?"

"A theorist," Lou Ballantine answered.

Then certain South Florida real-estate interests began calling the center. "This kind of talk is bad for business," they told the director.

When the barbs mounted, Steve was called in by Lou Ballantine. "Steve, I'm receiving criticism about your hurricane forecast."

"We're going to get a big one, Lou."

"All right . . . all right, but Steve, I want you to keep this to yourself. You're beginning to alarm people."

"What is the point, Lou, of keeping it to myself? I'm trying to save their lives."

"You don't know for sure that this kind of hurricane is going to hit South Florida."

"Lou, that warming trend in the tropical convergence zone is telling us something. Besides, we're due, according to statistics."

"You're a scientist, not a prophet. Scientists don't go around expressing whims. That's all you have . . . a whim wrapped in a few theories and facts that may, or may not, be on the button."

"It's coming, Lou. I know it's coming."

At that remark, Lou Ballantine drew in a sudden breath; he looked hard at the solemn, bony-faced man sitting across his desk. How stable was Steve Mitchell? Was he slowly coming unlinked with reality?

Lou was a spare, practical man who went by the book; he shied away from controversial bouts, messy dislocations of work. He probably would have discharged Steve Mitchell long before if he hadn't recognized in the man an earnestness, a sincere devotion to his work. The director realized there was yeast beneath Steve's storm fantasies: Mitchell had to be listened to, reckoned with. Maybe he had stumbled onto something no one else knew; who was to say that a super storm could not pounce out of the tropical Atlantic and lay flat an overconfident or "cocky coast," as Steve said repeatedly?

"Steve, I'll concede that a super hurricane could hit Florida, but what's to be gained by this kind of forecasting? It makes fools out of us. We're supposed to be the people who know."

"We don't know half of what people think we know."

"Yes," the director sighed.

"Lou, we have to get people to listen to us."

"They will . . . they'll evacuate when the time comes. How can you get people to listen when the weather's perfect and there is no storm in sight?"

"We'll have to force them to listen," Steve thundered. "Lou, I financed a private research study about evacuation and three quarters of the coastal residents I talked to told me they wouldn't leave. We've got to change that! One family up in Palm Beach gave us this special hurricane section from the *Palm Beach Daily News* . . . look at this ad sponsored by the Red Cross."

Steve shoved the paper across the desk.

HURRICANE EMERGENCY INFORMATION FOR YOUR PROTECTION

If you observe the following precautions, you need have little fear of an approaching storm. . . .

"What's wrong with that? We helped them write it ten years ago when I was deputy director."

"Go on . . . read the first statement."

Lou's eyes dropped to the list of instructions. Number one said:

Most people living in homes built to meet the current South Florida Building Code should remain in their homes during storms. If yours is a modern house, built to withstand storm winds, and kept in good condition, you should be perfectly safe in your own home where you can feel more at ease about your property.

"Well . . ." Lou said.

"That kind of talk breeds disaster. The people in Pass Christian stayed at home and they died. The instructions are wrong, Lou. It's not wind that kills; it's water . . . surge. But when you read this, you come away with the idea that the home is the safest place to be. That's fine as long as it's above water."

"Maybe we should update the information," Lou said slowly, glancing again at the paper.

"Damned right! It should say that high water is the killer."

"I agree with you, Steve . . . we'll update that. I'll make a note of it, but what worries me isn't newspaper language. There's no basis for your telling people that a hurricane could take ten thousand lives on this coast."

"It could."

"Everyone at the center disagrees with this prediction. I can't tell you how many times Keith and Billy have been in here asking what's wrong with you."

"Landon has his own thing going, and Billy packs it in with him. She'd agree with anything the little computer genius came up with," Steve said.

"Let's keep private lives out of this. Steve, how would ten thousand people be killed in South Florida? If you give me some platform for the theorem, I'll back you up, but running around with these idle speculations is crazy. We have a primary obligation to make the residents believe us when it's necessary, and you know how difficult this is already. When you insist on forecasting a storm that never comes, people begin to think . . . ask questions. . . . What storm? Show me."

"Lou, I have the figures and the plots. I think I can prove my theory."

"Go ahead . . . I'm listening."

"As you know, they dammed up Lake Okeechobee after the 1928 hurricane and dug a series of overflow canals through the Glades, which empty into the intracoastal."

Lou nodded.

"These canals relieve the inland water in five locations . . . Palm Beach, Lauderdale, et cetera. Now we start with the storm of the century, as I call it—winds in excess of two hundred miles per hour."

"Sustained?"

"Yes."

"We've never seen a storm like that."

"But the tropical Atlantic is warming up. You agreed with that fact."

"I did. OK . . . what kind of central pressure are we looking at?"

"Twenty-six point ten."

"That's lower than the Key West hurricane."

"Do you acknowledge that it could happen?"

"It's a remote possibility, Steve, but I'll go along. It could happen if conditions were exactly right."

"Fine. Now, let's continue to build the scenario. Twenty-two inches of rain are dumped on the Glades in ten hours. You have to admit that could occur in a storm such as this."

"Yes."

"So the theoretical storm hits our coast. Do you know how much overflow water is going to smash out of the Glades?"

"I could figure it out."

"You don't have to, Lou, I have. Eleven billion tons, Lou! Eleven billion tons!"

"Are you sure of that?"

"Worked it out with the Army engineers . . . they agree."

"But the intracoastal can absorb it."

"Ah, but what if there's convergence within the basins? What if Lauderdale is overtopped by surge? You have billions of tons of seawater colliding with tons of Glade water gushing out of the floodgates." Steve's eyes blazed at Lou. "Now we have a back-rise . . . twenty feet in the inland waterway at Lauderdale. The bridge accesses go under first. There's no way to escape. Lou, I saw this convergence in Pass Christian. I know! The water climbed to twenty-six feet!"

"But there are several weaknesses in your theory. First of all, Lauderdale would never be overtopped. Billy says the highest water rise there would be fifteen feet . . . no more."

"I think it could go to eighteen and just those three extra feet would cause the surge to pour over the beach and converge."

"Very remote."

"But possible."

"Maybe, but from what we know about surge characteristics, it's just about impossible. But let's suppose that Lauderdale is overtopped and we have convergence in the basin. People would have been pulled out long before this happened."

"Oh, sure. But my research says that most people won't leave. Articles like this in the paper tell them there's nothing to worry about. Remain at home, it says, safe with all your property."

"In Florida it is against the law to disregard an evacuation order."

"A thousand policemen are going to arrest a million people?"

"It wouldn't come to that. If residents saw the waves coming up, they would leave on their own."

"Lou, that was the story of Camille. The hurricane didn't have high waves, but when that surge started to boil the water came at us so fast we couldn't do a damned thing. That's how my wife died with ninety others at Pass Christian."

"But Pass Christian was a low beach community, Steve. We have reefs, some coral elevation, hundreds of high-rises. People could go up to the fifth floor, to the twentieth floor, and be completely safe. No hurricane is climbing up that far."

Steve thought a minute. "I wouldn't want to be in a high-rise with two-hundred-mile-an-hour winds bashing it. Every damned window in the place would be blown out."

"Most have storm shutters."

"That's the most overrated item in the world, Lou. With my kind of wind, they'd come off their tracks."

"Steve, let's cut through this. I didn't start this discussion to talk about your vision. I don't want any more of your interviews with the *Miami Star*."

Lou pointed to the thick black headlines from a Sunday feature story written by a José Gomez:

HURRICANE EXPERT PREDICTS SUPER STORM FOR SOUTH FLORIDA. COULD KILL 10,000

"The implication is that the center is issuing this kind of forecast," the director said. "Word has come down from Commerce. If one more thing like this gets out, I'm going to have to ask for your resignation."

CHAPTER

11

THAT SUMMER THE FIRST PILINGS WERE DRIVEN FOR THE PALACE
Beach project over the constant objections of Philip Guest. As the
days lengthened, the heat came to Palm Beach; the parties thinned
out and seasoned people left for Europe or northern resorts. Steve
Mitchell continued to speak about hurricane dangers, although he
didn't give out any more interviews to the press, and the center
denied emphatically that his predictions were authorized or official.

Nicole still met with Denise, although the relationship was straining the actress emotionally. She could not bring herself around to
enjoying sex with another woman. The strange arrangement with
Nicole, however, had the effect of improving Denise's sex life with
Mel who had always been dull and unimaginative in bed. Denise
would have gladly given up the relationship with Nicole had not
her picture begun to appear more often in the local papers. Twice
she was asked to lunch by Maggie, who thought that the Frenchwoman was not as bad as Cynthia had described her.

The surprise, which even shocked Nicole, was Maggie's decision to let Denise run the Home Ball, a small black-tie event that was held late every summer for the year-round Palm Beach residents. Cynthia was absolutely stunned; she wanted to chair the ball. It was not an important chairmanship in the roster of big P.B. balls, but to those moving up in the second covey, it did have a certain cachet.

"Nicole, you'll have to help me!" Denise said, on the edge of panic. "I don't even know how to order the flowers."

"Don't worry. Just do what I say. You should start by having a small, intimate party aboard the *Patna*." (The Hansens' Hatteras was named for the ship in *Lord Jim*.)

"Whom should I invite?"

"Not Maggie, of course. Her calendar is filled months in advance and it would be presumptuous. Invite a few of the gals in the court and, for God's sake, include Cynthia and John. It's bad form in P.B. to squabble openly."

"I don't have anything personal against Cynthia."

"I know, darling, but she stands in your way and there's always competition around here because we're all after the same things. Face it, there're only so many parties and who attends is important."

Denise had only entertained casually. Their yacht was small by Palm Beach standards, and she was unsure of herself as a hostess. She read book after book on etiquette.

The folk art of Palm Beach was party giving. The first covey entertained on a relatively small scale, not often, and their "sitdowns" were often black tie. No photographers were allowed in the big homes. A party's success was measured by the grace of the hostess and the food she served. Qualitative assessments.

The second covey entertained with more frequency; usually their parties were large, overstuffed, with orchestras, photographers, reporters, and catered food. Bashes!

At one of the larger second-covey affairs, some guests became sick after eating tainted shrimp; another person fell on the dance floor because it was too highly waxed; the air-conditioner in the rancid Mizner home failed; and there were two fist fights. The town clown, Jayson Kendall, was also there that night. Jayson was an Ivy League fellow who had lost most of his money and had trouble paying his food and bar bills, but he continued to live as if he still had it all.

He got drunk at the party, took off his clothes, and fell into the pool. He chose the wrong end, unfortunately, and smashed his head and the pool water immediately turned red. For all of this, the party was deemed a great success: The local paper published nine pictures of the disaster and all the right second-covey guests were adequately covered.

Denise did schedule a buffet aboard the *Patna*. It was too large for the small yacht to handle and she was ill at ease. Nicole did most of the work while continually reassuring the yearling hostess. Mel took the yacht filled with long-gowned guests up the lake for a short cruise during cocktails, and when they were snugged up at the Brazilian Docks again, the buffet of ham and chicken was served.

The party was enlivened by Jayson Kendall. He was one of the few P.B.'ers who could stroll in and out of the first and second coveys. He had family background, was well schooled—Andover, Princeton, Harvard Business—and at sixty-two played a better game of tennis than many younger men and danced well. The fact that his tuxedo was frayed was all right, a plus mark. Those in the first covey thought that Jayson was an extremely humorous bard, and he could talk on many diversified subjects: the stock market, which had sapped most of his money, his four wives who had sapped the rest of it, his racing-car days, when he had raced foreign cars with the early gentlemen drivers like Brigs Cunningham.

His reputation as a blue-blooded jester was well deserved. Among his merry pranks two were outstanding: One night there was a large dockside yachting party, a popular Palm Beach platform for get-togethers, and everyone, including Jayson, was into his cups. Jayson untied the yacht, an ancient 128-footer, and the whole fun-loving group drifted away on Lake Worth. Few realized what was happening, though some thought the yacht was under power, but the motors on the gleaming craft had not functioned for over two years. The Coast Guard finally rescued the yacht and tied it back to the dock where the gaiety continued as if nothing had gone wrong.

Jayson had also thrown the famous "in bad taste party." He had purchased cheap party invitations and he wrote a different message on each: Some said "pool party"; or "night tennis"; or "white tie with medals"; or "scarlet coats"; still others said "informal" or "black tie." The first and second divisions of people, about 190 guests, arrived, all wondering, of course, if they had misread their invitations.

Jayson served sweet grape punch and his buffet consisted of "heroes and subs" passed around on Saran-Wrapped paper plates. And he had hired an accordion player from the Elks Lodge to entertain, and he had strung crepe paper streamers from the ceiling of his large, crumbling Mizner house. When the edge was off and the joke revealed, everyone settled down to one of the best "un-Palm Beach" parties ever held on the finger island.

Nicole had suggested that Jayson be invited to the *Patna* buffet and the local scaramouch set the tone. He sang dirty Irish songs and everyone guzzled very stiff martinis as the yacht cut a small furrow up through the lake.

The buffet went very well and John Baxter, like the others, drank more than usual, and he was not a drinking man. Denise was drinking heavily to calm her nerves and after dinner John, who had always been secretly attracted to the Frenchwoman, met her on the foredeck. They kissed and he was amazed at himself; it was the first time he had ever given his attention to another woman. It might have been too much vodka or the scented night or the fact that Denise pushed herself hard against his chest, but John looked down to see her honey-colored breasts, firm and polished by moonlight, and he had a sudden desire for the woman.

"Can't we go someplace?" he whispered.

Denise was attracted to John because of his looks, position, and money, and she readily agreed. Her head was fuzzy, but she had often fantasized about being raped by this cool, handsome, conservative president of the Palace Beach System.

John Baxter was a sheltered, naïve man in many ways, especially sexual. His life had run along a single track from prep school to Harvard to summer resorts, such as Bar Harbor where the ideas and conversations flowed from the same tight, inbred group of eastern establishmentarians. Even World War II did not change this. John entered the Army Air Force with seven Harvard classmates; they trained together, flew together in the Eighth Air Force and the only disruption in John's social network was the noise and closeness of the German flak, but they all survived and he came home and his narrow life took up where it had left off.

Despite his education and travels, John had never met a woman like Denise; worse, he never knew they existed. When she took his hand that night, leading him below decks of the *Patna,* he was totally unaware she was pulling the oldest trick in the world.

They found their way into the last stateroom, which ran across the breadth of the yacht's stern. They locked the door and embraced passionately.

"I love fantasies, John," she murmured.

"Like what?"

"Pretend you're raping me," she laughed. "A good old-fashioned rape."

"OK . . . I'm raping you."

"No, tear my dress off. I'd like that."

He pulled slightly away for a moment. "Denise, that's a little crazy."

"Do it!" she said, kissing him.

"It's your dress," John sighed.

He clamped his big hands around the V of her neckline and yanked. The dress came away in shreds, revealing an almost perfect body, one gentle curve flowing into another. The cabin was dark, but filtered lights made effervescent puddles on the azure-blue carpet, and by the wide bunk stood a flickering alcohol ship's lantern. He caught his breath and studied her for a moment. She was even more beautiful than he had realized. He couldn't believe what he was doing and, for a fragment of a second, he wanted to dash from the cabin. Instead he took her in his arms and pushed her back onto the double bunk. He followed the soft curves of her body with his tongue as she slipped off his clothes. In a second she felt him slide inside her.

"Don't rape me! Let me go!" she cried out. "Let me go . . . don't rape me!"

Her husky French "acting" voice lent reality to the fantasy.

"Hey, keep it down! Someone will hear you," John whispered.

It was too late.

That someone was Cynthia Baxter, who was looking for her husband along with Mel Hansen, who was searching for his wife: They heard the cries and sobs coming from Denise.

"Oh, my God!" Denise shuddered.

Mel, who carried a spare key, quickly unlocked the door. The floor was littered with pieces of Denise's dress and for a second

Denise did not see Mel and Cynthia, and she continued her mock struggle.

"Please let me go . . . it's a brutal rape!" she cried out.

Five other guests who were stumbling around the yacht, including Nicole Bouchart, saw the same sight. Cynthia erupted into a savage temper, and she flew across the small cabin and dug her nails into Denise's face and started to peel flesh away from the French actress. John attempted to pull his wife off Denise and in the struggle the actress's flailing hand came into contact with the alcohol lantern and she flung it about in self-defense.

"You bitch!" Denise howled in French.

The lantern broke across Cynthia's left shoulder. Flaming alcohol rivered her face and she screamed as her hair caught on fire. Mel and John buried Cynthia's face in the blanket and the human torch went out immediately, but the carpet ignited and there was a rush of bumping panic. Someone called the Palm Beach emergency number from the shore-connected phone aboard the *Patna*. "There's been a rape . . . a riot aboard the yacht *Patna*! It's burning!"

Mel had smothered the flames with a CO_2 extinguisher in a matter of seconds, but the damage was done and acrid smoke billowed out.

For a small town, Palm Beach had one of the finest police and fire department systems in the county, plus a finely trained paramedic team driving an extremely well-equipped ambulance. The latter had been donated to the town by a woman whose husband died on the way to Good Samaritan Hospital in West Palm Beach, since Palm Beach did not have a hospital. As soon as a call came into the emergency number, 655-4000, a button was pushed at the police station that tied the fire department into the same conversation.

The *Patna* call was slurred by a drunken man and, according to practice, a police car was dispatched to the Brazilian Docks to verify the situation.

When Officer Forbes, a veteran on the ninety-man force, ran out on the dock, he saw clouds of thick smoke pouring from the stern of the *Patna*; people were screaming on the deck and Denise, her face crisscrossed with fresh blood, gripped the rail.

"I've been raped! Raped! Raped!" she kept screaming.

The officer, knowing that perhaps twenty million dollars' worth of yachts were resting beside the *Patna*, yelled into his walkie-talkie. "There's a fire aboard the *Patna*. Also seems to have been a rape . . . and there's people injured."

The Coast Guard was called and seven pieces of fire equipment, nine police units, and the paramedic ambulance rushed to the site, along with the hundreds of people who normally turned out to see such disruptions.

Denise collapsed theatrically; Cynthia collapsed physically, and both women were taken to Good Samaritan Hospital.

In the waiting room John and Mel stood talking.

"Mel, I'm sorry . . . I didn't rape Denise. She kind of, well, she wanted to play a rape scene. It was just a fantasy."

"I understand, John. Don't worry about it." Mel clamped a big hand on the other's shoulder. "There'll be no complaint."

(The architect was thinking gleefully what a fresh, good handle this gave him to hold over John Baxter.)

Denise's wounds were superficial and she was released after a gynecological examination that revealed sperm in her vagina. Cynthia was in far worse condition and she was rushed by helicopter to the burn center in Miami.

The next morning the daily paper in West Palm Beach, and a liberal journal that had often taken swipes at the "islanders" and their quaint folkways, ran a photograph and story on the front page:

PALM BEACH PARTY TURNS INTO FIERY RAPE AND RIOT

What started out as a typical Palm Beach yachting party aboard Mr. and Mrs. Melvin Hansen's 53-foot yacht, *Patna*, moored at the Brazilian Docks, turned into a near disaster last night: The motor yacht caught fire; there were two cases of aggravated assault, plus a rape, according to eyewitnesses and police reports.

There were conflicting stories of what happened. It appears that John Baxter, president of the Palace Beach System and elder of the Episcopal Church, was caught with Denise Hansen, the hostess, who claimed Mr. Baxter had raped her. She is the former Denise Dassault, a French film actress. A fight started when Mrs. Baxter attacked Mrs. Hansen and, by accident apparently, an alcohol lantern broke and the wife of the Palace Beach president was severely burned about the face. The flames spread to the carpeting, but they were extinguished quickly by the owner, Mr. Hansen.

Police reported finding an overloaded yacht teeming with drunken guests, shreds of Mrs. Hansen's clothing in the partly burned cabin, and witnesses were taken to the police department for questioning. According to Mr. Baxter, there was no rape.

"We were only pretending," he told police.

This seems to be supported by Mr. Hansen who said that no charges would be filed, but his wife who remained in a state of shock could not be questioned. Her condition was reported to be good. Mrs. Baxter is being treated for first- and second-degree burns in Miami and her condition is reported to be stable.

The police and Coast Guard are continuing their investigations.

And so, in an odd way, Denise Hansen got all the publicity she had always wanted.

PART TWO

BIRTH

There is, one knows not what sweet
mystery about this sea, whose gently
awful stirrings seem to speak of
some hidden soul beneath.

HERMAN MELVILLE

CHAPTER

12

THE DOLDRUM SKY IS ALWAYS BUSY, DOTTED WITH TOWERING CUMULUS puffs built from the evection moisture sucked from the warm surface. The lazy swells roll slowly, reflecting the metallic glaze of the large sun that never diminishes in size or intensity from one day to the next during the hurricane months from June to mid-October.

The sea below is jammed. Billions of microorganisms in the plant and fish chain populate the doldrum ocean, and if a tightly woven net is used to skim the surface of those tepid waters, the webs will be clogged with every conceivable sea creature—some so small that they must be washed from the meshing and examined under a microscope.

From the deck of a ship one can see the residents of the deeper tropical waters: gray-blue outlines gliding along, vivid against their azure background, a hammerhead moving and twisting for smaller fish. Sometimes a squid goes by. Then there is as well the bustle above: gray-snooted terns, ospreys, and other seabirds glide and flap about. They are working to stay alive, going to this place and that, diving for fish, bobbing upon the usually oily surface, ducking into the feeding grounds, raising their heads in gulps and shakes as they pluck out their part of the sea-air life chain.

Above it all are the usual groupings of convective clouds: white, high, magisterial, always moving, recurling, twisting into filmy strings, then reforming.

Though the doldrum sea, or the ITC (Intertropical Convergence) as it is called by the physical oceanographer and others, appears to be a band of tranquil water, never admitting the usual slant of chattering winds, like the trades or westerlies, it is the ever-pumping furnace for the world's thermal machine—its energy.

A particle of moisture drawn from these cunning oceans in the process of heat exchange or transference can affect the weather on a certain day in the city of Quebec. The source of water vapor in the atmosphere is derived from the oceans that bridle the equator, the warmest seas. The vapor condenses; clouds form and they are drawn out of the doldrums by the earth's spinning, the Coriolis force, and upper air steering currents take the condensed nuclei swinging the pattern along as pressure differentials. But what is taken from the warm seas must be returned.

Thus, energy changed into condensation from the hurricane seas becomes the rains of Quebec. As water vapor cools, it falls. The whole process goes on and repeats itself in a strange manner not totally understood.

Man doesn't know when a hurricane is about to be born, but the doldrum inhabitants do. They know long before it happens. Birds come to rest and take shelter well in advance of tornadoes, even before the Weather Services send out their warnings or watches. At Pass Christian the day before Camille some said that they noticed that the gulls and other seabirds had flown away; and three fishermen who were out after Gulf catches in the hours before the hurricane when the water was still unlathered, reported that they had not caught a thing. No nibbles that day.

It is suspected that the animal life of the sea is equipped with sensory radar, but this has never been confirmed by the ichthyologists.

A sea evacuation happened on August 17, in a five-mile area of the ocean just east of Cape Verdes, the ten-island chain controlled by the Portuguese 375 miles off the Senegal coast. On this particular day the fish were there and they knew something was going wrong.

At 5:30 A.M., on Camille's eighth birthday, the water east of the Verdes was 91 degrees, elevated two degrees from the usual pattern of surface heating. At 5:50 A.M., as the light bled into the cloud-flecked sky, a large tiger shark lazily propelled himself up to his morning feeding grounds in the waters ten feet beneath the luke-warm surface. He opened his mouth and cruised. Little was taken in during his feeding swim; his usual satisfying fill was gone. The smaller fish and organisms had drifted or swum away; something was amiss; things weren't the same for some reason, so the shark took it as a warning and he, too, flipped his tail and got out.

Overhead was an identical exit.

The birds from Verdes, the hawks, the tanges, the snoots had returned to shore.

The sea was ready.

The clouds clustered and there was a series of heavy rain squalls east of the islands just before eight. No one was in the exact spot when the heat machine started to go insane, but Dakar radar noticed the squall concentration around eight-thirty that morning and so did the man on duty monitoring the airport approach radar at Praia, capital of the Verdes.

The squall and slight pressure dip came up almost simultaneously on their Teletypes. The terminal and area forecast for the Praia Airport that morning said:

SIGMET ALPHA ONE. HEAVY CONCENTRATION OF SQUALL ACTIVITY LOCATED VICINITY AREA 16–10 NORTH, 21–40 WEST. EXPECT CEILINGS OF 500 FEET, TOPS TO FLIGHT LEVEL : 043. ACCOMPANYING WINDS RECORDED AT 20 KNOTS SUSTAINED, 28 IN GUSTS. EXPECT HEAVY RAIN CONCENTRATION AND MODERATE TO SEVERE TURBULENCE IN FORECAST AREA.

The surface readings were provided by a fisherman out of Praia who radioed to the Verdes central meteorological station saying that he was experiencing developing seas and heavy concentration of organized squalls with accompanying winds.

It simply rained a bit more than usual in the Verdes that day. By evening, the sun had burst forth and the gray, low nimbus had passed over the islands out to sea, westward.

The identical information had been fed into the worldwide meteorological reporting system and ten minutes after two in the morning eastern daylight time, it was relayed to the National Hurricane Center. The night operator in the Teletype room ripped off the broad tape and because it was technically a low-pressure formation in the convergence zone, the all-night man on the fifth floor took the blue print-out into the hurricane war room and slipped it on the clipboard. The specialist on duty looked at it and went back to his coffee, knowing that it was merely a routine dispatch from a reporting station thousands of miles from Miami.

Steve Mitchell arrived at the center shortly before eight that day. He was not a forecaster, or even a tropical storm specialist, but Steve probably knew more about the storms from experience and study than the other nine men working in the war room. During the winter months he seldom appeared upstairs except to speak to Lou Ballantine.

In hurricane season it was different.

Then he took the elevator each morning directly to the fifth floor and in the war room he would study the latest reports: synoptics delivered by wire and radio plus the night infrared satellite photos, barely dry from the printer in the room two doors down the south hall. Most of the specialists thought he was looking for his storm.

On this morning Steve studied the night input data. The disturbance, as it was technically called, east of the Verdes was noted by both the print-outs and satellite photos. But the infrared pictures only showed a slight smudge, evidence of a small cloud grouping with squall concentration. Steve picked up a magnifying glass to examine it.

Comparing and confirming data was usual practice among those who watched for irregularities in the thermal and pressure stability of the tropical ocean zones. The purpose of the dual investigation was simply to compare reports. Sometimes the satellite revealed that the surface input was more critical, more organized and broader than the human eye had observed. It happened the other way around, too.

Often the satellite would be the first eyes to see a cluster; even then the pictures told the specialist very little except the positioning of the isobar dent. That was all the Verdes disturbance was: a slight crevasse in the long sweeping lines of equal pressure that the weather-men drew to present visualization of global activity. This could not be Steve's private storm, for its positioning fell far from the hurri-cane spawning pattern. Steve thought it was probably a storm kicked off by an unusual warm, dry air current swept off the deserts east of Senegal. There were also two slight disturbances in the tropical seas that day, but like the Verdes cloud organization, they were small and insignificant. That morning at ten minutes after eight eastern day-light time, the hurricane center dispatched the following message on its wire:

THE NATIONAL HURRICANE CENTER REPORTS THAT PRESENT CON-DITIONS ARE NOT FAVORABLE FOR TROPICAL STORM DEVELOPMENT DURING THE NEXT THREE DAYS.

The report was accurate. None of the three notches in the isobar pattern could be legitimately classified as a depression—meaning a slight rotary circulation on the surface or aloft. And at that point the Verdes activity evidenced no closing of the isobar pattern. Nevertheless, for some reason, this odd migrant in the doldrums bore convectionary forces: vertical motion produced by thermal or mechanical instability in the atmosphere column.

No one ever knew just why this particular instability began where it did or why it suddenly began pumping moisture up into the atmosphere.

Satisfied that the hurricane grounds were resting this day, Steve took a cup of coffee from the hot plate in the military coordination room, which looked out on the hurricane nerve center by means of a glass panel. During the season of the great storms there was an Air Force or Navy officer on duty here twenty-four hours. His job was to form a continuity between the specialists and the hurricane hunters who flew reconnaissance planes into the storms to identify their makeup and anatomy.

Steve with his cardboard coffee cup in hand did not then go directly to his office. Rather, he stopped in room 408 to chat with another researcher who was paid $31,000 a year to investigate hur-ricane destruction of the red mangrove regions of Florida's Cape Sable. Steve felt this expensive study—and there were others like it —was irrelevant. How to plant new seedlings under the suffocating mud caused by hurricane surge appeared so insignificant. Choked rootlets and hurricane defoliation of the Florida stud growth did not seem vital when so many serious hurricane subjects were not fully budgeted. Several times Steve had asked the director how Butch, the roly-poly mangrove man in 408, had convinced Commerce that his was a substantive project. But the government adored ecological research and the more remote the topic happened to be, the better. Actually, Steve rather liked the cheery man whose walls were covered with photographs of hurricane damage to Florida's trees, as if these would justify the pursuit of his puny subject.

When Steve returned to his office, Billy was packing her attaché case.

"I suppose you and Keith are off to Palm Beach again?" he said.

"Yes, there's some very interesting work involving this new seawall proposal of Mr. Hansen's."

"But Keith doesn't need to go. He should be right here during the hurricane season."

"He's programming the characteristics of the basin. Lou thinks it's important."

Steve shook his head and Billy glanced up. "You just can't stand him, can you?" she said. Then she added off-handedly, "You almost sound jealous."

"I couldn't be jealous of that rip-off artist."

"Steve, you know what your problem is? You're into the language of ultimates. You see the 'worst' storm coming . . . you and Jeane Dixon. You judge Keith as a monster and he's not at all. He's a bright guy and if I were you I wouldn't go around tossing brickbats at him."

She walked out of the office with a stiff face. Steve sat down at his piled-up desk and thought that perhaps Billy Haughton was right. Maybe he was too committed to what he believed, and it was gnawing away at him again. Still, the appalling sight of Camille slid swiftly across his mind and he visualized each detail as if the tragedy had occurred only the day before.

CHAPTER

13

IMMEDIATELY AFTER THE *Patna* "RAPE AND RIOT," PALM BEACH buzzed. It was the most delicious hunk of scandal to ripple through the resort in recent years. Reactions varied.

How could John Baxter rape a woman?

That was the question most asked. People were shocked, and the first covey thought the episode was new evidence of the uncivilized manners practiced in the untidy lower groups. Denise did seem to be coming out ahead in the scoring. Her face bore thick brown scabs and she dined every day at Petite Marmite so everyone could see what Cynthia Baxter had done to her. The telephone aboard the *Patna* never stopped ringing; luncheon invitations poured in and Denise, good actress that she was, appeared to be in great distress in public.

When she had first arrived in Palm Beach as a social wall-scaler with her wobbly credentials, Denise was given some advice by an ancient climber who had succeeded: Hold down the big parties at first and hire a discreet public relations person. Denise followed the counsel. Some socially nervous people in the second covey and many in the third measured their success by the number of times they appeared in print. Most of those in the first covey considered the local press coverage to be an effrontery and one vicious P.B. joke said that the town was roughly divided between those who paid to keep their pictures out of the paper and those who paid to keep them in, which was not true because P.B. local reporting was generally accurate and not arbitrary.

Whatever, Denise had certain salient assets: She photographed beautifully, wore clothes extremely well, and after the *Patna* affair, she became not only a good visual subject for the local papers but also a mini-celebrity, the brutalized woman.

However, for Cynthia, confined at Jackson Memorial Hospital sixty-eight miles to the south, life was somewhat grimmer. The reconstruction surgery could not take place until her burns healed and that took three weeks. It was a painful, dull time for Cynthia, and John took a small apartment near the hospital, spending most of his time with his wife.

The operation was finally performed and it was not a total success since some scar tissue would remain forever. When Cynthia first looked at her unbandaged face, she burst into tears. She had thought that cosmetic surgery was going to perform miracles, even though the doctor had cautioned her that this was not the case. Five weeks after the *Patna* episode, Cynthia returned home devastated, angry, resentful, and sullen.

She immediately got into her Rolls-Royce, drove to a gun store in West Palm Beach, and purchased a purse-size twenty-two-caliber pistol.

Not long after Cynthia returned to Palm Beach Maggie Dunsmore summoned her.

"What really happened?" the old lady asked. "The whole thing is appalling."

Cynthia dutifully recounted the incident.

"I'm afraid I tend to believe what everyone else thinks," Maggie finally said.

"What is that?" Cynthia asked.

"People are sympathizing with Denise. Evidently your husband tried to rape her. You almost tore her eyes out. I saw her face. Her actions were provoked. After all, what's a woman to do when she is raped by a man and attacked by his wife at the same time?" the old woman added after a pause.

"But, look at my face! John told me that he didn't seduce Denise. That bitch led him in there!" Cynthia cried, holding her patched cheek.

"The facts just don't appear that way. Denise's clothes were ripped off. She brought them here to show me. Nicole Bouchart confirmed that she saw you attacking Denise, but I had to be sure of the situation before letting Denise handle the Home Ball."

"John would never rape a woman!"

"I hear you are suing him for divorce."

"We've only discussed it."

"I'm truly sorry about your injury, Cynthia, but I'm afraid you're no longer welcome in our group."

"Why? Because of what I did, or what you think my husband did?"

"Both. We just can't tolerate scandals like this in Palm Beach."

Cynthia broke down completely. "It's not fair, Maggie! My face is ruined forever and now you send me to Coventry. All because of that actress!"

Cynthia Baxter knew she was through socially and she was frantic. Her carefully planned ascent, fifteen years of always following the rules and doing the right thing, had suddenly come to an agonizing, tragic end. She was a woman driven by madness when she left Maggie's that day and she nurtured a seething desire to obliterate the Frenchwoman who had caused her downfall. The twenty-two-caliber gun she had purchased would be her last resort, but maybe there was another way of destroying Denise: Sue her for assault, claiming high compensatory damages, and open up the woman's shabby past for all to see. Cynthia immediately made an appointment with a firm of Palm Beach attorneys.

Just as Maggie had called in Cynthia shortly after her return from Miami, so Philip Guest had called in John. Philip believed John Baxter's story; the chairman understood how the ugly episode could have happened since he held little respect for the Hansens, and he accepted John's apologies. Also, Philip was still rankling over the condominium project that he had been talked into against his better judgment.

The following week the Palm Beach law firm of McKinsey, Hamilton & Smith, who handled all the Palace Beach work, called Philip Guest saying they had had preliminary talks with Mrs. Baxter concerning a possible lawsuit against Denise Hansen. They wished to discuss the matter with the chairman for possible conflicts of interest.

"It could possibly enter the criminal area," the attorney told Philip. "There may have been a rape and Mrs. Hansen's assault could be construed by the court as justifiable under the circumstances. We're anticipating a counteraction if the suit proceeds."

The implications did not please the chairman. The suit would be picked up by the local press, subsequently the wire services, and that would further damage the reputation of the Palace Beach System. Mel Hansen was a respected member of the Palace Beach team; his ideas and designs had proved out and he had made money for the hotel. The consequences of the president's wife suing Mel's wife and for her to counterclaim a rape could jeopardize the Regency Walk project.

Philip called John in again and he explained what he had heard and then told his president, "The lawsuit must be halted! You can't have your wife suing for assault and I hear there's a divorce action now. Denise Hansen will come right back with a rape charge."

"I didn't rape her, Philip."

"It doesn't matter; by appearance and evidence, it seems you did."

"Well, Christ, what do we do?"

"Cool those women down. Talk to the Hansens and get their promise not to pursue this. Get the same assurances from Cynthia. If you don't, and this blows up, both of you will be fired. Understand clearly what I say, John."

"I do," he said heavily. "I don't blame you, Philip."

John went directly to Mel and asked to see him and Denise together. They all met for lunch aboard the *Patna* and John carefully explained what could happen.

Mel was scared. Not only would such a lawsuit affect the proposal that was before the South Florida Planning Commission, but his association with the Regency Walk development would be terminated.

"You must be kidding, John," Denise said. "Why should my husband be fired because you raped me? What did Mel have to do with it?"

"I didn't rape you, Denise. You know that. Mel knows it."

"Everyone says it was a rape," Denise laughed playfully.

"Stop it, Denise, you bitch!" Mel blasted. "I know you're a tramp and everyone in Europe knows it."

"Mel, darling, how unkind," Denise purred. "I've acted with the highest principles in Palm Beach. I'll consider this at the proper time."

"Just what the hell are you going to consider?" Mel demanded.

"I hear that Cynthia is thinking of suing me for trying to defend myself."

"What do you really want, Denise?" John pleaded. "You have money, marriage, a ball chairmanship . . . whatever that's worth."

"I want everything, John. More and more of everything," the woman said.

John met later with his wife and they sat in the loggia of their large home after letting the help off for the afternoon.

"What good will it do you to sue me for divorce and then take Denise into court?"

"Look at my face!" she cried. "No one will talk to me around here. I'm an outcast. I want some compensation."

"But, Cynthia, the Hansens aren't rich enough to make it worthwhile, and I'll certainly be fired. What happened was inexcusable and tragic. I had too much to drink and I lost my head."

Cynthia gazed out over the soft spread of their lawn, realizing how long it had taken to dress their home. Now there would be no more guests and all their possessions and all their props meant nothing. Nothing in a wasteland created by the Frenchwoman.

Finally she said, "I want Denise to write me a letter explaining that you didn't rape her and that she seduced you."

"Denise would laugh at that."

"If it comes down to Mel's being fired, she might not laugh."

"She doesn't love him. I realized that today. She's using him too. Cynthia, please, drop the suit."

"If Denise writes me a letter."

"I'll ask her. I'll try anything. And, Cynthia dear, you must believe this: I do love you."

They kissed and she cried in his arms. "Why did you do it to me?"

"I was drunk. It was the first time, Cynthia, the first time. And my first mistake in all the years of our marriage."

14

MEL HANSEN WAS A LUCKY MAN. HE HAD NEVER BEEN CAUGHT ON his construction kickbacks and his plans for beach rehabilitation were beginning to be noticed and applauded—especially by those who would benefit economically. The most ironic aspect of Mel's strokes of luck concerned his seawall, a very worthy project that he had stumbled onto by mistake.

The seawall benefits would go much deeper than saving the swiftly eroding beach. After the disastrous 1928 hurricane a more extensive system of drainage canals had been dug between Lake Okeechobee and the intracoastal waterway. Originally Lake Worth and other areas of the intracoastal were clear bodies of relatively deep water, but as time went by they filled in and the canals began to lose the stability of their banks. Saw-grass rootlets, the natural binders, were destroyed, mostly because of pollution.

As Lake Worth silted in, it presented a shallow saucer that would quickly overflow since the only lateral runoffs were the narrow inlets twenty-six miles apart. Mel's seawall plan, given to him by the expert Dr. Van Betzig, included the dredging of Lake Worth and the pumping of the bottom sand across the island to the beach. Not only would a deepened lake prevent overflow in case of a major hurricane, but it would clear up the turbidity of the canal water. The saw grass would return and the banks would not cave in during extreme periods of torrential rain.

Billy Haughton saw how beneficial to disaster prevention the uncouth profiteer's suggestions were and she told him. This was supported by Dr. Van Betzig who looked upon the architect as some sort of visionary. Mel was ecstatic.

There was no doubt now that the proposal, 121.B, would be passed: The hurricane people were going to support it. Billy and Keith went to John Baxter's office and they explained the advantages of Mel's plan, and the troubled president repeated this to Philip Guest. The board was informed and John's credibility was somewhat restored.

John Baxter still faced the clamor that was about to be kicked off by two angry women. He was not sleeping, nor released; he had to make some deal with Denise Hansen. One morning he called from his office.

"Denise, we have to talk again. Let's go someplace private. I can't afford to be seen with you."

"How about El Lugar?"

"That's not a private place."

"But as president of the Palace Beach, you fly over all the time. You have a cottage there and who will know me? People from Palm Beach don't use the resort."

"All right, but we'll have to take separate flights."

"Darling, just go wind up that little bird and put her down at Lantana Airport en route. I'll be there. Magnificently simple, John."

After she put down the phone, Denise wondered what he wanted, for she had made her position clear. Nevertheless, she felt sexually aroused. She had ruined Cynthia Baxter.

Now she wanted John. And he was giving her the opportunity himself.

Her need for sex was always present, and though her sex with Mel had improved since the incident on the *Patna* Mel was still such a dull, mechanical man. Denise had never forgotten the excitement of making love to John Baxter, despite the ugliness of that night. Moreover, she wished to rid herself of Nicole Bouchart.

Denise, with her vast experience in seducing men, knew that the right perfume and dress were important. Trained to move well at an early age, she knew exactly how to use her body in expert, subtle gestures. Many directors had helped her along the way.

What to wear for the trip to El Lugar? Denise was not a "panty hose" or a "pants" person. She always wore dresses and she had discovered that stockings and a garter belt excited her targets; she would sit in such a manner that her skirts would ride up, exposing a bit of lacy garters and the bronzed thighs above. She wore no panties underneath.

But John would be suspicious if she showed up in too obvious an outfit, so she chose a simple pale gray Gucci skirt and a soft, clinging blouse.

She drove to the Lantana Airport in her Mercedes and stood in the warm August sun waiting for a speck to emerge out of the sky. Finally the twin-engine Apache settled over the slash pines and John kissed it on. With the engines still running, Denise got in and settled in the right seat. John eased the throttles forward; the plane crawled up the taxiway, turned into the wind, and as he ran up the engines he searched the sky for incoming traffic. John applied take-off power and the lightly loaded five-seater lifted off quickly, climbing into low cumulus, heading east over the Atlantic for El Lugar, less than an hour away.

The island was a small coral strip. The single-runway airport was on one side and Mel's Moorish dream come true was on the other side of the island. It was like a Portuguese transplant, foreign and exotic geography. That was probably the attraction of El Lugar: a different country so close to Florida. They walked along the narrow, twisting path fronting the fanciful cottages and then entered the last one reserved for the Palace Beach executives.

It was lavishly furnished with Moroccan antiques and artifacts and Turkish tapestries; brightly colored tiles ran up the wall; the windows were grilled slits and the sumptuous white sofas were deep and plush. On the far side was a bar made from a great Spanish chest.

"My . . . my . . ." Denise murmured as they entered.

"Drink?" John asked.

"Sure."

He fixed two vodkas at the bar and returned to the sofa, and Denise settled next to him.

"What's on the agenda?" she asked.

"I'll come right to the point," he said sternly. "My wife and I want you to write a letter saying that I didn't rape you."

She laughed. "Is that supposed to be a joke?" Denise set her drink down and leaned toward him. "You know something, John, I really loved fucking you that night, despite what happened, and my image is up. Everyone feels sorry for me. The only thing left for me to want now is you."

"That's impossible! You're crazy."

"I'm beautiful, they tell me . . . and a streamlined lay."

"Yes, you're a turn-on, but you're also vicious and cold."

"Oh, I think that's excessive," she said, recrossing her legs so her skirt lifted higher.

"You're a calculating woman who doesn't give a damn about anybody else. How long would I be your playtoy?"

"Forever, darling. You're what I've always wanted." She dropped her voice to a husky whisper. "I was drunk that night, John, and so were you. The fire was an accident. We both know that. Listen to me. I came from the Bordeaux slums. There was no finishing school in my life. My father was an alcoholic and my mother was a hooker. I had to get out of there. Of course I used my body, but I also educated myself and I'm a pretty good actress. Nobody ever gave me silver spoons. I fought for every inch. Don't forget that. And I came to Palm Beach and I kept my nose clean. You were the first man that I ever let touch me, and believe me, there were plenty of offers."

"I bet."

"I've had it rough, John, and I'm sick of fighting. Getting old, I guess, and I thought I'd pluck some security and comfort out of Palm Beach."

"Well," he shrugged, "what are we going to do, Denise?"

"Make an arrangement. How rich are you?"

"That's none of your goddamned business," he steamed.

"Do you want me to file a complaint?"

"Mel will be fired."

"What do I care? I want you to leave Cynthia."

"I happen to love my wife."

"How can you love that dull woman? If you go along with me, I'll never bring a complaint and I might consider writing the letter. But it will only sound plausible if we get together. Then you can say it was love all the time, not passion."

"You never stop, do you, Denise?"

"Do you want to get charged with rape and lose your job? We'll leave Palm Beach and forget the whole mad social scramble. What's your net worth, John?"

He took a sip of his drink and finally answered slowly, "Six hundred thousand."

"You're not even a millionaire!" she laughed. "Well, sacrifices have to be made. You see, dear, I like expensive things. Take my shoes . . . Celine. They cost one hundred twenty dollars. My stockings were handmade in Paris . . . fifty dollars. My garter belt, a chemise by Schiaparelli . . . seventy dollars. All the best."

As she showed off her undergarments she pulled up her skirt, rubbed her hand sensually down her thigh.

"Look at that leg. Perfect. I can please you, John. Don't say you're not turned on. I can see your nice thing on its way to work there."

"You're disgusting."

"But exciting."

"I wouldn't marry you if Cynthia were dead and you were the last woman standing up."

"I don't think you can afford not to marry me." She stood and slipped off her skirt and then her blouse.

"What in hell are you doing?"

"You're going to make love to me and I'm going to make you very happy."

She stood in front of him, her pelvis positioned forward, slightly stroking herself. "Isn't that a beautiful little thing? Come on, John, off with all those clothes. I really could love you."

When he didn't move, she sat down next to him and stroked his hair and whispered, "You haven't any choice and it's going to be so nice."

She pushed her hand down inside his pants. John resisted for a minute, but her warm fingers grasped him and she could feel him throb. He shoved her aside and went to the bar and hastily gulped down his drink. Denise crossed and took him by the hand.

"Right here," she said softly. "I like sofas . . . so big and cuddly."

Suddenly, with a groan, John capitulated. He jerked off his pants and grasped her breasts. Finally he lifted himself on top of her and she moved fluidly, exactly right under him. She was high voltage, John realized, and he came with a great gush, and five minutes later she had him coming again, and that had never happened to him before.

Back at the airstrip two hours later, Denise went up to the lineman while John was preflighting the Apache.

"My name is Denise Hansen. I'm doing some consulting business with Mr. Baxter. I'll be coming over here now and then."

"Yes'um."

"I'm so forgetful, but I have to keep a record of my trips for tax purposes. Would you jot down the times I come and go?"

She lifted a fifty-dollar bill out of her purse and slipped it to him.

"Sure will," he said, lighting up.

They got into the plane and a short time later they landed at the Lantana Airport.

"I want to go to El Lugar Thursday, John."

"Impossible. I have a budget meeting."

"Schedule around it."

"You're a bitch."

"Was I a good fuck?"

"Yes, goddammit! Yes!" John said with anger plowed into his voice.

John realized he had made a mistake with Denise and he was furious with himself, for she had him exactly where she wanted him. Everything was suddenly collapsing; it was as if a sledgehammer had pounded away the very pilings of a lifetime of propriety and all the ethics, breeding, and sensibilities that he had so valued.

CHAPTER

15

KEITH LANDON WAS ASSIGNED TO THE EARLY MORNING SHIFT IN THE hurricane war room and he arrived at eight, hung over, bleary-eyed after having spent the night aboard the *Patna* as Mel's guest.

Steve entered the war room later and he studied the night satellite photo tacked to the corkboard. There was a slight white smudge about a hundred miles west of the Verdes, soft-edged, elongated in pattern.

"How long have you been on duty?" Steve asked Keith.

"Came in about half an hour ago. Why?"

"What's the first thing you're supposed to do?"

"Look at the night data."

"Did you?"

"Yes. What the hell is this . . . a grilling? You belong on the floor below, not up here!" Keith shot back, hardening his voice. "I'm the forecaster, remember?"

"Did anything look strange to you on the night GOES transmission?"

Keith thought a minute. His mind was crocked in blurriness and he could not truthfully say he had studied the picture on the corkboard except for a fleeting glance. Specialists like Keith have trained eyes; in a microsecond they can evaluate a GOES transmission. They look for cloud organization, or circular forming, the frightful evidence of what the hurricane watchers called whirliness. But as Keith's eyes slid across the photo, he didn't see the visual evidence of pumping columns of warm air, being drawn tighter and tighter into the fearful, howling knot.

"What about the Verdes disturbance?" Steve asked.

Keith's head snapped around. He saw the blur west of the islands. "So?"

"It didn't arouse your interest?"

"No more than the other clusters." He walked over to the map and pointed his finger at the tropical population of white dots. "One's here at ten north . . . this one at five north . . . twenty-eight north . . . all these others." Then he stopped and regrouped his thoughts. "I don't have time for a meteorology lesson. I'm busy."

"You're inept, Landon."

"What was that?"

"You heard me. Any specialist who can't see something suspicious on the transmission knows more about computers than weather."

"I'm goddamned tired of your carping, Steve. Get the hell out of here! Play with your stuff downstairs."

"Yesterday's disturbance east of the Verdes is now west of the islands," Steve continued.

Keith tried to think clearly. "We watch all disturbances," he said, not knowing what else to say. He walked away from Steve trying to figure out why he had pinned his comments on the Verdes disturbance. It was west now, of course, but there was no indication of whirliness, so it could be dismissed. Steve walked after Keith and he touched his shoulder.

"Get away!" Keith barked in a quick rush of anger.

"You didn't learn your lessons well, my friend. Any disturbance that moves over land and doesn't dissipate should be viewed with suspicion. Rule one. Ask yourself why the disturbance didn't bust up. If I were you, I'd order an airborne penetration and check immediately with surface reports and local radar observation."

"You are nuts, man. I'm supposed to order a plane to fly all the way across the Atlantic, almost three thousand miles from Keesler, to penetrate a squall line!" Keith then began to laugh; it was so farfetched.

Steve walked out of the room and when Harry Grimes, the second specialist assigned to the war room that day, came in, Keith asked him offhandedly, "Harry, do you see anything on the night transmission that could call for an airborne penetration?"

Harry walked to the map. "Why do you ask?"

"Just checking . . . see anything?"

"No."

"I don't either."

The swelling antagonism between Keith and Steve was to intensify that morning and it would have nothing to do with the Verdes disturbance. Dr. Ballantine had received a call from Dr. Peterson in Washington.

"Lou, has the *Miami Star* called you?" the administrator asked quickly.

"No, sir, but I was late getting in . . . had to go over to Homestead to see my wife's mother."

"Have you seen this morning's paper?"

"No. What's the problem?"

"I'll tell you in just a minute. Let me ask some very direct questions first. Has anyone at the center had affiliations with either the Palace Beach System or a man named Mel Hansen?"

"Yes, two of my people—Billy Haughton and Keith Landon."

Lou could hear a sharp intake of breath on the other end.

"This is important, Lou. Did you authorize Keith Landon to talk to the press?"

"No, sir."

"Are any of your staff being retained on a consultancy basis by private interests?"

"Not that I know of. For heaven's sake, Marc . . . what's going on?"

"The undersecretary just called me in. He had the wired text of a

Miami Star front-page story. In a nutshell, it says that we endorse a setback proposal submitted by Mr. Hansen."

"I never made a statement like that."

"But Dr. Landon did."

"I'm surprised. He's an aggressive guy, but not irresponsible."

"It goes further. The *Miami Star* real-estate editor was fired for taking a bribe and it's suggested that the hurricane center might be involved in the whole deal."

Lou leaned back in his chair; his breath came quickly and he reached for the nitroglycerin pills in his drawer. "I can't believe such a thing!"

"It's on the front page, Lou."

"Hold on . . . let me see if I can find a paper."

Lou plodded to the outside office and rummaged around in his secretary's wastebasket; he returned with a copy of the early edition. "Give me a minute to skim through this, Marc."

The headlines were large and thick and the story was placed prominently in the upper-right-hand corner and rimmed with a six-pica gutter:

STAR REAL-ESTATE EDITOR ADMITS ACCEPTING BRIBE FOR HOLDING BACK STORY ON BEACH PROPOSITION. HURRICANE CENTER AND PALACE BEACH SYSTEM POSSIBLY INVOLVED IN PAYOFF

Henry Daniels, longtime real-estate editor of the *Star,* was terminated this morning pending an investigation by the state attorney's office growing out of an alleged bribery scheme to shield the fact that a new setback line, Proposition 121.B, will change building restrictions in the three-county area. . . .

Lou threw the paper down and spoke into the phone. "This is crazy. Nobody here would accept an outside fee. I'll get onto this right away . . . the bribe implication is nonsense."

"Why did you allow your people to work on this?"

"Because it seemed worthwhile when it was explained to us. All we're doing is sharing expertise . . . our data on bottom conditions. What's wrong with that?"

"Lou, it was poor judgment."

"Under the circumstances, I agree."

"All right. Find out all you can. Don't talk to anyone, not even the Justice Department if they should call. Our general counsel will make any necessary statements from this end and get back to me."

There was a click.

Lou picked up the paper again and began reading:

The *Star* has carried three stories on the new seawall and beach restoration, a program being suggested by Mr. Mel Hansen, vice-president for development at the Palace Beach Hotel System headquartered in Palm Beach. The seawall was only part of the new proposal to be laid before the South Florida Building Commission on October 18. Mr. Hansen and, allegedly, the Palace Beach System are recommending that the bulkhead line be moved possibly fifty feet closer to the high-water mark. This would open the beach to additional construction and realty experts indicate that increased condominium units would number in the hundreds of thousands. Sources familiar with South Florida planning told the *Star* that the new construction program could place strains on existing roads, bridges, sewage, and utility services.

The *Star* learned of the setback proposal from the South Florida Brotherhood of Construction Workers who are endorsing the project. They stated to the *Star* that if the new setback line is adopted, it would not only save the beaches, but it would create ten thousand construction jobs.

The *Star* also learned that two members of the National Hurricane Center have been working on the project with executives of the Palm Beach System. Dr. Keith Landon, deputy director of the National Hurricane Center, told the *Star* that the idea is excellent and that the hurricane center is behind it. The *Star* was also informed that the Palace Beach Hotel has already started a vast condominium project that is to be built fifty feet beyond the present setback line under a variance granted by the Palm Beach Town Council. When questioned about the alleged bribe to Mr. Daniels, Mr. Philip Guest, chairman of the hotel chain, said he knew nothing about it. Under advice of counsel, Mr. Daniels would not indicate the amount of the payment, nor where it originated.

The *Star* tried to contact Dr. Louis P. Ballantine, director of the National Hurricane Center, to ascertain their official interest, if any, in the proposal, but as of nine o'clock press deadline, Dr. Ballantine could not be reached. Ralph Thompson, publisher of the *Miami Star*, stated that the paper would begin an immediate investigation working with the state attorney's office. Since the proposal involves the alteration of federally controlled waterways, the United States Attorney for the Southern District has also been brought into the investigation.

Lou Ballantine was an ill man, with high blood pressure and angina pectoris. He swallowed his pills quickly and when he had regained control of his jumping mind, he called Billy, Keith, and Steve into his office.

"Look at this," he said. "Read it."

After they had finished, Keith said, "The article is misleading."

"I want the truth. Were any of you involved in this bribe? Did you know about it?"

"Absolutely not," Keith said.

Billy shook her head.

"Did the Palace Beach people pay you anything?"

"No," Billy and Keith said in unison.

"Did you talk to any reporters, Keith?"

"Yes, Mel Hansen had a guy on the phone one day from the *Star*."

"And what did you tell him?"

"Just that we were working on the project because from a hurricane standpoint we agreed with the value of pumping sand out of Lake Worth."

"Did you say that the center was endorsing it?"

"No. The man inferred those things."

"We can't put our name to private projects!" Lou said, becoming short of breath again.

"Lou, everything Keith is telling you is true," Billy said. "We never took any money and I was aboard the yacht when the call came through. Keith didn't say we were backing it. He only remarked that we were studying the situation and that it appeared beneficial."

"How the hell do you think this looks?" Lou puffed.

"Lou, you were the one who sent us up there," Keith said in his cold, deliberate manner.

"I did not authorize press conferences. It was a mistake to talk to anyone. Government work is delicate. You should know that, Keith."

Steve, who had remained silent throughout Lou's inquiry, spoke up, carefully pacing his words, "Let me ask you an important question, Keith."

"What the hell do you have to do with it?" Keith bounded back with glaring eyes.

"We're all in the same business," Steve said, getting to his feet. "Did you know anything about this extension of the bulkhead line?"

"Yes, I knew about it."

"Did you tell Lou?"

"No."

"Why not?"

"What's the difference? Draining Lake Worth was the important issue, not some new building project."

"The building project is important because the beach can't take another five hundred thousand people! If a classic hurricane were to strike now, we'd have problems with evacuation."

"Oh, Christ, I don't agree," Keith said. "And neither does anybody else around here."

"You know half the people never believe us to begin with," Steve argued, "and the other half are too dumb to care. Rather than get out, they organize hurricane-watching parties . . . big candles and booze."

"We've been through all this before," Lou sighed. "Steve, there's always vertical evacuation and residents can go to higher floors."

"Those windows can be blown in. A big 'cat five' would kill thousands of people. And, Keith, you should have come to me on this. You knew I was working on surge."

"You and your goddamned big storm! Draining the lake is much more important!"

"Keith's right," the director said.

"No, he's not!" Steve said, pitching his voice. "The roads over the inland waterway won't hold any more cars. The statistics are there."

"So are the drainage figures out of Lake Okeechobee," Billy added.

There was a pause, and then Steve said, looking straight at Keith, then at Billy, "I just can't believe that money wasn't passed around someplace."

Keith sprang from his chair and made a lunge at Steve who pushed him away. "Take that back!"

"Cut it out!" Lou yelled with a reddening face. "Sit down, Keith."

The younger man went back to his chair. His smooth face was flaming and his thin hands were twitching slightly. He pushed back his hair and took out a cigarette. "We might as well have this out right now," Keith said. "Because if we don't, there'll be more problems around here than hurricanes."

"That was a terrible thing to say, Steve," Billy interjected.

"I didn't like it either," Lou added. "Billy and Keith aren't liars."

"OK, I apologize," Steve said, "but you should have told us about the setback proposal."

"Steve," Keith began, "you've been at my throat ever since I came here. I can't do anything without being criticized by you in that arrogant way. I know you went through Camille and lost your wife, and I'm sorry about that, but it doesn't make you some kind of hurricane prophet. You won't bury your wife; you make fools out of us with this two-hundred-mile-an-hour hurricane you say is coming."

"Camille came and no one said it would."

"All right. Maybe the storm of the century will arrive any moment. This isn't an exact science. But I'll tell you how this vendetta began, and that's exactly what it is."

Billy started to interrupt but Keith waved her protests aside and continued, "Billy Haughton stopped going out with you. She thought there was something wrong with a guy who chartered a yacht and then proceeded to take temperature readings all over the Atlantic. I agree with her. Then, you came up to the war room and started lecturing me, telling me that I wasn't doing my job. You suggested that we probe a little disturbance thirty-five hundred miles away, off the Verdes."

"We should."

"We shouldn't," Lou said.

"And whether we should or not isn't the point," Keith continued. "You don't even belong on the fifth floor. You're not assigned to the war room. Do I come downstairs and do a number on your surge stuff? No. You tell people I'm here only to rip off the director's job so I can cut out someday and start a private forecasting service. I might want to start a private company in the future; nothing wrong with that. Now either you get off my back or I'm leaving the hurricane center. Both of us can't work here!"

"I might just save you the trouble and leave myself," Steve said. "Lou, proceeding with a program to stuff the beach with more dumb fools is a crime. You're dealing with life and death here. Someday that storm will come!"

Steve left the office, slamming the door, as they all looked after him.

"He gets upset when we start talking about his storm," Billy said. Then she turned toward Keith. "I didn't appreciate your dragging my personal affairs into this."

"The man's clearly unbalanced . . . ought to be fired!" Keith said contemptuously.

"I'll decide that!" the director snapped. "Now, let's get down to this problem. I want both of you to write me short memos on everything that happened in Palm Beach. Don't leave anything out. I'll arrange a meeting at the Palace Beach Hotel this afternoon if possible. I want to see who's behind this." Then Lou stopped and said slowly, "Keith, do any of your people see anything suspicious about that Verdes 'hotdog'?"

"No, we've discussed it. Seems to be just another disturbance . . . odd-shaped and elongating, but there's no tightening."

"Maybe we should probe it."

"It's up to you."

"I want it observed very closely."

"You mean you bought Steve's message?"

"I just have a hunch that something is going to go wrong. Odd . . . I don't have any basis for feeling this way. Keep a close watch on it, though, and pound out those memos immediately."

Keith and Billy left Lou's office and they walked down the hall toward the war room. "I think old Lou's caught Steve's vibes," Keith said.

"Is there anything to worry about, Keith?"

"No, Billy, I really don't think so. That Verdes hotdog is just another insignificant disturbance."

By one-thirty that day, August 19, there were three sets of eyes watching the hotdog disturbance moving westward from the Verdes: two mechanical, one human. The satellite was picking it up; so was the Verdes Islands approach radar, but the disturbance had moved beyond the limits of the powerful Dakar scanning network. The human eyes watched and felt the concentrated squall cluster from a small trader that had entered the disturbance early, making her run down the entire length of the slinky cluster, now elongated to ninety miles.

She was the reefer vessel *Bergen Star,* a 6,200 tonner, loaded to her marks with frozen beef out of the River Platte for Stockholm. The master, a Mr. Kuhlne, with twenty-four sailing years behind him, had bumped about in his bunk most of the night. At times he thought it was a dream as the bows dug into the rising seas, then pushed off the mountains of foam. The old vessel groaned and shuddered as black water tore down her bulwarks toward the scuppers and the rest of the waves were split and shredded into whitish froth forced up into a V-shaped spume.

"What's the trouble?" the master said into the bridge phone by the side of the bunk.

"Heavy stuff, sir . . . getting dusty for some reason."

"What's the wireless report?"

"No warnings."

"Reduce your RPMs."

During the night the diesel was cut back from 60 to 40 percent and near dawn as the gray light pushed through, the captain pulled on his terry-cloth robe and clamping one of his meaty hands on the grab rail, he worked his way along the passage just below the bridge and yanked himself up to the wheelhouse. A frightful sight met him beyond the water-beaded windows: Gray, roaring combers were crashing in from the southeast and what had begun hours before as a ripple upon the calm, warm surface had somehow persisted and deepened. The master looked for a moment as his slim bow pushed back the angry water. Then he called for a third power reduction and went into the chart room, bracing himself against the bulkhead. Winds were peaking forty-five, he noted, tapping the anemometer.

"You sure there're no storm warnings out?" he asked his Number One.

"Wireless hasn't given us anything."

A minute later a sallow-looking radio officer struggled up to the bridge.

"How can we be in this situation?" the master asked.

"Don't know, sir. Here's the last meteorological report . . . nothing about a gale."

"All right. Take down this message for Dakar radio."

Ten minutes later the operator was tapping out a high-speed continuous wave transmission:

DAKAR RADIO. REEFER VESSEL BERGEN STAR. CALL LETTERS WRUR. POSITION 20.1 NORTH, 60.6 WEST. EXPERIENCING HEAVY CONFUSED SEAS ASSOCIATED WITH TROPICAL GALE. WIND SPEED 20–30 KNOTS. BAROMETRIC PRESSURE 29.80. REQUEST METEOROLOGICAL UPDATE.

The operator at the Dakar listening station didn't think very much of the message traffic from the *Bergen Star*. He retrafficked it routinely to the worldwide reporting network.

The following morning the APT rolled off the printer showing resolutions of the three disturbances that the center was tracking. They had drifted only slightly on the easterly wave, but each was moving toward land.

Steve made extra copies of the transmission and brought still damp photos into his office. He sat down at his desk, nodded to Billy Haughton who was still attempting to digitize the Tampa basin. After a few minutes Steve broke the silence. "I don't like it."

"What?"

"This disturbance off the Verdes."

"What's wrong with it?"

"I'll show you."

She left her desk and crossed over to Steve's side.

"The damned thing's in the wrong place." He pointed to a print. "She's here in the Intertropical Zone, a low-pressure band between the trades of both hemispheres. She can't develop into a hurricane as long as she's plowing around in the doldrums. She'll have to turn north to where the earth narrows so the spinning force can set her in motion."

"And you want that?"

"Of course not!" he snapped.

"Why worry? As long as the disturbance stays in the doldrums, we're safe."

"But why is she enlarging every hour? Most of these doldrum babies shrink and die. This one won't quit. I've never seen a disturbance this large before, and neither has Lou."

She studied his perplexed face and then returned to her work.

While each of the disturbances had to be watched, and they were, there was nothing that day, as Keith said, to give rise for concern. The surface synoptic reports indicated that the windfield in each area had not exceeded much over twenty knots sustained with periodic gusts to thirty. If there were a next step up the hurricane ladder, it would be a depression emerging from one or, possibly, all of the disturbances.

This would signal a new alarm; they would observe the isobars carefully and if one or more closed with indicated rotary circulation at sea level, combined with winds of thirty-nine miles an hour, it could be reasonably assumed that a hurricane was under way. Nothing like this had happened yet.

CHAPTER

17

MEL AND DENISE WERE SITTING ON THE AFTERDECK OF THE *Patna* having breakfast; it was cool and clear that morning. She was shuffling through a mound of handwritten notes, annoying preparations for the small Home Ball, only a matter of days away.

"Denise, you're not going to scuffle with Cynthia anymore, are you?" Mel asked casually as he thumbed through *Variety*.

"If she sues me," Denise replied without looking up.

"I think it's better to forget the whole thing. We have too much riding on the Regency Walk project for any more scandal."

Denise was about to answer when the phone rang.

"Mr. Hansen, this is Philip Guest."

"Yes, Mr. Guest?" Mel said brightly.

"Have you read this morning's *Miami Star*?"

"No. I don't take it."

"It says the Palace Beach might be involved in a bribe handed to their real-estate editor," Philip said in his Locust Valley voice, aged, but firm.

Mel hesitated; he caught the authority and the crispness in the words. He lit a cigarette and after a pause said with just the right amount of sureness, "I know nothing about it, sir."

"Are you positive?" Philip asked with more alacrity.

"Absolutely!" Mel said.

"And what about the hurricane people . . . are we paying them to work on the project?"

"Not that I know of."

"Dr. Ballantine down at the center just called me. He's coming up here this afternoon with some of his people. Be in my office at four."

Mel's face whitened as the phone clicked on the other end.

"What's the matter, Mel? You look flabby, love."

"Someone bribed the *Miami Star* . . . their real-estate man."

"Was it you, dear?" she asked.

"Drop dead, Denise!"

Mel fumbled for the phone and called John Baxter at home.

"John . . . Philip called and . . ."

"I know," John said sourly. "When are these problems going to end? I just read the article. Did you pay anybody, Mel?" John asked, his voice filled with frustration.

"Did you?"

"Of course not!" John's voice came back sharply.

"That's my answer, too," Mel said.

"Who could have been involved? You ought to know . . . it's your baby."

"I just can't imagine . . . the unions maybe?"

"Mel, if you know anything, don't hide it. Philip is a very thorough man. He's scrupulously honest and he doesn't put up with very much. We're lucky to have jobs after that unfortunate incident."

"You're lucky, John. What did I do?"

"I told you we're both involved. If a new chief executive officer came into the Palace Beach, I doubt whether you'd be continued. I'll see you this afternoon."

Mel knew exactly who was connected to the bribery scheme: Glen

Markum. He had spoken in vague terms of buying people off before. Mel rushed from the Brazilian Docks and sped down North County Road toward Century Towers. When he reached Glen's apartment, he found Gloria to be in excellent spirits as if nothing had happened.

"My son and his family are coming down Thursday," she said gaily.

"That's good . . . fine . . . I'd like to meet them," Mel said. "Is Glen in his office?"

"Yes, but he's upset . . . I don't know why with the children coming. He's always trying to get them down from Chicago."

"I know what's upsetting him," Mel said as he moved swiftly down the hall.

He entered Glen's office and saw the man sitting on a high stool staring blankly from the window toward the endless line of high condominiums glistening in the pure morning light.

"Why the hell did you do it?" Mel demanded, flushed with anger.

Mel realized that Philip Guest would probably begin to take a closer look at things now. The whole Regency Walk project had been placed in jeopardy by Glen's actions and it could flow to the land deals, to the St. Paul's and El Lugar projects.

Glen remained silent.

"Answer me, you goddamned, crazy bastard!" Mel screamed.

"Calm down, Mel," Glen said, lifting his bloodshot eyes. "It came from one of the commissioners. He asked me to deliver it to Daniels."

"Why, for God's sake?"

"Because the commissioners were picking up static. Residents were telling them that if more condos went up, the highways would be overcrowded . . . that kind of thing."

"So what? We got a whole ecology story out of this. We were going to save the beaches by pumping out the lagoons and the inland waterways. It was going through, Glen. We had it made!"

"But you held out on me, Mel. I didn't know anything about the Regency Walk proposal until I read about it in the papers. Wasn't there room for me in the deal?"

"No. There wasn't. Glen, how much was the bribe?"

"Five thousand."

"Beautiful! That's just beautiful. Don't talk to anyone about this, Glen. Don't mention my name, even if you're hauled down to the state attorney's office. Just lie and lie and lie, and get yourself a good criminal lawyer."

Mel left shortly afterward and returned to the *Patna* just as Denise was leaving for a poker game at Maggie Dunsmore's.

"That jerk, Markum, delivered five thousand dollars to a real-estate editor. We might be in serious trouble with the project. Philip Guest would just love to discover that I'm up to my ass in the whole thing."

"Are you?"

"No."

Denise was concerned. If Mel's financial security collapsed prematurely, so would hers, and without other arrangements she'd be back where she started, her Palm Beach work reduced to a fruitless exercise.

She picked up a copy of the *Star* on the way to Maggie's and as soon as she arrived at the Dunsmore home, a large, smelly Mizner, she called John Baxter. She knew he would be troubled and weakened. "John . . . Denise. Can you talk?"

"What about?"

"Mel had nothing to do with it."

"Neither did I, but Philip is fuming."

"I bet he is. Listen . . . I'd like to spend part of Sunday with you at El Lugar."

"Denise, I have too many problems right now."

"We'll leave the same way as before."

"Denise, I can't."

"See you at Lantana Airport . . . Sunday at two."

Denise returned to the main loggia of the house where three poker tables had been set up. Cynthia, who normally played, was absent, but Nicole Bouchart showed up and Denise whispered to her that she wanted to talk after the game.

Gambling and Palm Beach were united very early.

Most people in the resort played backgammon and tournaments were held frequently, but there were a few groups, comprised of both men and women, who met for afternoon or evening poker with medium to high stakes. Gambling had started with Colonel

Bradley, a Catholic who came there with his brother in 1895. Bradley established what he called his "beach club," a typical P.B. misnomer, for the club wasn't on the beach any more than Palm Beach originated with palms. The club was a gambling casino, perhaps the poshest, most exclusive in the world, with higher limits than Monte Carlo and much stricter rules. Members had to wear white tie at the tables, though this restriction was gradually eased to allow black tie, and if a person ever hinted that he was cheated, the loss was refunded and the member was politely sacked, never to be seen again in the casino. No Florida residents were permitted to bet because the Colonel didn't feel that true blue blood trickled into Florida, and at that time the locals were on the bottom half of a tight two-class society. Indeed, Bradley was considered one of the founding fathers of Palm Beach, along with Flagler, Mizner, and Paris Singer.

The gambling casino existed in violation of the Florida laws, but who was going to arrest the Vanderbilts and Whitneys? There were many tragedies connected with Bradley's beach club: Money was lost by those who couldn't afford it; there were fights by borrowers elegantly attired in white ties, and one night when Jim Donahue lost two hundred thousand dollars at one of the faster tables, he went home and killed himself.

In the twenties, a prominent member of a New York family was once asked why he went to Palm Beach every year and he replied, "It's the only place that I can go in my private railroad car and play tennis in the sun and gamble my heart out and have affairs with gorgeous women. If I did some of those things in New York, my wife would leave me . . . in Palm Beach she asks me if I'm having an enjoyable season."

Denise lost four hundred dollars that afternoon at Maggie's. Her mind wasn't on the game and after she wrote her check out to the Queen, who was the treasurer and a skilled poker player, Denise took Nicole aside.

"Can we go back to your place?"

"Sure, honey," Nicole said, thinking that a brief afternoon fling would be nice after the game.

The Bouchart home was big, well built, and ventilated, styled in Regency, by Fatio, one of the architects who followed the Mizner

Spanish period. The house faced the lake and before it ran the famous P.B. bicycle trail. Reaching out into the waters of Lake Worth was a wooden dock where the Boucharts used to moor a custom Berger yacht before the old man became senile. (Nicole had come to Palm Beach for the same reasons as Cynthia and Denise, and she had found what she wanted.)

The entrance hall was tiled and columned and from it ran a series of suites overlooking the lake. It was late afternoon and a soft light flowed into the large, hushed rooms. Nicole often spent hours looking from these windows and she never tired of watching the swiftly changing formations in the sky.

The Florida summer not only arrived with a big, blazing sun but also displayed towering cumulus clouds that were often rimmed with flickering backlight in the afternoons when the ball drew in and dipped over the Glades. The heavenly parade was much more dramatic in summer than winter. The cumulus tops were higher then, the evection over the steaming swamp pumped the moisture up into the seventy-thousand-foot range, and the sky seemed more brittle as the soft blue of winter turned crisper with washes of azure, crimson, and ultraviolet. In late afternoon the clouds would gang up and having absorbed all the moisture they could hold from the Glades, the white would darken to dove gray and the lower edges of the cumulus clusters would form a ragged, threatening base. It would rain lightly, then clear for the last brilliant stages of a Glades sunset.

This particular afternoon the display was unusually dramatic and the two women, in silence, paused at the window watching the flow of amber and bronze light that fell in long swatches upon the still lake.

Finally Denise turned and said, "I have to discuss something with you, Nicole."

"Come upstairs where we can be more comfortable." She took Denise's smooth hand and led her up the winding marble stairs and they settled in the study next to Nicole's bedroom.

"Nicole, I think it's time we stopped our little get-togethers."

"Am I running into competition with John Baxter?" Nicole laughed, tossing her long hair back.

"Absolutely not."

"I know he didn't rape you. You pulled that same scene once before with a French director."

"Who told you that?"

"Oh, a friend of mine in Paris who's aware . . . shall we say . . . of how you operate. I've kept my side of the bargain, haven't I, Denise? You would never have been in Maggie's house this afternoon if I hadn't paved the way for you. Why do you think you were given the Home Ball over a lot of others, and do you possibly believe you can run it yourself?"

"I know what you've done for me, but I'm just not comfortable with this sort of relationship. I have to get bombed every time before we even begin."

"I had no idea I was that revolting."

"Nicole, you're not, but don't you see . . . it's the idea of a lesbian affair."

"I'm not a lesbian!" Nicole said defensively. "I like men, too. I hadn't been with a woman for three years before I met you."

"Then why me?"

"Well, you know you're a very exciting and beautiful woman. I don't blame John Baxter."

"Leave him out of it . . . I'm talking about us now."

"All right. I want to continue seeing you now and then . . . I'm not going to be greedy, but we do have an arrangement."

"You made me in Palm Beach and now you can unmake me. Is that the message?"

"Darling, I just want you to consider everything."

Nicole smiled and kissed Denise on the cheek as she arose.

Denise walked stiffly from the house, her heart pounding. It was not a direct threat, but the implication was clear. She had been a fool to think she could abandon the affair whenever she chose. The medicine Denise usually dished out was suddenly being fed to her.

It was very unpleasant, but she was a survivor. She would think of something.

CHAPTER

18

THE PALACE BEACH HOTEL, A FIVE-STAR ENTRY IN THE *Mobil Guide,* was a six-story Spanish Renaissance building with a thick facade, erected in 1931. Over the years there had been many additions. It conveyed the magical illusion of Palm Beach perfectly with its sunken gardens, overrun by peacocks, three-tiered fountains, all orders of classical columns, pilasters, balustrades, urns, great relief panels, courtyards—and all this baroque splendor had been accomplished without Mizner. The Palace Beach stood twelve feet from a crumbling seawall and when the brochure claimed the hotel was directly on the beach, it was not a boast. Some said it looked like a boxy galleon about to be landed. The present hotel was constructed in a fourteen-month period after its wooden predecessor was reduced to a pile of charred litter following a spectacular housewarming. The workers were imported from Italy and they lived in tents on the grounds until the building was completed.

Leading up to the hotel was a long drive flanked by imported royal palms girded on both sides by the golf courses; to the right of the imposing structure was a parking lot and a secondary U-shaped drive bordered on the west by the golf club and on the east by the pool and pavilion area.

Steve Mitchell drove to Palm Beach with Lou Ballantine and they met Billy and Keith in the Palace Beach parking lot.

Lou said emphatically, "I don't want to have a shambles in there."

"Well, Steve, you'd better not even hint that Billy and I had anything to do with a payoff," Keith said.

"I won't, but just so you're not surprised I'm going to say that the proposal sets up a dangerous situation. I'm planning to show my film, too, if they let me."

"Lou," Billy spoke up, "isn't it poor judgment for the hurricane center to appear here with two opinions? Either we're for the proposal or we're not."

"We can't take a position," Lou repeated.

"But Lake Worth ought to be dug out," Keith said.

"I've never disagreed with that," Steve answered.

"All right," Lou said, ". . . a compromise. Steve, you agree with Billy and Keith that the drainage situation in the lake is critical?"

"From what I know, it's a valid issue."

"And Keith, you must admit that bringing a half-million more people on the beach is dangerous?"

"Maybe."

"Then, there's our position. We're for beach dredging but against the movement of the bulkhead line."

"It's all the same proposal," Keith said.

"Doesn't have to be," Lou answered.

"Mel Hansen's not going to go for that at all," Keith said. "He's counting on his extra beach footage . . . that's what he really wants. This business with Dr. Van Betzig and the seawall has always seemed to me to be just a cover."

"Well, at last, we agree on something," Steve said, smiling. "That's exactly what I think."

As they continued to talk in the parking lot trying to reach a unified opinion, Mel Hansen, John Baxter, and Philip Guest were seated in the chairman's office, and once again the senior man asked them if they had any knowledge of the bribe. Mel lied very well and Philip Guest believed the architect. Glen Markum's name had not come up, and Mel wondered if it would, and whether the state attorney might say at some point, "Mr. Markum, if you want to save yourself, you had better tell us everything."

That would signal the end for Mel Hansen.

As soon as Steve entered the hotel, he went to the phone outside the boardroom and dialed the private number of the war room.

"Hello, this is Steve Mitchell. Anything new on that Verdes disturbance?"

"Yes, Dr. Mitchell," the specialist said. "Quite a few developments emerged on the latest APT. The hotdog has deepened and enlarged. She's a full depression now. That's not all . . . two other disturbances located off the Windwards are also deepening. We have surface and satellite confirmations."

"What's the diameter of the hotdog?"

"I'll have to measure it from the APT. Hold on."

The specialist placed dividers across the breadth of the whitish smudge, and then he returned to the phone.

"Two hundred miles," he said, "maybe a little more in some places."

"Two hundred!" Steve shot back.

"That's right."

"I'll inform the director and we'll be in touch."

Steve approached Lou who was in the midst of introductions outside the boardroom.

"This is Steve Mitchell from the center," Lou said, turning toward Steve, "our co-deputy director."

"How do you do? I'm John Baxter and this is our chairman, Philip Guest."

"We appreciate your taking the time to come here today," Philip said.

"Thank you, sir," Steve said, and then turned to Lou. "Lou, may I speak to you for a second?" Steve indicated this was to be private. They walked a few feet down the corridor.

"We've got trouble. The three disturbances have deepened. I just called the war room. The hotdog is two hundred miles across. She's now a depression and growing fast."

"That's gigantic," Lou said softly.

The two men stood looking at each other, both feeling distinct uneasiness. For a very youthful cyclone to be two hundred miles across was unheard of, and Lou tried to recall if in all his years at the center anything like that had ever happened before. Keith, an engaging young man, was already laughing with John and Philip when Lou took him aside.

"Is there anything wrong, Dr. Ballantine?" Philip said, walking over to the corner where the three experts now stood.

The chairman wondered if these people were about to admit that money had been passed to them by someone at the Palace Beach.

"We have a little problem out in the Atlantic," Lou said as he guided Keith and Billy over to the phone and explained the report from the war room.

"Is the diameter of the activity confirmed?" Keith asked.

"Yes, by surface and satellite."

"Never thought it would grow like that," Keith said. "We should probe it immediately."

"We should have done it a day ago," Steve answered.

"That can't be helped now," Lou said. "I'll order a plane out of Keesler Air Force. What does this mean to you people . . . such a broad depression?"

"I don't know," Steve said thoughtfully. "Camille was tight but small. If this one begins to form . . . wow!"

"Then you might finally have your big storm," Keith remarked in an acid voice.

"That's a cheap shot, Keith! You think I want a dangerous hurricane! I've had my dose already."

They entered the boardroom finally, but Lou was worried. He had had a strange feeling about that Verdes low from the beginning. It could well be Steve's storm of the century, or any century. The director knew that a large hurricane was not necessarily a vicious one; size and wind speed have nothing to do with each other. Some large hurricanes are mild in the core without an acute deterioration of central pressure. On the other hand, a very small but well-organized hurricane, such as Camille or the 1935 Labor Day storm that hit the Florida Keys, could be brutally intense.

Lou's thoughts drifted to the combination that no hurricane man dares imagine: a mammoth storm five hundred miles across with an extremely low central pressure. That catastrophic situation would go far beyond Steve's model storm. Could it happen? Lou asked himself. What were they really seeing out there west of the Verdes? His mind was so riveted to that appalling possibility that the director hardly acknowledged the introduction of Dr. Van Betzig and the Palace Beach management.

Philip Guest was relieved when he saw the appearance of the team from the National Hurricane Center. They were all Ph.D.'s, the men conservatively dressed in coats and ties, and Dr. Haughton wore a dark-green dress. She was neat and businesslike. The chairman found it hard to believe that these people would take the risk of accepting money.

Philip began the meeting. "We're happy to have you at the Palace Beach. I'm sorry it's under such circumstances, but we wanted to clear the air. I'm sure you wish to know our position, Dr. Ballantine."

"Yes. My administrator in Washington called this morning. The Secretary of Commerce is, naturally, upset. The implications in the *Miami Star* are very serious."

"I agree. Our general counsel has written the paper a letter saying that the reference to us was highly unfair and arbitrary. Mr. Hansen came to us with the idea of a new condominium project. He said that the new setback proposal would be passed. Dr. Van Betzig is a consultant to Mr. Hansen, not the Palace Beach, and he told us that Mr. Hansen's seawall code would help reclaim our eroded beaches. We started to build, although I personally was against it; I took the position that we should wait until the proposition was passed. My thinking was economic because, you see, our permission to build was provisional and we stood to take a serious loss if the proposal isn't passed. I was outvoted by the board.

"The Palace Beach did not engage any of your people, Dr. Ballantine. Mr. Hansen asked them for data to assist in a dredging of Lake Worth. In other words, we are not supporting Mr. Hansen's proposal, even though it appears that we are because, unfortunately, we're constructing a condominium where we shouldn't."

"Thank you, sir," Lou said. "The hurricane center must remain neutral. We neither approve nor disapprove of private projects. We can and have said that opening up places like Lake Worth will improve drainage conditions."

"I understand there is some merit to Mr. Hansen's proposal from that point of view," Philip added.

"Definitely," Keith said.

"May I speak?" Steve asked.

"Certainly, Dr. Mitchell."

"I agree wtih the plan to dredge the inland waterway to create a better flow pattern in and out of the inlets, but letting the line move toward the high-water mark will have a serious impact upon the beach population."

"Overcrowding?" Philip asked.

"Exactly. I brought a short film with me today that illustrates my concern. If you'll bear with me for a minute or two, while I set it up, I think you'll better understand my sentiments afterward."

Three years earlier Steve Mitchell had seen the growing danger: too many condominium residents loading the beach with too few bridges over the inland waterway to evacuate them in case of a category-five hurricane. At that time Steve requested money from Commerce to produce an educational documentary film, but the idea was turned down because of fiscal problems, so Steve went ahead on his own. Using his personal funds, he hired three Fort Lauderdale film makers and made a sixteen-minute color and sound movie that bore neither the stamp nor official authorization of the United States Department of Commerce.

After a few moments, the screen Steve had brought with him had been set up and the lights were dimmed. The movie dealt with two central issues. Traffic department data showed that only 67 percent of all the registered vehicles on the hurricane coast—the area of tightly wadded condominiums running from Miami north to Pompano Beach—would be able to escape over the existing bridges. Should the bridges become flooded or a number of cars break down during a torrential hurricane rain, the figure would be much lower. Conditions existed for a potentially great disaster.

The other point of the film regarded vertical evacuation. How safe was it to take refuge on the higher floors of a beach condominium, and the film announcer said:

"Condominiums in South Florida are built to a strict code, which presumably protects them against hurricane shearing winds, but the control storm used to determine engineering and construction criteria was based upon historical data of the worst storm to hit the east Florida coast. The top wind speed used as a reference point was one hundred and sixty miles per hour. Hurricane shutters are designed to those speeds, but consider a more intense storm with winds of two hundred miles an hour and over. What would happen to the occupants of a condominium if the wind moved up to that regime? Manufacturers of storm shutters say that their products would blow apart at wind speeds above one hundred and sixty and engineers report that windows would shatter at wind speeds of two hundred miles an hour. It is reasonable to believe that the vertical evacuees would be seriously injured, perhaps killed.

"The only safety from a severe hurricane is lateral evacuation, but to accomplish this efficiently more roads and bridges must be built. And there still remains the question: How many residents would leave if they were ordered out? Research indicates that at least sixty percent of the people occupying condominiums believe themselves to be safer in their own homes than anywhere else and these people would not evacuate. So, hurricane education along with additional escape routes must be designed, financed, and implemented. The Gold Coast is an endangered coast."

When the lights came on, Philip Guest said, "I wish I had seen that film before our board met."

"Had I known about your project, sir," Steve said, "I would have talked to them."

"It's a scenario for a catastrophe," Philip continued. "Dr. Ballantine, I didn't see the name of the hurricane center on that film."

"Steve financed it himself and as a private citizen he has been exhibiting it to various groups around South Florida."

"Isn't that unusual? Do you agree with the contents of the documentary, Dr. Ballantine?"

There was a long pause and Lou thought again about the situation developing in the tropical Atlantic.

"How realistic is this idea of a two-hundred-mile-an-hour storm?" Philip Guest pressed. "Has it ever occurred?"

"Not around here," Lou said. "But there have been cyclones with measured wind speeds clocked over two hundred miles an hour."

"May I, Lou?" Steve said, trying to get his director off the hook. "There is no doubt that a storm of these proportions could hit South Florida if the right atmospheric conditions existed."

"Then why wasn't the building code amended to reflect the worst storm possible?" the chairman asked. "I served with the intelligence end in the Air Force in London during the blitz and when the English built their shelters, they were constructed to take the largest blockbuster in the German arsenal, not an average bomb. Why isn't it the same with the building code?"

"A matter of economics," Steve said. "They took reasonable hurricane data. The builders and engineers told me they could design for storms with two-hundred-mile-an-hour winds, but the costs would be prohibitive. Nobody would be able to sell the units. The answer is *not* vertical evacuation; it *has* to be *lateral*. What I object to in Mr. Hansen's plan is the fact that he proposes to put more buildings on the beach, and we can't even evacuate the existing population now."

"That's clear to me," Philip said. "John, did you know about this evacuation problem?"

"I thought all that was investigated by Mel since it was his proposal."

"Mr. Guest," Steve continued, "just the appearance of your condominium going up past the bulkhead line suggests that you endorse Mr. Hansen's proposal."

"I know how it looks," he said. "I realized that way back when we voted for it. Now it's compounded by this bribery allegation."

"I would suggest, Mr. Hansen, that you redraft your proposal to exclude the extension of the building line," Steve said.

Mel sprang to his feet. All his dreams seemed to be withering before him. He knew that Philip Guest was about to halt the Regency Walk project and he spoke firmly, pounding his hand on the table. "I thought my idea was worthwhile! Dr. Landon and Dr. Haughton said it would help reclaim the beach, and the world's expert on seawalls, who was retained by me personally, agreed with its ecological advantages. I've put my time and money into this. I'm creating jobs. Now, if we cut off the building program, what's in it for me? Hell, what am I supposed to be . . . some goddamned Jesus Christ of the beach?"

"Mr. Hansen, watch your language, please!" Philip said. "If you had checked with the hurricane center, you would have been exposed to Dr. Mitchell's theories."

"I contacted the head of the center, the director. Dr. Ballantine, why didn't you tell me about the existence of this film and what Mitchell was going around telling people?"

"You said your plan was just to reclaim the beach. You didn't say anything about the bulkhead extension."

"Then it was up to you," Mel said, jabbing his thick, ugly finger at Keith. "Why didn't you mention Mitchell and all this crap on the two-hundred-mile-an-hour storm!"

"Mr. Hansen, please control yourself," the chairman fumed.

"Well, dammit, I'm mad. I try to do something beneficial and look what happens."

"Beneficial, Mr. Hansen?" Philip said. "You were after a boondoggle, weren't you?"

"I might have gained some work, but there were no guarantees. I don't have a single commission in my pocket at the moment, and you're blaming this entirely on me. That's the man who should have told me about Mitchell's campaign. He knew what we were doing."

"Is that true, Dr. Landon?" Philip asked.

"Yes."

"Then why didn't you advise Mr. Hansen accordingly?"

Lou Ballantine slumped down in his chair, dreading the possibility of an open split, and he wondered if he should be talking for the center. Keith, however, shot back at Mel, "Because I do not agree with the contents of that film! The language is excessive. I told Steve that three years ago and I advised him then to stop showing the film."

"What is it that you disagree with, Dr. Landon?" Philip asked.

"The chances of a storm like that are infinitesimal. As far as evacuation goes, we can give twelve hours warning with eighty percent accuracy. You can't tell me that we couldn't get everyone out in that time."

"If you could offer twelve hours warning with accuracy, my wife would still be alive," Steve said softly.

"Dr. Mitchell lost his wife during Camille up in Mississippi," Dr. Ballantine said, looking at the chairman.

"I'm sorry to hear that. Were you there, Dr. Mitchell?"

"Yes. There was terrible confusion and people reacted ignorantly. Everybody didn't have twelve hours and, in fact, the experts don't know much more today than they did back in 1969. We had all the fancy satellites, the radar then; still ninety people died on that one beach. They never had a chance. I saw it happen right before my eyes."

"Then you speak from experience?" the chairman said.

"Yes, I do."

"The real danger," Keith said with a sting to his voice, "is not south of here, but three quarters of a mile west. Drainage out of the lake and margin lands is a serious problem and I'm afraid if we alter the proposal, as Steve suggests, it won't go through."

"I'll say it won't! It must carry some economic benefit for approval!" Mel blasted.

"And the lake will never be dredged or improved," Keith said.

"Dr. Haughton, you haven't said anything."

"Mr. Guest, I frankly agree with Keith Landon. The proposal should go through."

"And you, Dr. Ballantine?"

"As director, I can't agree or disagree. There's merit on both sides."

"You have a divided opinion within your ranks, Dr. Ballantine."

"Yes, we have. But there are many different opinions in the hurricane business. Sometimes, I think we're still groping in the wilderness."

"John, I feel it was your duty to research this adequately," Philip said with a reproving glance at his president.

There was more discussion, but by the end of the meeting the chairman had made up his mind. He was going to halt the Regency Walk project and investigate their expenses to date. In the hall outside the boardroom Philip invited the hurricane team to a party he was giving at his home that evening. They said they would have supper but had to leave early because of certain business developments back at the center. No one said what kind of business.

19

WHILE THE DISCUSSION WAS GOING ON AT THE PALACE BEACH THAT
day, Jayson Kendall visited Cynthia Baxter. She was sunning by the
pool and the phone next to her chaise had not rung all that afternoon. As Jayson approached in blue jeans and a wrinkled shirt and
carrying his bathing suit, she could smell the odor of whiskey that
hung around him like a smothering cloud.

"I'll turn the sauna on, Jayson," she said routinely.

He often visited Cynthia on afternoons when his morning drinking had taken more of a toll than usual.

"What happened today, Jayson?"

"The head of the Finance Committee from the club stopped by.
I've taken the 'arrears prize.' "

"Are you cut off?"

"Temporarily . . . Do you have any loose lolly?"

"You didn't pay me back last time, you rascal."

Cynthia was fond of Jayson. When the Baxters came to Palm Beach, Jayson introduced them to several right people in both camps, and despite his drinking and practical jokes, Jayson was a kind man who never made up stories about other Palm Beachers and did nothing to feed the gossip machine that always worked overtime, damaging many innocent people. He had stuck by Cynthia after the *Patna* incident and he went to great lengths to tell everyone he knew (an extensive population) that John Baxter was seduced that night and there was no rape.

Unfortunately, few believed him.

Jayson tucked his *Wall Street Journal* under his arm and entered the sauna. It was located in the Baxters' pool house, a white structure with a mock Mizner roof, and out in front was a blue baldachin, which gave one the impression of a whimsical French Riviera setting. When Mizner built his great homes in Palm Beach many were constructed without pools and they did not include the fanciful pool houses that became popular in the thirties and forties for afternoon entertaining.

After John Baxter bought the rancid, overgrown "El Lugar" (Mel had thought it judicious to name his Bahamian resort after the Baxter place), he and Cynthia had worked for years, waging a war of attrition against age, poor construction, and faulty design. John's starting salary at the Palace Beach, even though he enjoyed a prestigious position, was not sufficient to complete the necessary work on the two-acre estate, which had gone to seed. But little by little, he and Cynthia had put the house, the grounds, and pool into condition, never admitting, of course, that they were doing their own work. Palm Beach was not a "do-it-yourself" town; professional servants, handymen, carpenters, plasterers, pool boys were the common currency and to be seen clipping one's own hedge in front of a large facade was a tip-off that there might be financial wobbliness behind the Ficus trees.

The pool house was a mark of stature. John designed theirs and built it himself with Cynthia's help. Slowly and secretly, they renewed "El Lugar," to a point where important guests could be entertained with ease and style. It took almost four years and they were happy years for the couple, and their love grew as they hammered the nails, hitting their fingers at times.

John and Cynthia had lived in New York previously where he practiced as general counsel to the American Resort Company; at a hotel convention he had met Philip Guest who offered the presentable New Englander the job of general house counsel to the Palace Beach System, and when the president, Colonel Appling, died, John moved into his spot.

Still, the new couple were far from being hoisted to the top ranks of the second covey and Cynthia began to work on it. She was not a superficial publicity hawk. She was outgoing and wanted to be liked and if anyone in Palm Beach had to characterize Cynthia Baxter, her graciousness would be mentioned first. She served on various charitable boards to help raise money rather than to evoke publicity. And then came the evening aboard the *Patna*.

The Baxters did not deserve the terrible consequences from that event. Cynthia, who was not able to have children, felt that perhaps she had not rewarded her husband sufficiently, but she had, indeed, served his career until Denise Hansen came to town. It was all the more agonizing that someone so shallow, so sleazy, and so obvious as Denise Hansen could have wrecked the lives of two good and careful people.

Cynthia realized very quickly that it must have started with Nicole Bouchart, but she did not know under what circumstances. If she had, it might have settled some of Cynthia's shaken spirits. She had not thought any more of the gun buried under the winter clothes that she wore on trips to New York; the desire to kill Denise left her mind soon after she purchased the weapon. Cynthia knew no way to fight Denise at this point; she lived in solitude day after day and the phone was stilled.

Cynthia went inside now and prepared a cold steak sandwich and a bowl of nourishing soup for Jayson. She knew that the sauna and the soup would bring him around, and he always looked better after the dry heat and a swim. The therapy worked and he emerged a different man forty minutes later.

"Cindy, I don't know what I'd do without you."

"You'd be a little hungrier now and then."

"Are you going to Philip's party tonight?"

"I don't know," she said hesitantly. "John says I have to. What's the point of drawing this out . . . putting us all on display? I don't even want to be within a hundred feet of Denise and Nicole. They're ruthless, Jayson."

"I ran into Philip on the Everglades course the other day. He asked me if you were really going to divorce John."

"What did you say?"

"Told him I didn't know. Are you?"

"My head is so cracked up over this, I don't know what I'll do. Leave Palm Beach, I guess . . . might go back to Atlanta." She said half under her breath, "Why is Philip having Mel and his wife at the party? He never included them before."

Jayson shrugged. "Probably the idea is to get everybody together in a homey kind of way to prove that our little clique has patched its social sails."

"And I'm supposed to dance with Mel, and John is supposed to dance with Denise, while Maggie looks on and smiles. That's a lot of BS!" She shook her head and swallowed the rest of her gin and tonic in one gulp.

"Cynthia dear, you've got to understand that this whole thing has kicked the hell out of Philip and the hotel's reputation. Did you see that business in the paper about a bribe?"

"Yes. John's been in a meeting all afternoon with Mel and some hurricane experts from Miami."

Jayson finished his soup and sandwich and he sat at the end of the taffy-colored chaise looking first at the blazing sun, then over at Cynthia, whose face seemed to be recovering well from her burns. Then his eyes slipped down to her full breasts and then to her finely formed tanned legs. His hand slipped into hers and he brought her face toward him and kissed her lightly on the cheek, then she turned her lips toward his and they embraced for a long moment.

"Wait, Jayson, the gardener's around. This is all I need."

"Then let's go down to my house. The advantage of being poor is that one isn't disturbed by servants and gardeners."

"I can't go to your house. It'd spoil our perfect record."

"You've been very kind to me, Cynthia."

"Well, Jayson, that's because you're such a desperate, lovable old scoundrel. Now, how much money do you need this time?"

"Five hundred would see me through nicely. Things just got a little tight all of a sudden."

"All right, but under one condition—promise you'll drop down to three drinks a day."

"Aw, Cindy, I don't think I can do it."

"Yes you can."

"OK, I'll try. For you, I'll try."

A few minutes later Cynthia went inside, and shortly after that, returning with the money, she gave Jayson a gentle kiss on the cheek. "Remember, Jayson," she said, looking him straight in the eye, a look of warmth on her face, "a promise is a promise."

With that she gave Jayson the money, which he pocketed with effusive thanks.

CHAPTER

20

THE NORTH AND SOUTH ENDS OF PALM BEACH WERE DIVIDED AT ROYAL Poinciana Way, one of the main streets running across the island. On the far north end the houses were small and modern; most did not occupy either beach or lake frontage, and they rested on very low ground—grade, they said—not more than three feet above sea level. When the county engineers carried out their storm data topography studies indicating which parts of the county would be overtopped first, the streets running south of Palm Beach Inlet—Arabian, Caribbean, Mediterranean Road, and others—were found to be the most vulnerable on the island, perhaps in the county.

The real rich didn't live there; most of the residents were retired people and a few, younger divorcées and lawyers, doctors, accountants involved in town business. The houses clustered on the middle properties of the north end, in what was called the Boca Raton subdivision, were for the most part cinderblock and cement, single-storied, some with pools, most without; not unlike other Florida neighborhoods. But since this was Palm Beach, where land was at a premium, the houses sold for more than $100,000.

Going south toward town the cross streets became wider and lusher and the homes were larger, moving up into the $200,000 category. Their architecture was inspired by Bermudian and Bahamian designs and eclectic French Regency. The streets bore characteristic names such as Sandpiper Drive, Tradewind Drive, Jamaica Lane, and Bahama Lane; and all these clusters rested on a grade level that was only four to five feet above the sea on one side and the lake on the other.

Bordering the middle properties were the waterfront sites. Homes on Lake Worth were priced in the $300,000 to $500,000 range. They faced the bicycle trail; they were much larger than the middle properties and some of the homes had yacht docks in front. On the other side were the choicest properties: estates directly on the ocean. The Kennedys owned an ocean-front home on the north end; the Du Ponts lived on that strip and it was probably Mrs. Stotesbury's selection of a north-end property that resulted in that section of the town being opened up. Also, a portent that the Palm Beachers were inching up the island was the 1928 construction of the north-end fire station designed by Clark Lawrence; it was far from an ordinary old firehouse, American style; the Palm Beach fathers would never have been satisfied with something mundane and so they constructed a three-level Spanish-type building with barrel tiles and ornamental rafters, pecky cypress ceilings and even the fire engine doors were paneled.

On the south end of Palm Beach, below Worth Avenue, the grade level ran up to an average of nine feet, and there were outcroppings of coquina rock fourteen feet high near Mar-a-Lago. This was Palm Beach's outstanding architectural embarrassment, a 122-room mansion built around 1930 for Marjorie Merriweather Post, who had been married to E. F. Hutton among others and who had sat in the regent's chair during the golden years of Palm Beach society.

It had been rumored that when Harry K. Thaw, who gunned down Stanford White in a hot dispute over Evelyn Nesbit, took a look at Mar-a-Lago, he said, "My God, I may have killed the wrong architect."

The Post palace, built by Toasties, was designed by a team of architects including Joseph Urban, a set designer for Florenz Ziegfeld, who was also the architect of record for the Bath & Tennis Club across the street from Mar-a-Lago. The Post home was one of the few estates in the Palm Beach area that ran from the sea to the lake; one other located in nearby Manalapan was built by Gerard Lambert, of the Listerine fortune, but that was a modern house and it ran under the road, A-1A, and was later sold to a member of the Du Pont family.

There were no small, plain cinderblock houses in the south end of town and, unlike the squads of typical Florida homes on the opposite end, the middle properties here were spotted with clusters of Spanish and Tuscan estates, some large, others enormous.

The two extremities of the island were different physically. The north end was flat, sandy, and dangerous from a hurricane point of view, but the lower end was deceptive: While the higher grade level set up a partial barrier against surge overtopping, a rocky base of lime sand and shells, Anastasia, ran downhill from the ocean to the lake at an inclination of four to seven degrees. When the ocean surge overtopped the south end, the water was prevented from returning to the sea in a process of runoff. Since the sea always sought its own level, once over South Ocean Boulevard, it rushed downhill to the lake like a raging cataract. The lake filled up and overflowed since it had little lateral release except for two inlets spaced twenty-nine miles apart.

Philip Guest's house was located on the north end five doors down from the Kennedy place; it was designed by Maurice Fatio in 1924 and it stood 140 feet from the high-tide line. Philip's wife, Laura, was a stylish horsewoman, originally from Upperville, Virginia, who inherited a fortune when she was young.

The Guests were spikes of Palm Beach authenticity.

When Philip was nine years old his father first came to Palm Beach and stayed at the Royal Poinciana Hotel. He had known Flagler and Bradley and he and his wife often gambled at the beach club. (Bradley's was the first casino in the world to allow women to bet.) But Philip's father, a man who established his fortune in raw minerals, had had an argument with Paris Singer who was the owner and kingpin of the Everglades Club. Singer handed out the memberships that had to be renewed each year on a totally preferential basis; if he didn't like the way someone combed his hair, that man's membership was not renewed and no reason was given. After the argument, the senior Guest (no relation to the Winston Guests, also P.B. people), left the club forever, and it was only after World War II and long after Singer's rule was over, that his son, Philip, joined the Everglades.

The Guests did not care for the saccharine Romanesque and Spanish tradition of Mizner; it probably was rooted in the fact that Mizner in the beginning was supported by Paris Singer. The Guests built a winter home along the Regency lines and it was an outstanding example of finer Palm Beach architecture, having a classical facade of 154 feet fronting the ocean. The home of fifty-six rooms formed an atrium effect around a large pool bordered by lush plantings of hybrid hibiscus, Bougainvillaea, and trimmed Ficus hedges. At one end was a large marbled patio that was used for dancing with a stage rise for an orchestra along a scalloped balustrade.

Philip always gave a "non-covey" party one week before the Home Ball. It was one of the few times that those on the first level opened their homes to respectable members of the other groups at an annual event. Three hundred guests would be invited. They came informally dressed in Rolls and slightly battered Chevrolets; that indicated a mixed party, but all the cars were parked by attendants. (The Executive Parking Service, perhaps the best on the island, was a specialized profession. The fellows never forgot who went with which car, and some of them had about four hundred faces paired off to the right cars locked in their memories.)

Laura Guest was one of the most skilled hostesses in Palm Beach and she gave her parties with gracious ease. She had been at it so long that there was never a nervous moment, and she was helped by the reinforcement of funds and a permanent social secretary. This year's party was about the same as the others, but the cost was now estimated to be around $19,000 for the evening, up $3,000 from the previous year's event. The $19,000 went into two large tents, fresh flowers, four bars, two buffet tables laid out with eight kinds of fresh fish, including lobsters flown in from Maine and Dublin Bay prawns direct from Ireland, wild boar, turkey, Virginia ham, hot and cold roast beef along with seven other dishes from squab to curried chicken.

The meal was partly catered and served by nineteen waitresses and six bartenders; the guests danced to a nine-piece orchestra. The fresh flower arrangements which were on every table cost $3,900, and the party favors, shell necklaces for the women and gold-plated lighters for the men, $2,700.

This year's party would not only continue the tradition of the Guests' annual open house; it was designed to clear up the social tangle of the year.

Philip had set up a small bar in his paneled study and during the evening he sent for those individuals whom he could depend upon to help diminish the escalating problems facing the Palace Beach System. People listened to Philip Guest and he was a king of sorts to all levels of the tight society, having served as mayor at one time. He was first approached by Jayson Kendall, who came especially early to speak with Philip.

"Close the door, Jayson," Philip said, as he built drinks for himself and Jayson. "I know you've got something on your mind. What is it?"

"Cynthia Baxter. Phil, she's terribly distraught."

"John told me. I know all about it and it's damned embarrassing. And now I have a bribery to contend with. My board of directors, needless to say, is quite upset at the moment."

Jayson and Philip were close friends, and Philip, knowing that the bard never became entangled in idle talk, confided in Jayson from time to time.

He continued now, "I asked Mel Hansen and his wife here this evening because I want that sordid episode to blow over as soon as possible. Everyone must see that the two women are friends."

"But they're not. Cynthia hates Denise."

"She'd better not show it tonight."

"Philip, I know Cynthia. She's in a terrible state, and I wouldn't be surprised if it all ends up in court. And that could be ghastly because Denise will cry 'rape.'"

A painful expression shot across Philip Guest's smooth face. "I know and the board's aware, too. They're very nervous."

"Phil, Cynthia's been completely cut off by Maggie. No one calls her. Maggie has the power to fix what she unfixed, and if she were to wipe the slate clean, there would be nothing to worry about."

"Is it that simple?"

"I think so. Cynthia sits by her phone hoping it will ring. If Maggie and the others called only to see how she was, her attitude would improve."

"Jayson, you may just have hit on a very good idea. If you'd only stop drinking, I'd hire you."

"I wish I could."

"Go get some help while your mind is still keen. I will talk to Maggie when she gets here. She was on my list anyhow."

The two men wandered out onto the terrace where Laura was greeting her friends. The night was warm, fanned by a slight breeze, and Philip began to introduce the team from the hurricane center; slowly people worked their way through the four bars and the laughter heightened.

"Maggie, how good of you to come," Philip said as he kissed the sprite Queen.

He introduced her to Keith Landon and Billy Haughton and told the old woman who they were.

"Isn't that marvelous! Are we safe from hurricanes up here?" she asked them.

"I think so. As long as you pay attention to our warnings," Keith smiled.

They chatted awhile and then Steve and Dr. Ballantine were introduced to Maggie and Jayson Kendall. John Baxter moved into the group and he had a long conversation with Steve about his study of storm surge.

"Let me know if you ever fly into one of those things," John said. "I'd like to go along . . . I was with the Eighth Air Force. That film you showed this afternoon . . . I can't get it off my mind. Mel should have gone into that with you."

"I think my associate stood in the way."

"I could feel the hostility between you two."

"Well, the hurricane business is full of contradictory opinions."

As the two men continued to talk, Philip took Maggie into his study.

"Maggie, I need your help."

"Anything, Phil. What is it?"

"Do you really think that John raped Denise?"

"It looked that way, but I must say I find it hard to believe."

"He didn't. They were both drinking heavily that night and Denise was as much to blame as John. In fact, more, according to his story."

"Phil! Denise is not that type. Nicole Bouchart told me that Denise comes from a fine Parisian family. She was educated by nuns and she gave all the proceeds from her acting to charitable causes."

"And you believe that?"

"Well, of course. Why shouldn't I?"

"What if I brought Mel Hansen in here and he told you differently?"

"That man works for you. He'll say anything, even about his own wife. What happened that night was a disgrace."

"John made a mistake, but why take it out on Cynthia? Maggie, I've never asked you for a favor in all the years we've known each other . . . when did we meet?"

"At a ball in 1932 and I thought you were the handsomest man in Palm Beach."

Philip was constantly amazed at the lucidity of Maggie's mind, and he laughed and said, "We're old, old friends. So, will you do me a favor? Cynthia is very upset about her injuries and about being left out of things. She's talked about suing John for divorce and Denise for assault. If she does, Denise will charge John with rape. It will all reflect on Palm Beach . . . the town and the hotel. Not only that," he sighed, "we have new problems."

"I read about them. Is that why the hurricane people are here?"

"Yes. We had to get some matters straightened out. We're stopping the Regency Walk project, but that's highly confidential."

"I understand. What about the people who've already purchased units? I was thinking of buying one myself."

"We'll get to that later . . . work something out. Now, I want you to patch things up with Cynthia."

Maggie was about to answer when someone knocked on the door. One of the seven photographers entered.

"Mr. Guest, excuse me. Oh, I'm sorry, I didn't see Mrs. Dunsmore."

"That's all right."

"It's about the matter of photographing Mrs. Hansen and Mrs. Baxter."

"Yes?"

"The ladies don't wish to be photographed together."

"Would you ask the Hansens and the Baxters to step in here, Tom?"

The man nodded and left and Philip went to the bar and poured a second drink.

"Do you see what I'm going through?"

"Yes. It's showing up on your face."

"Could you help? Say that you've forgotten the incident and as a token gesture, take Cynthia back."

"That will solve Cynthia's problem, perhaps, but I don't think Denise will go along."

"Even if you ask?"

"If Nicole Bouchart and I ask together, she may. Let's get Nicole in here."

Philip made his way through the growing crowd and found Nicole talking to Steve Mitchell.

"Excuse me, you two. Nicole, Maggie and I would like to talk to you a moment."

"Sure. See you later, Dr. Mitchell."

Denise approached Steve. She looked absolutely stunning in Cardin evening pajamas. Steve could not help the admiring look that crossed his face. Denise quickly caught it, but just as quickly put him at ease. "I'm Mel Hansen's wife, Denise, Dr. Mitchell. Keith Landon pointed you out."

"Hello, Mrs. Hansen . . . pleased to meet you."

"I guess you two squared off this afternoon. My husband isn't happy right now, but he's a practical man."

"We'll have to compromise our viewpoints."

"Why don't we dance?"

She took him by the hand and they headed toward the floor.

Just about the same time Nicole reached Philip Guest's study. Philip explained the problem and stated how important it was to Palm Beach to have Cynthia and Denise patch up their differences. "We have to pull together. Nicole, how much influence do you have with Denise Hansen?"

Nicole smiled to herself and she was filled with a warm feeling. "We've been fairly close, you might say. I know she's provoked at

Cynthia and John for all the embarrassment they've caused her."

A few minutes later the Baxters and the Hansens entered the study. They knew immediately why they were there: The voices of Maggie and Philip were powerful.

"I'll come right to the point. I want you all photographed together talking and laughing and dancing with each other," Philip said.

Maggie chimed in. "Ladies, I think Philip is right. Let's forget the whole incident, and, Cynthia, perhaps I was hasty in talking to you so forcefully that afternoon. I'm sorry."

"I'm not being photographed with her," Denise said, realizing that as soon as she was seen joined in a truce with the Baxters, her possible charge of rape would be groundless.

"Now, don't take it that way, Denise. Forget and forgive," Nicole said. Her cool blue eyes never left Denise's face as she spoke slowly and deliberately, enjoying her power. "I would suggest that you be photographed as Philip asks."

There was silence.

"Why not?" Mel said. "I think it's the only thing to do."

Nicole went over and took Denise by the arm and ten minutes later Denise and Cynthia were photographed together.

"This is purely a tactic," Cynthia whispered to Denise. "I abhor you."

"No more than I detest you."

Denise was then photographed dancing with John Baxter.

"John, darling, this doesn't mean you're not coming to El Lugar," she said.

He did not answer, but a muscle in the side of his face twitched as he stared across the room.

On the other side of the floor Billy and Steve were dancing, and Steve after a few drinks had lightened up considerably.

"It's good to see you smiling again," she said.

"Not bad up here in Palm Beach. Must be nice to be rich."

"Do you know what impresses me about all these people?"

"They're all monied lovelies."

"Besides that. They're very friendly . . . not a bit snobbish."

"I think that John Baxter and his wife are very pleasant. What happened to her face?"

"Didn't you hear?"

"No."

"It was the scandal of the season."

They left the dance floor and walked out toward the beach, and sat down looking over the calm sea streaked with moonlight.

"I'm glad you admitted that Keith had a point about the dredging," she said.

Steve laughed.

"What's so funny?"

"Here we are sitting in magic land on a beautiful estate under the palms and all of a sudden you're talking about dredging. What other woman would do that?"

"Well, when we went down to the sexy Caribbean aboard the *Pleasure Pie*, all you talked about was sea temperatures."

"I know. Maybe I'm changing as I get older. There has to be something else besides hurricanes." He waved his arm toward the house. "Do they worry about hurricanes?"

"They don't get paid to."

Steve leaned back and rested his head in Billy's lap and she stroked his forehead.

"Are you going to marry Keith?"

"I don't know. Maybe."

He reached up and brought her face down to his and kissed her lightly on the lips. "Billy, please don't do anything hasty. I know we've had our differences but you and Keith aren't . . ."

He stopped short as he heard a rustling nearby.

Standing off under a clump of swaying royal palms was Keith Landon, who was just approached by Lou Ballantine. Steve saw them engaged in conversation and could hear Ballantine say, "Keith, where are the others?"

"Out there!" Keith was boiling.

By the time he and Ballantine reached Billy and Steve they were sitting straight.

"I just called the center," Lou said. "The three depressions have gone to storms. The Verdes hotdog is now named Claudine and she's almost three hundred miles across. We'd better get back to Miami immediately."

The four quickly said their good-byes and in only minutes were driving at top speed down I-95 toward Coral Gables.

CHAPTER

21

SUNDAY.

Palm Beachers had always closely associated themselves with God and prayer. Perhaps P.B.'s devotion to the higher order arose as expressions of gratitude for gifts received and for those not yet bestowed; and also, Sunday church attendance was thought to be proper, correct, and social.

While Bradley set the tone of Palm Beach behavior at the gambling tables, it was Henry Flagler who first made it practical for the resorters to pray on Sunday morning. In addition to his Royal Poinciana Hotel erected in 1894, the Palm Beach Inn in 1895, and his columned home, Whitehall, in 1901, Flagler built a colonial church called the Royal Poinciana Chapel in 1896, which still stood in the summer of 1977.

Although it was one of the oldest churches in the county, the Royal Poinciana Chapel was not the finest nor the most social; that distinction belonged to the prestigious Bethesda-by-the-Sea. This bastion of Episcopalianism, a Spanish Gothic design completed in 1928 with contributions from the Chicago McCormicks, was constructed without regard to cost, and it remained one of the finest miniature Spanish Gothic cathedrals in the world. Its inventory of liturgical art included a Murillo, a Diepenbeeck (student of Rubens), and stained-glass windows designed and fabricated in England and shipped to Palm Beach during the war on three different freighters so that the godless German subs wouldn't destroy what was destined for the praying peacocks. The stage-like church was named by the Cluetts, an old Palm Beach family who stacked up its funds from the invention of the Sanforizing process.

One churchgoing visitor to Palm Beach said that only at the altar rail in Bethesda-by-the-Sea could one look down as the holy communion was distributed and see the rector padding along in white Gucci loafers.

The third of the Palm Beach churches was again a Spanish-styled mini-cathedral erected with the assistance of the Catholic elite who wintered in the resort. Colonel Bradley gave the first donation to break ground, but others such as Joseph P. Kennedy and William Randolph Hearst contributed stained-glass windows. St. Edward's has been alternately called the gamblers' church and the Kennedy church, mostly by Protestants, and few could decide which was worse since both gambling and the Kennedys were not looked upon with much admiration just after Bradley closed his house of chance in 1946.

The Kennedys were considered to be Irish upstarts and were not invited to many parties, nor was Joseph Kennedy's application accepted at the Everglades Club, so he played golf at the Jewish club. The Kennedys were never noticed or taken seriously in Palm Beach until the patriarch became the ambassador to the Court of St. James. In the end when the resort finally deigned to accept Catholics capable of merit and stature, Rose Kennedy was one of the most admired.

But of all the liturgical towers in Palm Beach, the one that bore the finest design and appropriate simplicity was the Jewish temple on North County Road, a modern, functional house of worship that many claimed was the finest small synagogue in the world.

The Baxters and the Hansens were attending the same eleven o'clock service at Bethesda-by-the-Sea the morning after Philip Guest's party. Cynthia was eyeing her husband who had once looked around toward Denise sitting on the far side of the nave. At first she thought it was a glance of simple recognition, but the second time it happened she noticed Denise bowing her head as if to say yes. Yes to what? Cynthia asked herself. Her suspicions increased when John told her shortly after they returned to their house that he had to fly over to El Lugar, especially since he had never gone there on a Sunday.

When he left in his Mercedes, she followed him in the Rolls, thinking that she would see Denise board the plane. She stood on the far side of the field and watched John enter his Apache alone and take off; but instead of heading directly east in the direction of El Lugar, the plane banked to the right heading south. After the plane had disappeared, Cynthia drove to the Butler Aviation Terminal, parked, and at the flight operations desk, she said, "I'm Mrs. John Baxter. Did my husband file a flight plan for El Lugar this morning?"

"Just a minute, Mrs. Baxter. I'll check."

He returned from an adjoining room and read from a card, "Yes, ma'am, via Lantana Airport, direct El Lugar. He just took off."

"Thank you."

Cynthia was a slow, cautious driver who had never received a warning or a ticket for a moving vehicle in her fifteen years in the tightly patrolled and well-radared resort, but on this afternoon through a veil of light summer rain, she drove her 1967 Rolls Silver Shadow like a madwoman, desperately hoping to catch the Apache at the Lantana facility fourteen miles south of Palm Beach International Airport.

As she pushed the car to ninety along I-95, the front end began to shimmy, but Cynthia couldn't have cared less. She exited from the highway and sped west toward the Glades. Finally the Australian pines and scrub palms disappeared and she approached the field. She hoped that she still had time to intercept the plane, but when she pulled into the parking lot and slid to a halt upon the crushed coral, she heard a familiar roar of two Lycomings at takeoff power. She knew the sound of the company plane, especially in the thrusting moments of takeoff. There was no doubt it was the red and white Apache.

By the time she reached the fence, the light twin had rotated and she was looking at the underbelly as the wheels retracted and the roaring ship was sucked up into the soft-edged rain cumulus. She had not been able to see who was in the plane. She turned to go back to her car and as her eyes glanced over the vehicles in the slots, she noticed Denise's blue Mercedes with the license plate: MH-100.

Mixed feelings overwhelmed her. First the satisfaction of having caught her husband and Denise, then fury and vengeance and sorrow. She felt herself shaking slightly, but she straightened up, sucked in a deep breath, and walked slowly, casually, toward a pimple-faced kid who was fueling planes on the ramp.

"Hello," she said brightly.

The boy almost jumped to attention seeing the stunning lady— Cynthia had taken to wearing large glasses and wide-brimmed shade hats to force a shadow upon her forehead and maybe one cheek if she stood to the sun in just the right manner.

"Were you here when that Apache took off?"

"Sure. It just took off a couple of minutes ago."

"Did my sister, a pretty blonde girl, get in?"

"Same one as last week? Yeah. She got in."

"Oh, I just missed them then. She comes out fairly often, doesn't she?"

"No, I've seen her only twice. Tuesday, I think it was, I was talking to her that day. Was she really a French movie star?"

"Yes. She still puts on a few acts. Thank you."

Cynthia drove much slower back to Palm Beach, barely aware of which road she was taking. Denise was the ultimate tormentor. This woman had taken away her facial beauty, her husband, and her place in Palm Beach society. Cynthia knew Maggie very well, what she would do, what she wouldn't do, and she realized that the old bee was *not* one to alter a decision. It was so obvious what had happened. As a practical matter, Philip Guest had to show everyone that peace had been made between her and Denise and he had demanded Maggie's mock approval. Cynthia also realized that as soon as the effect of false friendliness had done its job, she would be right back where she started: in Coventry.

But she had one advantage: She knew Denise did not know she was aware of the affair between her and John. Cynthia would keep it that way. By the time she had passed the Bath & Tennis and swung north along A-1A, she knew that she would kill Denise. That was now certain.

And what happened the night before when the strobe lights were turned on their renewed friendship could be used to save her should the need arise. If she were discovered and questioned, she'd say, "We did have a little misunderstanding, but the olive branch was passed. Look at these photos in the paper. Does that look as if I hated Denise?"

To implement her plan, Cynthia would call Denise, saying that she could have John. She would suck the Frenchwoman into a trap; they would be seen together at lunch, buying clothes, and the town would know that the *Patna* incident had been forgotten. Then she would murder Denise somehow, somewhere. Then she would divorce John, accusing him of infidelity, and leave the resort forever. And with most of John's money. Denise had turned a gentle woman into a monster.

Before going home she stopped off to see Jayson Kendall.

As she turned into the entrance of Kendall's place she immediately knew that things were going far worse for the man than he had admitted. The lush old plantings were hanging over the road and the ever-anxious Florida weeds were pushing up through the separations in the coquina-blocked driveway that curved around toward the long, forbidding house.

And the house—beards of green-whiskered moss hung from the limestone facade. The sickening growth oozed and the afternoon rain brought out the smell of unraked leaves that had turned to soggy lumps of muck and mire. Decay was everywhere.

She rang the bell, a tinkle now nursing only a few notes, and Jayson came to the front door wearing the tattered green blazer of the Everglades Club. Yet there was something different on this Sunday. He was perfectly shaven. His deep blue eyes were clear and they were shining as they must have in other years.

"Hello, Jayson. How well you look."

"I've decided to reform for the four hundredth time. Come on in."

She was led into the vaulted living room crowded with old,

bruised furniture and pale, threadbare heavy hangings. All about the hideous room there were small tables with lifeless coverings that dropped to the floor, and on each were armies of little faded photographs in dull silver frames.

Jayson's past. All he had left.

"How about a drink?" he asked.

"I may interrupt your reform program," she said, knowing that it took very little to sway the man from his good intentions.

"Oh, but it's an afternoon for drinking. I detest this house when it rains; not that I like it too much when it doesn't."

Jayson made two drinks and crossed to sit beside her on the pillowed couch that drooped at one end from a missing leg and was propped up by a pile of books on Greek mythology.

"I'm happy that you and Denise made up last night."

"Well, I think I understand Denise better now. We had a long talk and we both decided to forget the past. She's really a very gentle person."

"I wouldn't have said that, but anyhow I'm glad things are glued back together."

"Jayson, I do appreciate your interceding on my behalf. I know you did."

"Just for a friend. This town is too small for wars."

"But they do exist, Jayson, and it's the only thing I don't like about Palm Beach . . . such a delicate society . . . one day you're in, the next you're out, and you wonder if it's all worth it."

They talked on and Denise's name was mentioned several times; Jayson thought Cynthia was going too far. She had become too obvious in her praise, and Jayson said, "Cynthia, don't overdo it." When eventually their hands found each other and they embraced, both Jayson and Cynthia seemed a little embarrassed.

"I have a feeling, Cynthia, that this might be our day. We've played it so straight all these years," Jayson said solemnly.

"Perhaps you're right, Jayson. Let's call it an expression of friendship, a seal."

They embraced again. "I even made my bed up this morning, Cynthia. Come with me, I'll show you."

He took her up the damp winding stairs to the long gallery spotted with old family portraits. At the end the choked light filtered

((173))

through a typical Mizner window stained by salt and collected dust.

Cynthia thought that all this eerie place needed were the far-off chords of an organ—the crazy brother playing his heart out while locked in a tower room.

They came to the bedroom and Jayson swung back the thick Spanish door to reveal a canopied bed and walls covered with sepia-toned photos of Jayson when he was young and hopeful at Harvard.

Cynthia quickly unbuttoned her blouse revealing the full breasts, which bulged over her brassiere, and she held them up to Jayson.

"Let's make it good. We've waited so long, haven't we?"

Jayson had always wanted Cynthia; still he couldn't understand her sudden aggression and shifts of mood; but, whatever, he would make it good. He pushed the straps aside and kissed her breasts and the nipples rose in excitement. He didn't even know when she stepped out of her skirt and panties. For years he had imagined seeing Cynthia naked in front of him, and he had always had a feeling that it would happen someday.

He took her in his arms and they caressed each other. A softness came over her as she vibrated under Jayson's gentle movements. Her hips moved in semicircles and she felt the warmth deep inside her swell, echoing the vengeful thrust of her new head and heart. It was a brutal brand of ecstasy. Total ecstasy.

She was breaking loose. Faster and further. A wildness rushed over her mind and body and into Jayson in an outpouring of energy she never dreamed she had. After she had climaxed with Jayson, the only man she had ever been with besides John, she thought how easy the rest would be. The thin thread that leads people out of dull respectability was already beginning to thicken with new strands.

There was very little left of her life now, and she was going to grasp the remaining bits with everything she could.

22

HURRICANES HAVE STAGES OF GROWTH LIKE PEOPLE: INFANCY, ADO-lescence, maturity, decay, and finally the inevitable death. The Verdes hotdog, now Claudine, had a long infancy. She was merely a disturbance for four days, big and odd, but, nevertheless, there was no rotary surface action for a long time, too long, the specialists said. This seemed to support Keith's original theory—that she would die out or move out of the doldrums to form a front in the higher latitudes.

But quickly she sprang up, as a child does sometimes in the first years of adolescence. Claudine passed through her teens with great alacrity and brazenness, becoming a depression, and then a storm in a matter of hours.

An odd feeling permeated the war room that Sunday. It was not fear or alarm, but a sense of helplessness. They were seeing three storms develop at once, not a totally unique phenomenon, but in the case of Claudine, they were watching something that had never come their way before: a doldrum storm enlarging by the hour. And there did not seem to be a rational explanation for this meteorological monstrosity. The concern was reflected that morning when the first of the daylight APTs came off the printer. Steve, Keith, and Lou were waiting for the red light to signal that the transmission was on the line from the Maryland receiving station when a technician from the communications section rushed into the room.

"Claudine's gone to a hurricane!" he shouted.

"What's the input?" Lou asked.

"A tanker . . . they just measured wind speeds to one hundred and fifteen."

"Here we go," Steve said.

"God, look at it!" Lou exclaimed as he bowed his bald head over the transmission slowly unwinding. "What's her diameter now?" he asked the technician.

"Six hundred twenty miles," the man said after placing the dividers across the whitish smudge.

"There's something else," Keith said.

"Yeah, the other two depressions are almost gone. But let's verify with surface reports," Lou ordered. "And get a plane in there."

Steve walked to the far end of the APT room and leaned against the workbench with arms folded.

"Lou, there's something here that scares me," he said. "I think we'd better have a quick meeting. What we do now might save lives later."

"Like what!" Keith snapped. "Tell the goddamned thing to go away?" He turned toward Lou. "Let's get one thing straight right now. I'm the forecaster, not Steve, and he's not going to give orders in the war room. He shouldn't even be up here. He's a researcher, not a forecaster."

"I gave Steve permission to work the room if anything big happened."

"All right, but he takes his directions from me," Keith said, his voice leaving no doubt as to what he meant.

"Fine, but let's hear him out . . . OK?"

Keith was sullen and resentful as they sat down in Lou's office where the bright Miami sun dappled the room as if nothing in the atmosphere could possibly be wrong.

"Tell us how you're going to put Claudine to bed," Keith said.

"I'm not putting her to bed, but if you'll listen to me, I'll tell you what killed people up in Pass Christian."

"Not that again," Keith groaned.

"It was the unpredicted high water," Lou said. "We all know that."

"Sure," Steve said, "but there was something more. Everyone could have got out. One of the killers was the inane hurricane language."

"What do you mean?" Lou frowned.

"The night before the hurricane struck I was listening to the local radio. The New Orleans stations were issuing advisories. You know, general stuff about where the storm was going. At the very same time, the stations around Pass Christian were issuing local bulletins."

"Standard procedure," Keith said.

"Of course. But the local statements were conflicting with the advisories."

"How?" Lou asked.

"As I remember, the New Orleans advisories said that all persons in the affected coastal areas should take shelter on high ground. They kept talking about high tides and waves. We were supposed to follow the latest advice from public officials. So I asked myself, what coastal areas? No one defined them. What tides? There weren't any that night and the waves weren't very big. It all came in the morning, and by that time, it was too late to do anything."

"What did the local stations say?" Lou asked.

"Just a little bit about the storm and preparing for evacuation. But the station didn't spell it out right away, and afterward none of us could get off the beach."

"What's your point?" Keith said with a bored look.

"A couple of things. In the days before the storm, there was a cavalier attitude around Pass Christian, a kind of joy almost. It had been so hot that the news was welcomed. People prepared for parties, not evacuation!"

"What do you recommend, Steve?" Lou asked.

"Alert people to the worst that can happen. Scare the hell out of them! Make them terrified of Claudine and make sure we send out very precise statements."

"But that's a local authority. Each county gives its own orders."

"In this case, we should do it. The civil defense people aren't hurricane experts."

"That's knocking the system, Steve," Lou said, shaking his head.

"What the hell do we care about the system when there's something like Claudine out there!"

"But we don't know if Claudine will landfall and who says her winds will accelerate?" Keith cried, jumping to his feet.

"We do know we have one hell of a wild storm on our hands. We should break the rules, petrify people, so they'll listen when and if the hurricane landfalls."

"Do you have something definite in mind?" Lou asked, arching his brows.

"I'd call the local press in here right away and tell them to start winding up their scare copy. Then I would get this out on the line to all stations."

Steve handed a typed yellow sheet to Lou. The director read it and a stunned expression flooded his roundish face; then Keith took the paper and read it:

THE NATIONAL HURRICANE CENTER ADVISORY NUMBER ONE CLAUDINE. SUNDAY, AUGUST 21, 1977. CONFIRMED SURFACE REPORTS INDICATE THAT TROPICAL STORM, CLAUDINE, HAS NOW REACHED HURRICANE STRENGTH WITH WIND SPEEDS TO 115 MPH. CLAUDINE LOCATED VICINITY 19.05 N., 54.68 W. FORECASTED TO MOVE ON NORTHWESTERLY COURSE. ALL INTERESTS SHOULD PAY SPECIAL ATTENTION TO THIS HURRICANE, WHICH IS 620 MILES IN DIAMETER AND EXPECTED TO INCREASE IN SIZE AND INTENSITY.
REPEAT: HURRICANE CENTER VIEWS CLAUDINE AS A POTENTIALLY DANGEROUS HURRICANE WITH POSSIBLE WIND SPEEDS FORECAST TO EXCEED 200 MPH. ALL INTERESTS IN LEEWARD ISLANDS, NORTHERN CARIBBEAN, INCLUDING HISPANIOLA, PUERTO RICO, AMERICAN-BRITISH VIRGINS, ENTIRE BAHAMAS, FLORIDA ON WEST COAST NORTHWARD TO PUNTA GORDA, ON EAST COAST NORTHWARD TO THE JUPITER INLET ARE NOW WARNED OF POSSIBLE HURRICANE WATCH IF STORM DEEPENS OR CONTINUES ON FORECASTED TRACK.
REPEAT: THE NATIONAL HURRICANE CENTER VIEWS CLAUDINE AS EXTREMELY DANGEROUS. EXTREMELY DANGEROUS.

Keith slapped the yellow paper back at Steve. "That's the most irresponsible piece of junk I've ever read!"

"Why?"

"First of all, you're alerting the entire Caribbean and Bahamas. Second, this business of winds over two hundred. Where did that come from?"

"It could happen."

"Maybe, but it's totally premature to say things like this right now. Claudine is still eight hundred miles away from land."

"She's over six hundred miles in diameter and well organized." Steve got to his feet and his face reddened. "We should get this out and repeat it, repeat it, repeat it! And if she does landfall, people will take notice because they'll be programmed."

"Our mission isn't to frighten people," Lou said.

"If we don't frighten them, they won't move off their asses!"

"Steve," Lou said in a lowered voice, "sit down. Let's be reasonable. We can't send something like this out. It's not correct, for one thing, and it doesn't follow procedure for another."

"Goddammit, when you have a storm like Claudine, the procedures should be torn up! You want another Camille?"

"Of course not. We won't have one," Lou said.

"I hope you're right, Lou, because we have a responsibility here. I hope everyone realizes it."

At ten-fifteen that morning a routine, watered-down advisory went out on Claudine.

Two hundred and nineteen stations picked up the message, but just as Steve feared, there were only yawns and cursory scannings of the short, noneditorialized dispatch.

CHAPTER

23

IF A HURRICANE WAS ERUPTING SOUTH OF EL LUGAR, THERE WAS NO evidence of it as the Apache was greased onto the coral strip and braked to a halt. The local rain squalls had passed to the east. The sun shot out and it was big and blasting, and soon the hibiscus uncurled.

After the previous night at Philip's party when she and Cynthia had been forced to smile at each other, Denise realized that she could not proceed with the same strategy to haul John Baxter in, if indeed it was possible at all. The actress pulled a one-eighty.

Instead of dressing in her usually provocative clothes—the stockings and perfume and the slit skirt—she showed up at Lantana Airport in a pair of slacks and a tailored white blouse. When they landed on the island, she turned to him and said, "John, let's not go to the cottage."

"If you don't want a fast one, what are we doing here?"

"I just thought it would be nice for us to be together . . . that's all. Let's go fishing."

John was stunned.

"Look at those boats at the end of the pier. Why can't we pack some sandwiches and make a few floating martinis from the bar and go out and try our luck with the rods?"

"Denise, this is a waste of time. I don't know what game you're playing now, but I'm sorry I came. This must be our last meeting. If you still want to bring a rape charge against me, go ahead."

"I was never going to do that."

"Well, in that case you sure caused a hell of a lot of trouble for no reason."

"So did your wife."

"Let's not get into it."

"The proof was last night." As he looked at her inquiringly, she continued, "Cynthia and I became friends again, remember?"

"Only because Philip Guest demanded it."

"I just wanted to say good-bye privately and prove to you that I'm not a terrible person. You must go back to your wife. She loves you."

John was perplexed. This was a curious about-face for Denise and finally he said, "All right. Let's have a nice afternoon. Then we'll shake hands at the Lantana Airport and that will be the end of it."

"Good," Denise assured him. "Then let's go."

El Lugar was a small island in the Berry chain north of Nassau and near this ring of coral ran a flush of warm water, the route of many migrating game fish such as the mighty white and blue marlin, sailfish, and the wahoo. There was a forty-two-foot Rybovich, *Carol II*, a well-equipped big game fisherman, at the dock and John told the skipper, George Mason, to load up on live bait, ice, drinks, and food; they were going after marlin. John wanted to see the delicate "sex machine" at the end of a mighty five-hundred-pound angry fish, which would probably wrench the actress's arms out of their sockets.

"'George, how are the marlin and sails running?" John asked the crinkled and deeply tanned skipper.

"Not bad, Mr. Baxter. Boated a four-hundred-twenty-pound blue marlin two days ago."

"Well, my friend, Mrs. . . . ah, Jones, wants some action," he said with a wink. "Think we could give it to her? She's an energized lady in more ways than one."

The skipper smiled. He took one look at the actress and knew what John meant.

"Let's just have a pleasant afternoon without any wisecracks," Denise said.

"All right . . . we fish and shut up."

Twenty minutes later, the twin diesels of the Rybovich were turning over and, loaded down with bait and gear, George and his son, Clint, eased the fishing machine away from the El Lugar dock and sped over the coral-bottomed sea toward the deep blue edge where the mighty marlin swam.

Denise went below and returned shortly in a bikini. The seventeen-year-old mate could not keep his eyes on his work as he watched Denise stretch out in the fighting chair anchored to the cockpit sole. The boy pulled himself up to the tuna tower where his father was steering the boat.

"Ever see anything like that?" Clint whispered.

"Some piece," George said, sliding his eyes around and down to the aft cockpit.

"Who is she?"

"Friend of the Baxters from Palm Beach."

"Bet she's more than a friend," Clint said, poking his father in the ribs.

"OK, we ought to be out there in ten minutes. Prepare two rods. Get 'em on eighty pound test. That chick'll snap anything lighter. Doesn't look like she's ever had a rod in her hand."

The boy climbed down from the control station and went into the aft cockpit. He took two reels from the saloon and attached them to big game fishing rods.

"What test is that, Clint?" Denise asked.

"Eighty pound, ma'am."

"Go to fifty, please."

John swung his head around toward Denise. "Fifty?" he laughed. "You couldn't take a marlin on fifty. You have to know what you're doing."

"I know what I'm doing."

"When's the last time you had a fish on a hook, Denise?"

"About four years ago. We were shooting a picture off the Great Barrier Reef in Australia. One of the best guides taught me."

Knowing Denise, John waved away the boast and he chortled, "Let her use fifty test."

"That's very light stuff if you set a hook into a big one, Mrs. Jones," the skipper said.

"Let's just see what my guest can do, George. I'll pay for the lost equipment."

"No equipment will be lost, John!" Denise snapped back.

"All right, Clint, go to the fifty pound," his father said.

The boy took the reels and lines back to the cabin and returned with two others, which he attached to the rods. Then he reached into the bait box and took out a couple of mackerels, which had been rigged ashore to twelve degree Mustad hooks. They trolled for marlin on two outriggers and time eased by.

The afternoon sun was brutal and the sea was mirrored, only disturbed by the wake furrow of the fast Rybovich. An occasional sailfish broke the surface and flapped in the air, only to fall again in the endless pursuit of smaller fish.

"Marlin!" Clint called suddenly from the tower. "Fifteen degrees off starboard."

George pushed the throttles ahead, spun the wheel over, and the bow lifted out of the calm water.

"Come port . . . a little more!" Clint yelled in excitement. "Big bastard!"

"Sure you want to go through with this?" John asked Denise.

She did not answer but changed her position in the fighting chair, placing her feet on the footrest while pulling the thick, cracked leather belt around her slender waist, so that the boat, chair, and the fish fighter became one. (To be pulled overboard in these shark-infested seas while struggling with a dying, thrashing fish would mean certain death.)

"Denise, the fish is big and you only have fifty pounds on there," John yelled over the roar of the diesels.

"My fish, John, I'm in the chair," Denise shot back.

"There's the animal!" George yelled down from above. "Must be six hundred at least. Look at it!"

John leaned over the rail and saw the mammoth dark shape, perhaps fifteen feet in length, swiftly swimming off the stern quarter.

"You'll never handle it, Denise!"

"Wait and see."

George throttled back so that the bait was directly in front of the cruising fish.

"Hold on, Denise! This guy might weigh six times what you weigh."

"I've seen black marlin, much bigger!"

John shook his head, thinking that this woman was about as arrogant and sure of herself as anyone he had ever met.

"He sees it!" George shouted, spinning over the helm so that the mackerel flashed right in front of the giant blue marlin.

"There he goes!" John yelled. "Be careful, Denise."

The marlin opened his cavernous mouth, rose, and in a second the mackerel and the hook were deep in his gullet. Denise tightened her arms and every muscle stood out as if she were a thin, well-proportioned weight lifter; finally she eased the drag lever back as the marlin swam to port with his catch, and George cranked over the helm again to keep the fish directly astern.

"Revolve that chair," Denise yelled. "Keep me positioned. Come on, John, move your ass!"

Her voice was deep and authoritative and knowing how dangerous a fish like this was, John sprang for the chair along with Clint.

"Be careful, Mrs. Jones," he panted. "Easy now."

"Cut the directions," Denise ordered. "I have it."

Skillfully Denise pushed the drag lever into the striking position to set the hook. When it was just about taut, but not too taut, for a fish of that size would snap a light line as if it were a strand of thread, Denise yanked upward in a fast positive action. George had never seen a woman set a hook so adroitly.

"Nice work, Denise. You set it," John yelled.

"I know. I can feel it."

At precisely the right moment she backed off on the drag. The marlin's big bill came up and then his mouth broke the surface, and there was a spray of bubbles and a plume of hissing seawater.

"Look at the size of that mother!" Clint called out. "It must be near the record."

The reel unwound and the fish dived. Denise kept the line going as George maneuvered the boat so that the angry fish was positioned. As John and Clint swung the fighting chair around, neither thought that this fish would ever be boated on a fifty pound line. (Even champion fishermen would normally use an eighty pound test.) The motion of the played-out line ceased and again Denise adjusted the drag on the reel. Then the grueling fight began.

She doubled up on her downward motion; she reeled and reeled on the upswing of her body; she pulled with all her might and stringy muscles popped to the surface of her lush skin. She pumped and reeled, pumped and reeled and sweated, getting a few inches onto the reel each time. The fish broke surface, desperately trying to shake the hook. He dived, rested, rushed to the surface again. Denise kept up her rhythmic pumping. Sweat poured out all over her and the top of her bikini snapped off. Clint's eyes boggled as John made a move to fix it.

"Don't touch me!" she screamed, knowing that in the rules of the sport another person may not touch the fisherman or the pole. He may only swing the chair for positioning.

"This is something, Mr. Baxter," Clint whispered during one of the lulls. "Want to bet?"

"What odds?" John whispered back.

"I heard that," Denise yelled. "Don't bet against me, Baxter!"

"All right. I'll bet for you."

"What do you say?" Clint asked.

"A hundred to one."

"You have no faith in me, John."

The fat fish jumped, thrashed, pulled himself along the surface, then contorted, spinning over nearly on his back to break the contact, and each time Denise made a little more line. The pain in her arms was excruciating. "I'll get you yet!" she screamed.

Determined not to give up or let him go, Denise played by the sportsmen's rules. But time was working against her, and John knew it would only be minutes before the 115-pound woman was defeated by the great fish that must have weighed six to seven hundred pounds. The belt dug deep into her flesh, and red marks crisscrossed her heaving stomach and pelvic areas. She dripped sweat as her arms pitched back and forth in the battle to gain an inch of line.

John was amazed. He had never seen such a fight.

((*185*   ))

Two hours had gone by and the fish was no nearer. The reel was still half empty.

"Denise, you'll kill yourself," John said.

"Get away!" she cried, tossing out the last bit of breath from her lungs.

The fish was as determined to remain in the sea as she was to haul him in, but gradually, painfully, Denise began to conquer the great marlin, taking in more and more line. The sight of the reel filling up with gut gave her the final shot she needed to succeed.

"Surfacing!" George bellowed as he jumped down from the tower.

Clint pulled on a pair of work gloves and grabbed the wire leader in what was the most critical part of catching a giant fish. Manually he pulled the marlin within reach of the eight-foot gaff which he then drove through its back.

"What a catch, Mrs. Jones!"

Quickly the leader was snapped off the line and onto the tackle hoist, for the fish was too big to boat manually, and all they could do was haul him clear of the water on a short tackle mast fixed to the side of the cockpit. Denise fell back exhausted into her seat.

It was over.

Suddenly George shouted, "Dammit, we've got tiger sharks!" He strained to pull the fish free of the water.

Denise moved out of the chair and collapsed into the cockpit, then she pulled herself up.

"Stay out of the way, Denise. This is dangerous!"

Three ten-foot tigers rushed for the tail section of the marlin. They extended their teeth and yanked at the fish. The meat was pulled away from the bones in massive bites that were flooded with spurts of blood. The immense power of the sharks pulling at the gaffed marlin began to jerk the boat around. George sprang for the controls as Denise grabbed a gaff hook and started beating the sharks.

"You shits!" she screamed.

"Denise, get away from that rail!" John yelled. "You'll go over!"

She swung the gaff around toward John, trying to keep him back. More sharks joined the first group and one of them bit off the gaff that Denise was struggling with and she was almost pulled into the water.

It was too late for the marlin.

He had been chewed in half and his huge head rose out of the water gushing blood and juices and innards. The sharks tried to jump for the dripping, hanging meat, but they cannot break the surface like other fish, so they swam away. The sea returned to placidity. The pools of blood floated off the stern and dissolved.

There was complete silence aboard the *Carol II*.

Denise sank into the chair, trying to regain her breath.

"That was a fantastic fight, Denise," John said softly.

"Mrs. Jones," the captain said, "I'll always remember that. I've never seen a woman put up such a battle. But we can't help the sharks . . . these waters are teeming with them."

Denise didn't say a word, but finally she hauled herself up from the chair and wrapped her bikini bra around her bruised breasts. She looked at John and smiled forlornly.

"That's the breaks," she said, "but I think I deserve a big martini, John."

"You do. Cut the marlin's head loose, George, and let's go home." He turned back to Denise. "You're not angry?"

She shrugged. "What can you do? I learned early not to cry over the things I can't have . . . or can't fix."

As John stood in the cool of the cabin preparing their drinks, he began to see something else in the fierce Frenchwoman. In one sense it frightened him and in another sense it was exciting. They hardly said a word on the way back to El Lugar but quietly sipped their martinis, and when the fish boat had been tied up they walked to the arabesque cottage to take showers before flying home.

Inside the door John kissed her passionately and whispered, "You were great today."

"Thank you, John."

"Come to bed with me . . . now."

"Will it be the last time?"

He looked at her, not saying anything, and she walked on into the bedroom. They made love and she used the last bit of passion that was still in her. He tried to be as gentle as possible.

Two hours later the Apache landed at Lantana Airport.

CHAPTER

24

WHEN JOHN DROVE UP TO THE HOUSE, CYNTHIA WAS WORKING ON HER begonias.

"Did you fly to El Lugar all alone, dear?" she said, smiling.

"Yes. Why?" He got out of the car and watched his wife for a moment as she worked.

"Just asking. I'm glad you had such a nice day," Cynthia said, kissing him.

John went upstairs to nap and Cynthia picked up the phone and called the *Patna*.

"Denise, this is Cynthia. How are you?"

"Fine," Denise said dully from the other end.

"Have a pleasant day?"

"Yes. I went fishing."

"Oh . . . where?"

"On a friend's boat out of the Jupiter Inlet."

"I didn't know you fished."

"Haven't lately. But I used to, a lot."

"I'd like to speak to you."

"About what?"

"I can't tell you on the phone. We must meet right away. Would you have supper with me at Capriccio's tonight?"

"Cynthia, I've had a tiring day. Another time."

"No, please, I beg you. This is extremely important. It concerns someone we both know."

Denise acquiesced and they made a date to dine at seven. Both Denise's arms were battered and she could hardly walk, her muscles were so sore. But she appeared on time, wearing pants and a long-sleeve blouse to hide the welts.

The restaurant was crowded. Cynthia arrived a few minutes late and Denise was waiting just inside the door. Cynthia paused and studied her for a moment before entering. The actress's eyes were bloodshot and her face seemed puffed and sunburned. Somehow she looked old as she stood dejectedly in the midst of the gay throng. Cynthia knew that the fishing story was a lie; her husband hadn't fished in years.

"Must have been some expedition, Denise, you look terrible," she said by way of greeting.

"Well, I caught a big blue marlin, but the sharks ate him before we could boat him."

"Whose yacht did you say you were on?"

"The . . . ah . . . Campbells."

"Oh, yes . . . that's the Hobe Sound Campbells?"

Denise murmured something as they threaded their way between the tables of the tightly packed restaurant. Cynthia stopped often and talked to friends and kept her arm tucked through Denise's. After their slow movement to a far table in the corner had been completed, people began swiveling their heads.

Maybe it was true what the local paper had hinted: that the two couples had forgotten the so-called rape.

Cynthia didn't say much during their cocktails and she kept studying the face of the woman opposite her. She wondered if her husband had suddenly turned into a sadist; perhaps he *had* raped

Denise aboard the *Patna* that night. After dinner she finally said to Denise, "You might think this is strange, but I want us to be friends again."

Denise gazed levelly at her over the cup of coffee she held.

"This town is small. Life is short," Cynthia continued, "and there's nothing to be gained by feuding."

"You said you abhorred me the other night when they snapped our 'gluing it together' picture."

"I've thought things over since then. I don't know what's going on between you and John. . . ."

"How do you know anything is going on?" Denise interrupted.

"Denise, I don't care. I'm trying to tell you that John is yours if you want him."

Denise could not believe what she was hearing. She set her cup down and said, "Just a minute, Cynthia. Did I hear you correctly?"

"Yes, you heard me. I've been thinking about all of us, Denise, and I want John to be happy."

"Don't you love him anymore?"

"Well, seventeen years is a long time." She paused and then said, "Do *you* love him?"

"He's attractive," Denise said in an even tone. "But even if you don't love John I don't understand how you could possibly want to be my friend."

"I've always thought you were interesting, Denise, and unusual, so why don't we get together again often? It'll smooth things over for whatever happens."

Denise was a highly skeptical woman. The circumstances of her life had made her that way, but her head on that Sunday night after the hours in the fighting chair was dulled, whirling, and she couldn't seem to understand what Cynthia had on her mind; yet deep down she knew it couldn't be good. Nevertheless, it was Denise who turned the conversation to serious things. She had remained quiet for a time but finally said, "Cynthia, I know you think I'm a tramp, and I am. Just so you understand, you're on the right track. Why else would I have married a man like Mel, and have to come to Palm Beach and scramble? Someday Nicole will tell you the truth. I screwed my way into the film business, into my first marriage and so on and so on and so on."

Cynthia was shocked at this sudden outpouring and could barely muster the courage to say, "With my husband, too?"

"Of course, you saw me."

"I mean, were there other times?"

"Yes."

"I knew it. I was at the airport today shortly after you left for El Lugar."

"And I saw your Rolls in the parking lot. I looked down just as we were taking off. I'll tell you one other thing just for the record," Denise continued. "I've been making it with Nicole. She goes both ways."

"I'm not surprised. She made a pass at me one time."

"But you know, Cynthia, it's interesting. You, Nicole, and I are all the same."

"How?"

"The three of us came to Palm Beach to fortune hunt."

"That's not true. I was already married to John when we came here."

"Well, you and John came down here to make it. The intent's the same."

"I can't argue with that. But Denise, remember even Maggie came down to find a husband. She wanted to marry the ambassador all along. Being his secretary was just a ploy. As for myself, I knew I couldn't get anyplace in Atlanta society. I worked my way through college and my father was only a milkman. I married John in New York, and down here no one knew who I was. But I did make a good wife, and I contributed. Anyone will tell you. When I was suddenly cut off, I thought it was a terrible offense. What had I done?" Cynthia was surprised at herself, speaking in such a candid open way to the woman she regarded as her enemy.

"Nothing," Denise answered. "That's Palm Beach. Your flag came down for the wrong reason, or no reason at all. You were treated unfairly, Cynthia. The Queen decided and the others followed, too weak to make up their own minds. I wouldn't have done that. I may be guilty of many sins, but no one can say I'm two-faced or weak."

"I doubt whether you'd ever be accused of weakness. It's odd, Denise, there's quite a lot about you I admire . . . and there's quite a bit about you that I detest."

While the two women continued their "cleansing" conversation, Mel dressed quickly aboard the *Patna*. The real-estate editor, Daniels, had talked to the state attorney's office in Miami, and Glen Markum was being called in the following morning. Mel had just hung up the telephone after speaking to Glen.

"I'll come right down, Glen. Meantime, don't say anything to anybody! Got that?" Mel screamed into the phone on the after lounge of the vessel.

As he was leaving for the trip to Century Towers, Mel recognized the tall, slender figure of Nicole Bouchart, dressed in a light summer caftan, approaching him across the Brazilian Docks.

"Hi, Nicole, I'm in a hurry . . . on my way to a business meeting."

"On a Sunday night?"

"Yes, yes," Mel said nervously. "Something came up and I have to leave. Denise isn't here. She's having dinner with Cynthia Baxter."

Nicole looked at Mel quizzically. "Cynthia?"

"Yeah, look . . ." He fumbled in his pocket. "Here's a duplicate key. Go on aboard, make yourself at home. Denise should be back soon. Sorry, I have to run."

Mel left Nicole standing on the dock and his thick legs trotted quickly toward the parking lot. Nicole looked after him for a moment, then she turned and boarded the *Patna*. She helped herself to a drink in the aft saloon, put on the hi-fi, and settled down to read an old copy of *W*.

Finally, she heard the thumps of heels coming down the dock; she stood and looked from the window of the yacht. Denise was moving along slowly, stooped, as if the world had come down upon her, and Nicole pushed open the after door and ran out on the dock.

"Denise, dear, what's wrong?"

"A little stiff, that's all."

"I tried to get you all day. Where were you?"

"I went fishing."

"For what . . . a whale?"

"Can't laugh, Nicole . . . hurts too much. No, a blue marlin, but I lost him."

Nicole came down the gangplank and helped her friend up and slowly they moved into the yacht.

"I used to be in great shape when I was acting," Denise groaned, "but you sure lose it quickly."

"A hot bath would help. Have you had one?"

"No, Cynthia called as soon as I got home demanding that I meet her for dinner."

"What did she want?"

"My friendship. Can you believe that? Palm Beach likes to forget the nasties. I don't understand anything anymore."

"I was kind of lonely today," Nicole said as they reached the saloon.

"Nicole, *not* tonight. I've been in a battle."

"Please?"

Denise didn't have the strength for an argument with Nicole and she simply looked at her and crossed to the bar and made herself a vodka martini. Nicole came up behind her and kissed her friend on the back of the neck, whispering, "We'll just go below and talk. That's all . . . talk."

She took Denise's hand and they moved toward the companionway leading to the stern quarters of the yacht, toward the same cabin where it had all started months before. Once inside, Nicole closed the door and locked it. Then she went into the head and drew a hot tub and when she returned Denise was lying on the bed, almost asleep. Nicole bent over her and started undoing her blouse, and Denise did not resist.

"What is this!" Nicole cried, staring at her bruised breasts.

Denise rolled over and Nicole quickly unzipped her pants and pulled them off, noticing the deep-blue marks and the welts of her fight for the marlin.

"Christ, look at you," Nicole said, grabbing the actress by her arm and jerking her upward. "What the hell happened?"

"I told you."

"Those aren't fishing welts, sweetheart."

"Of course they are . . . the fish was just goddamned big."

"I don't believe it. Who were you fishing with?"

"People you don't know."

"Tell me, you little bitch!"

((*193*))

"What the hell's wrong with you?"

"You were beaten up, baby. Who beat you . . . a man or a woman?"

"It was nothing like that, Nicole!"

Nicole was suddenly excited as she gazed at the naked, bruised body of Denise Hansen. "I've seen a few beatings before. Tell me who did it."

"A fish."

"Stop that, goddamn you, Denise. Who got hold of you? You wanted it, didn't you? It was another fantasy, just like having John Baxter rip off your clothes right here in this cabin. I want to know right now or I'll tell Maggie how you're getting your kicks!"

As Denise stared up at the wild-eyed woman, Nicole became tender again and she reached out and gently touched Denise's injured flesh. "Honey, I really didn't know you were into all this. Why didn't you tell me you liked it?"

"Guess I never had time," Denise said.

Realizing that Nicole was really turned on in a morbid kind of way, Denise thought, what the hell? Why not give her what she wants? Denise certainly didn't feel physically able to satisfy the woman that night, but being an actress it would be easy for her to simply lie there and talk provocatively and sensually, making up the wildest, most improbable stories; the black and blue evidence was striped across her body so there was nothing that Nicole would not believe. So she closed her eyes and played along with Nicole.

"Who was involved, Denise . . . one person, two people?"

"It was a crazy group . . . in Hobe Sound. A party . . . there was a huge estate and gorgeous women."

"Oh, that's wild. What guts you have!"

"Yes, it was . . . almost indescribable."

"Go on," Nicole said eagerly, "what were you wearing?"

"I had on my short chiffon dress . . . you know, the red one, and very high heels."

"Don't leave a thing out, Denise. We're friends. Tell me about the other gals. How did they look? What were they wearing?"

As Denise proceeded through the make-believe story, detailing the beatings of wealthy snobs, the chains, the whips, the shackles, she suddenly became aware of something about her small, adopted hometown. The place itself was a fantasy; the houses were dream-like; the elegant Worth Avenue, a shored-up movie set. Many inhabitants of the wonderland were veteran dreamers barely held in check.

Nothing was ever quite the way it appeared, Denise thought: the *Patna* party, that afternoon on the fishing boat; when something was real, it was not believed; when it was totally false, it was taken as fact. So that night she told Nicole the most absurd and outrageous things she could think of. The excited woman sucked it all in and became breathless listening and believing the stories about aberrations that had never happened that day or probably any other.

Denise knew that all dreams came to an end eventually. How far would this one go? The answer was inching closer.

CHAPTER

25

THE WAR ROOM WAS STUFFY AND PACKED THAT MONDAY MORNING. Steve was working the night shift after catching a few hours sleep on Lou Ballantine's couch. The director was off; he had worked sixteen hours straight and his wife, worrying about his heart condition, had come down to the center to beg him to go home, which he did. The place smelled like a locker room from the sweat of the fourteen men trying to track and forecast the whirling monster.

It happened at ten after twelve that day, August 22, 1977. A small unshaven man rushed into the room.

"Dr. Mitchell, Claudine has wind speeds of one hundred and seventy-eight!"

"What's the input?"

"A tanker bound for Aruba just went through it."

"How could she accelerate like that?"

"Look at the message traffic."

Steve read the print-out communication that had been relayed to the center by San Juan Radio. If this was true, Steve thought, the hotdog might be on its way to becoming the worst hurricane on record.

It was *his* storm, maybe, but he hoped not.

He felt sick about it, knowing what it could do.

The switchboard at the end of the hall near Lou Ballantine's office was flooded with calls. One lady had even found the private number.

Steve got on the phone.

"This is Mrs. Gold in Miami Beach."

"How did you get this number?"

"Through a friend."

"How can I help you?" Steve said, exhausting a long breath.

"We want to know if Claudine is going to hit Miami Beach."

"That is a possibility. Just keep listening to the radio and TV. I'm sorry, I have to go. And please, Mrs. Gold, don't use this number again. We have to keep it open to the center."

That same day five people showed up at the hurricane center asking what they should do, and on the six o'clock advisory a Miami radio station mistakenly positioned Claudine west of Puerto Rico, rather than east.

At eleven that night Keith Landon came into the war room and went up to Steve.

"How's it going in this hell box?" Keith said, looking around at the bent nervous men hunched over the plotting board, littered now with the hundreds of surface and air reports.

"Just look at this shambles," Steve said, pointing to piles of growing data.

The center was a receiving house for information and it all had to be checked and cross-checked. The contradictions had come quickly. There were two ships northeast of Claudine. One reported wind speeds of 190 and the other reported 120 miles per hour. Something was, obviously, wrong: a misreading, an unstable or faulty anemometer; regardless, it generated problems.

The satellite told them little about wind regimes or central pressure. Their only reliable tool was the hurricane reconnaissance plane. To probe the storm continuously was almost impossible. The meteorological crews who monitored the instruments in the belly of the four-engine Hercules prop-jet were exhausted; flying into a big hurricane day after day, being rattled, shook, shoved, dropped, lifted, bounced, vibrated inside the swirling winds was too much for the men who manned the equipment.

They had to rest.

Keesler Command told the hurricane center that it would be eight hours between probes.

"Get other equipment and crews in here," Steve ordered.

There were eight weather planes in the Air Force, several based in the mid-Pacific and two attached to the western air bases. By two o'clock Tuesday morning an emergency request had been received at the Pentagon and two Hercules and three crews from the Midwest began their flights down to Keesler.

Realizing that the Miami situation was deteriorating, both criminally and meteorologically, Dr. Marc Peterson left his office in the Commerce building that morning under special orders from the Secretary. He was to find out how far the bribe went and why suddenly a huge hurricane was springing out of the Caribbean when only a few days previously the center had indicated that conditions were not favorable for tropical storm development.

Tuesday morning Steve and Keith were both working in the war room when the phone rang.

"Keith, there's a call for you," Steve yelled.

Keith went over and picked up the green government telephone on the far wall.

"Keith . . . Mel Hansen. I know you have problems down there."

"A few."

"I'll be brief. An associate of mine, Glen Markum, handed over that bribe. He's a realty man in South Palm Beach."

Keith was stunned. "Did you know about it, Mel?" he asked.

"No. Came from some building commissioner, but Glen will probably mention me to the state attorney. You'll be called in, too, and I want us to have a little rehearsal to make sure we both say the same thing."

"I'll simply tell them the truth, that's all."

"Of course. But I think we should talk. Any chance of you shooting up here?"

"I don't get off until three, then I'm back on again at twelve."

"I'd come down, but I have to give a statement to the lawyers at the Palace Beach this afternoon."

"I guess I can come up. See you sometime after four."

When he returned to the plotting desk, Steve turned to Keith and asked, "Want to fly into Claudine? There're three or four extra seats on the Wednesday morning probe. Lou thinks it would be educational."

"I'll get my education another way."

"Too close, huh?"

"Steve, I have no interest in being tossed around up there. My job is here."

Ignoring Steve's grin, Keith went back to work, but the phone call from Mel Hansen had started him thinking. As he and Billy researched the architect's project in Lake Worth, Keith had begun to feel that something else might be wrong with the flood-control system besides the absence of saw-grass rootlets. He decided to pay a visit to the director of the district that afternoon before he went to see Mel Hansen.

Several hours later he was sitting in the office of Dr. Robert Morley. He explained that the center was tracking a dangerous hurricane. (Keith was now using the word *dangerous*.)

"I don't think the saw grass is our problem, Dr. Landon," the director said. "It exists, yes. Some of our banks are unstable, but we have other concerns, too. Improvements to the system haven't been made. Take these documents, go into the library and you'll see what I mean."

The truth quickly popped out.

A survey report dated September 29, 1961, described the difficulties facing Florida's coastal areas. The horrifying facts were on page 20; it said that after a detailed study of hurricane frequency and characteristics, a "standard project hurricane" was evolved. This theoretical storm formed the design criteria for the levees, bulkheads, breakwaters, and hydraulic structures in the Okeechobee flood zone. For the Atlantic Coast, between latitudes 26.10 and 27 degrees north, the report listed the model hurricane as having a minimum central pressure of 27.5 inches, a radius of maximum winds up to 26 miles, and the maximum ten-minute average wind of 100 miles per hour.

Keith was shaken.

The storm moving toward Florida was much more intense!

The other bulletins dated 1955 and 1958 suggested improvements to the flood-control system, but pages had been marked out in red pencil: "not built," "not built," "not built," "not built."

One U.S. Army engineering project was entitled: "Survey-Review Report on Central and Southern Florida Project, West Palm Beach Canal, January 23, 1958." On page A-18, paragraph f. under "Discussion," the bitter truth unfolded. (The information was never reported in the papers and at the bottom of the report was a notation: "not for public release.") Keith read, "Performance studies of the existing canal during design floods indicate that water levels and average velocities would exceed those permissible under standard design criteria for new work."

Translated, this meant two things: The system wasn't adequate and there was an indication that design criteria were faulty.

The next sentence qualified and limited the first, saying that the flooding would be of short duration only. However, two thirds through the paragraph, the engineers said, "The existing canal and structure would not provide complete protection during the 60 percent standard project flood. Considerable flooding up to twenty-nine days' duration would occur in the agricultural area west of Highway 441."

After making some quick notes, Keith walked back into Morley's office.

"Were those helpful, Dr. Landon?"

"Yes, but you people admit that the system is overtaxed."

"We admit nothing," the man said. "We run the flood-control system. We don't design the parameters . . . that's the Army engineers . . . you can see them up in Jacksonville."

"Did you ever question your standard project hurricane?"

"Why should we question it?"

"It's all wrong!"

"In what way?"

"The wind speeds and central pressure standards are way too low. We have a storm out there right now with wind speeds in excess of what this page says."

"We didn't write that page, sir," Morley said stiffly.

"Do you believe it?"

"Of course. What other source do we have?"

"Then you're a fool!"

"Dr. Landon, please do not talk to me that way. Who are you to come in here blowing your top?"

"Dr. Morley, dammit, you've got to listen to me. The figures are wrong. The whole system is outdated and built to inadequate standards, and we have a big one out there that may be headed straight for Florida!"

"What are you talking about?" Morley asked.

"Let me tell you something about the Army engineers. Remember a hurricane called Camille?"

"Everyone does."

"A man from the Weather Service in New Orleans predicted that the storm surge east of the Mississippi would rise between six and eight feet. He based that on Army engineers' figures. Dr. Morley, the water came up over twenty-six feet in Pass Christian. One of our men at the center, Steve Mitchell, lost his bride because someone made a drastic forecasting error. Ninety people died there."

The executive director, an elegant man in his late sixties whose face was so bland and serene that it appeared never to have been ruffled, smoothed back the few hairs over his tanned bald scalp, and he lit his pipe.

"You sound like an investigator."

"I'm drawing your attention to something important."

"We only know what we read. The Army engineers deal with flood control in this country."

"But they're not meteorologists, climatologists, surge or hurricane experts. They're trained in roads, bridges, and dams."

"Dr. Landon, I think you're unnecessarily concerned."

"What's the level of the big lake now?"

Morley reached slowly for his daily report from the Okeechobee flood-control station. "Sixteen feet at Hoover Levee."

"Is that usual?"

"It's about three to four feet higher than normal. We've had a lot of rainfall this summer."

"How low could you drain the lake?"

"Down to six feet, maybe."

"I suggest you empty Lake Okeechobee."

The executive director pushed straight up in his thick leather chair. "Why?"

"If one of these storms hits, we might have a rainfall of up to thirty inches. Your system can't handle it. The report says so."

"I don't simply push a button, Dr. Landon. A chain of command is required to flood the margin lands. These things are carefully worked out. The farmers are just laying in their winter seedlings. If we emptied the lake the banks would overflow and the crop damage could run into the millions."

"You're facing a potential disaster."

"I resent your coming up here like this, Dr. Landon. I'll get onto Dr. Ballantine immediately. I know him."

Keith left the office and drove east toward Palm Beach. He parked at the Brazilian Docks and boarded the *Patna*. Denise was sunning herself on the forward deck, trying to minimize the new red and blue marks that had surfaced that day, and she waved as he passed by and continued aft.

"Hi, Mel," Keith said, pushing back the door of the saloon. "What happened to your wife . . . an accident?"

"Claims she was fishing. I have my doubts."

"Do you mind if I make a quick call to the hurricane center?"

"Go ahead."

Keith dialed and asked for Lou Ballantine. The secretary told him the director wasn't feeling well and he wouldn't be in until after six.

"Then give me Steve Mitchell and, Karen, can you patch us into Dr. Haughton's office?

"We may have a genuine horror scene up here," Keith started as soon as they were both on the line.

"Where are you?" Billy asked.

"I'm aboard Hansen's yacht right now."

"Did you know that the administrator is coming down from Washington?" Steve said. "This business of the bribe has them all shook and Lou's home sick today."

"What a time to get sick," Keith sighed.

"You and I might have to fill in, Keith. Why are you talking to Hansen?" Steve asked.

"Because an associate of his has been subpoenaed by the state attorney's office and I guess he wants to make sure we all say the same thing. Anyhow, to hell with the bribe . . . that's not why I called. There're more important things." Keith went on to explain what he had learned at the flood-control district office and his subsequent demand that they lower the lake.

"If they don't prepare, there's going to be a disaster for sure," Keith said.

"Why won't they lower it?" Billy asked.

"Big, long story. If they flood the margin lands, the farmers will scream. They can't stand flooding right now because of their seedlings, but if a hurricane hits around here when the big lake is high, the system will fold. There won't be adequate runoff and we'll have a massive flood."

"What do you think we should do?" Steve said.

"It seems the only thing is to contact the Army engineers in Jacksonville and start the wheels turning as soon as possible."

"I'll call 'em right away," Steve said briskly.

"What's the afternoon report?"

"Claudine is seven hundred miles across. The APT just came in."

"Good God! Steve," Keith said after a brief pause, "do you think we should call for a premature evacuation?"

"How premature?"

"Maybe a full thirty hours. I'm thinking mostly about the Florida Keys."

"Well, if we order people out and they go, and if the hurricane *doesn't* hit, we'll catch hell for being alarmists and liars," Steve said.

"I realize that. We're screwed either way."

"Let's sit on it. I think we have time. When are you coming back?"

"Just as soon as I've heard what Hansen has to say, and that won't take long . . . I'm sick of listening to him."

When Keith returned to the afterdeck, Dr. Van Betzig was seated at the table talking to Mel. Keith shook hands with the old man and sat down.

"Can we make this short, Mel? We have a lot of problems down at the center."

"I heard about Claudine, Dr. Landon. Will it hit around here?"

"There's over a sixty percent chance. It's too early to tell. Let's get to the bone here. As far as the state attorney's investigation goes, I did what I was told to do by Dr. Ballantine, I didn't know about the bribe, and I never met this Glen what's his name."

"Markum. But you could be helpful. You do want the lake dredged?"

"And a lot of other things. The whole flood-control system should be rebuilt. I just came from their district office."

"I agree," Dr. Van Betzig said animatedly. "It's most inadequate. I've studied it from the day I arrived. In Holland we wouldn't have such a system."

"Let's get back to this problem," Mel said. "I'd like you and Dr. Van Betzig to support us, Keith . . . say that as experts you were behind the whole proposal."

Keith jumped to his feet. "Mel, I'm not going to be somebody's scapegoat, by implication or otherwise!"

He started to leave the *Patna* and Mel called after him, "But you're both involved already."

"I'm not involved, Mel, and I don't intend to become involved. Sorry . . . Our meeting is over."

Keith strode from the *Patna* and Dr. Van Betzig ran to the rail and leaned over. "Dr. Landon . . . Dr. Landon . . . I wasn't in on anything. I'm also telling the truth."

"That's fine," Keith said as he quickly walked off the dock, "I'm sure you are, Dr. Van Betzig."

THE SECRETARY OF COMMERCE WAS PACKING HIS VALISE AT SIX o'clock that evening preparing to take some work home before attending a White House dinner party that the President was giving in honor of the Irish ambassador and his wife. The private phone rang.

"Mr. Secretary, this is General Anderson."

The Secretary very seldom received calls from the Chief of Staff. He took the long phone line and went to the other side of his desk and sat down.

"Yes, sir?"

"You know about the hurricane heading toward the U.S. mainland?"

"Of course. I just sent the administrator of NOAA down there to supervise personally."

"It seems that a certain Dr. Mitchell at the hurricane center has been very active on the phone. He's asking the South Florida flood-control district to drain Lake Okeechobee."

The name Steve Mitchell seemed familiar to the Secretary. Of course, he was the hurricane activist who had been giving private screenings and lectures.

"According to Mitchell," the general continued, "and his associate, a Dr. Landon, the flood-control facilities in South Florida are inadequate."

"We never made such a statement!" the Secretary said, raising his voice.

"I realize that, sir, but they're asking the Army engineers to drain the lake. They want the water at the lowest possible level to accept a hurricane rainfall should it come. General Barnes, head of our Corps of Engineers, called me."

"Well, it sounds like a sensible idea," the Secretary said, "not that I know that much about flood control."

"There are problems. When General Barnes heard of the proposal, he contacted the executive director of the flood-control district, a Dr. Robert Morley. Dr. Morley told the general that the canal system would overflow if they emptied the lake. There'd be flooding in the farmlands. The Okeechobee growers' co-op heard about it, a leak from the flood-control district office, I suppose. They got onto the Secretary of Agriculture. He concurred with the growers. What else could he do?"

"I don't understand the significance of all this, General. If the hurricane people want the lake lowered for precautionary reasons, then it should be done."

"Palm Beach County is the largest producer of winter vegetables in the country, Mr. Secretary. The seedlings would be washed away and probably there'd be no crop. The loss could be in the millions . . . millions of dollars."

"So, you're asking me to stop my people?"

"That's the idea. No one knows if Claudine will hit. Naturally, if she does, then the floodgates will be opened; but only in an emergency. It's a very delicate time of year for the farmers."

"Whose side are you on, General?"

"I'm in the middle, of course. I understand you're going to the White House reception tonight."

"That's right."

"The Secretary of Agriculture will be there, too. He views this as extremely serious."

"So do I, General. I'll be back to you shortly."

The Secretary immediately placed a call to his administrator who was supposed to be at the Biscayne Plaza Hotel in Miami. He hadn't arrived there yet. Then he called the center and asked to speak to Dr. Ballantine, but he was told that the director was ill.

"Well, who's in charge there?"

"Dr. Stephen Mitchell, our co-deputy director, is on duty now, sir. Shall I put you through?"

"Yes, put Mitchell on."

The phone rang in the war room and an assistant said, "Steve, it's the Secretary of Commerce!"

"Yes, sir?" Steve answered.

"Dr. Mitchell, the Chief of Staff just called me. I understand you're suggesting that we drain Lake Okeechobee?"

"Yes, sir. I've consulted with two of my associates, Dr. Landon and Dr. Haughton. They're of the opinion that the lake can't take hurricane rains on the level of Claudine's. We've suggested that it be emptied to the lowest permissible level and *right now*. I told the engineers that in Jacksonville."

"By whose authority did you request this?"

"Our own. Dr. Ballantine is ill and Dr. Landon and I are acting in his place."

"Is the hurricane threatening now?"

"At the moment it's headed toward South Florida; it could turn, die out, or increase its intensity."

"What are the probabilities?"

"We think it highly likely that some sections of Florida will be hit."

"I wish Dr. Ballantine were available. Have you heard from Dr. Peterson?"

"Not yet, sir."

"Do you know the crop impact if we open the gates?"

"Yes, sir. The divisional office at Jacksonville told me all about it."

"And you still feel this is a necessary precaution?"

"I think it's vital, sir. We might be facing the biggest natural catastrophe in our country's history."

"Dr. Mitchell, I don't want you to misconstrue what I'm about to say, but you're considered a scaremonger by some people down there. In fact, there have been a lot of complaints about you."

"I know that. But this threat is *real*," Steve said, hardening his voice. "Even my colleagues agree that these precautions should be taken *now*, no matter what the price. We're talking about saving people, not lettuce!"

"I'm going to a White House dinner tonight, Dr. Mitchell, and I'll have to confront the Secretary of Agriculture and the President who sides with Agriculture. If you were in my shoes, would you still feel the same way?"

"Absolutely, sir! Empty the lake and to hell with the seeds. We're looking at a possible human disaster here!"

It was five minutes to ten in the war room when Steve was handed a message from the CARCAH (Chief, Aerial Reconnaissance Coordination, Atlantic Hurricanes), saying that the Hercules hurricane hunter plane would pick him up at Homestead Air Force Base the next morning at eleven o'clock.

Attached to the print-out there was permission for two civilian observers to ride in the cockpit jump seats.

At the party in Palm Beach John Baxter had told Steve he would like to see the hurricane close up from the hunter plane and he planned to take Cynthia along. As soon as Steve got back to the center, he had put the requests through channels, saying that a former Air Force officer and his wife desired space if available. Hurricane reconnaissance was not considered a strategic mission by the Air Force, nor did the hunter planes transport classified equipment. They often carried observers, sometimes senators or perhaps other civilians, in their public relations efforts to keep the planes flying. Many of the budgets presented to Congress called for cuts in weather reconnaissance, and the Air Force was determined to continue this vital service for the Department of Commerce.

Steve picked up the phone and called John Baxter. "Do you remember the other night when you asked to fly into Claudine? The permission just came through. You and your wife will have to sign a series of releases, but if you still want to go, be at Homestead Air Force Base at ten-thirty tomorrow morning."

"How safe is it, Steve?"

"We've never lost a plane. It's a jaw-rattler, but we don't penetrate these things to get killed. The plane is specially stressed."

"I don't know about Cynthia, but I'll be there. By the way, did you hear that the state attorney wants to talk to us Friday in Miami?"

"Yeah, I heard. See you tomorrow morning. Get plenty of rest."

John Baxter hung up and turned to Cynthia who was watching television and said, "That was Steve Mitchell, honey, down at the hurricane center. He wanted to know if we'd like to fly into a storm with them tomorrow. I think it'd be kind of exciting."

"No, darling," she smiled. "I'm not very adventurous. Why don't you ask Denise? She'd love it. Really . . . I'm sure she would."

John didn't know whether she meant it or not; lately Cynthia had been different, ironic, but she and Denise seemed to be getting along well. He said nothing but went upstairs and picked up the phone and called the *Patna,* asking Mel's wife if she was ready for some more excitement.

"I've never refused a kick. I'll have the maid prepare my latest parachute."

Lou Ballantine came into the war room just before eleven that night; his face was drawn and sallow and he looked as if he had aged twenty years since Steve had last seen him.

"You OK, Lou?"

"Just tired," he said slowly.

They went into the APT room for the ten o'clock infrared photo; they stood silently waiting for the printer to signal that the transmission was about to roll off the scanner, knowing full well that the news could only be bad. As they grouped there in the semidarkness, Marc Peterson arrived. He had already spoken to the Secretary about the growing conflict: whether to open the floodgates or not.

"One thing I want to make clear," he said autocratically upon entering. "We must present a unified position. This center has far too many divergent views. Doesn't inspire confidence in Washington."

"There'll be one opinion tonight," Lou said.

Twenty minutes later the picture slowly unwound from the receiver roll; it was partially dried and placed on the light box.

"God, look at Claudine!" Steve said.

"Her track is swinging north," Keith commented.

"What does it mean?" the administrator asked.

"If she continues on that path we're in for a hit!"

"I'm supposed to call the Secretary at the White House," Marc Peterson said. "What do I tell him? There's still some uncertainty about all this, it seems to me."

There was more discussion, but the center's final opinion was expressed by Lou Ballantine.

"I don't think we can afford to take a chance. Open the gates."

"But the area isn't even under a hurricane warning," the administrator said. "The Army engineers don't agree with you. I've talked to General Barnes."

"Dr. Peterson, we're the meteorologists, not the Army engineers," Steve said. "You're looking at a critical situation on that night photo. It could develop into a calamity. The canal system and levees around Lake Okeechobee weren't designed to carry the impact from such a large hurricane."

"All right . . . all right . . . that's our decision and now it's up to the higher powers," Peterson said, puffing on his Scotch pipe.

Peterson used the director's office to inform the Secretary of Commerce who said that he had been in private conversations with the President and the Secretary of Agriculture.

"If we issue orders to open the gates and the storm doesn't hit, the federal government will probably be sued for millions of dollars. Our general counsel and the counsel from Agriculture want to study it further," the Secretary told him.

"What does the President say?"

"He doesn't have enough inputs. We'll get back to you when we have an opinion of counsel. Maybe we can secure a quick court immunity."

"That might be too late, Mr. Secretary."

"We're requesting acceleration. The Attorney General's already been notified."

As the administrator walked back down the hall toward the war room he was recognized by several reporters who were lounging around with TV and still cameras.

"Dr. Peterson, what about the floodgates?"

"No word on it yet."

"How much danger is Florida facing?"

"We don't know at this time."

"Are you down here because of the bribe or the hurricane?"

Peterson hadn't planned to get into that, but he replied, "The hurricane, of course. There's nothing to these bribery allegations. Rubbish."

He entered the war room where the specialists were busily plotting Claudine's new position.

"I think she'll curve more northward," Steve said. "Notice the slight undulation in her track."

As they bent over the light table carefully searching for the slightest clues to course changes, comparing the visual information with the upper air steering currents, Lou Ballantine coughed and slowly his wrinkled hands grasped his midsection below his heart as if he had a pain in his stomach. Then he fell forward and Steve caught his head just before it hit the ground glass of the tabletop.

"Lou, what's the matter?" Keith yelled.

"Call a doctor!" someone said.

He came to rest on the linoleum floor of the war room and his face was white and sweaty.

Steve raced for the phone and called the emergency number; when he returned, he saw that Lou's face had gone from white to blue, and Steve began mouth-to-mouth resuscitation. In minutes the rescue squad from the Coral Gables Fire Department was on the scene and an oxygen mask was clamped around Lou's stilled face. Steve stood back and felt his own heart pound, knowing that Lou Ballantine was the one stabilizing force that had kept the center together; his glance crossed with Keith, who Steve knew was sharing the feeling.

There was silence in the war room as they all stood staring down at the director. The paramedic finally pushed to his feet, his stethoscope still swinging across his chest.

"I'm sorry, but he's dead. We can't revive him."

Steve walked out of the room and he padded around the dark halls on the far side of the building. He felt a stickiness spread over his cheeks and tried to hold back the tears, but he couldn't.

THE DEATH IN THE WAR ROOM SEEMED TO BE A PORTENT. A TERRIBLE chill went through even the most hardened hurricane men, not only because Lou Ballantine would be remembered as having devoted his whole life to the study of hurricanes—granted he started in the early days and saw big storm forecasting move to a quasi-science— but his dying seemed to say that there would be other expirations.

No one could escape from this ghoulish thought.

Later the administrator took Steve, Billy, and Keith to Lou's office. They sat in silence drinking coffee. Dr. Peterson shuffled papers on the desk. The man was shaking inside. There was almost too much for him to handle at once—the huge storm moving toward Florida, the dispute over the floodgates, the bribery allegations, the conflict between the two deputy directors and, now, the death of the man who seemed to lace all this together somehow. For a time he didn't say anything. Then, finally, he lifted his head and cleared his throat several times.

Billy wiped her eyes and so did Keith and, still, they all sat there, not knowing what to say or how.

"I'm very sorry," Peterson began. "I know you all thought a lot of Dr. Ballantine."

"He was a moderate and we weren't," Steve said.

"I guess we gave him a lot of trouble," Keith added slowly.

The administrator continued, "Dr. Ballantine was a very dedicated person and we'll miss . . ."

Suddenly Billy broke down in tears and Keith placed his arm about her.

"But what are we going to do now?" she cried. "These two men can't even work in the same room!"

"Well, ah, certainly, this is a very tragic loss, very tragic, but we must all make adjustments," Dr. Peterson said.

"Lou was the referee," Keith said simply, patting Billy's shoulder.

"Didn't he designate one of you to be director in case of an emergency?"

"He was never able to make up his mind," Steve said. "Poor Lou. He would like to have pleased everybody, but we can't have two people giving orders."

"Are you implying, Steve, that I should withdraw?" Keith snapped.

"If I remember correctly, Keith, we've both threatened at one time or another to withdraw."

The administrator held up his hand. "Gentlemen . . . Lou told me you two have always had divergent ideas on forecasting and policy."

"That's true," Steve said. "We have agreed on some basic points, but we could never run the center together. There can only be one leader."

"I think you're right because I get the feeling there's still tension between you."

"There is and it'll continue," Keith said. "Call it differences in age, theory, education . . . anything you want."

"All right, but for the time being can you people work this hurricane together? Stick it out and Commerce will name one of you or someone else. We need you both now, and remember your responsibility is grave if I understand the situation out there."

They agreed. Starting that night there were two directors of the National Hurricane Center, but the harmony of such an arrangement, even in its temporary nature, was not to last long, for at nine o'clock the following morning Keith called Steve into Lou's office.

"Steve, I don't feel you should be flying into Claudine."

"Are you worried about my life?" Steve smiled.

"Frankly, no, but I think your place is here. You're needed. And you asked Billy to go."

"So what? She's not assigned to the war room."

"And I understand you're taking John Baxter and someone else from Palm Beach. Why don't we just conduct tours like the Greyhound Lines?"

"Keith, it's not us . . . it's the Air Force. Anytime they can get people into those hurricane hunter planes, they think they're spreading the word. It's the same as opening up their air bases for public shows. The Air Force considers Baxter an important Florida business executive, which he is. He knows the state senators and representatives."

"All right, forget about Baxter, but I think you should be on duty here."

"And, Keith, I think you need to see at least one hurricane with your own eyes."

"That's where we've always differed!"

"We'll only be out there for a few hours. Claudine's not moving that fast anyhow."

"What's the purpose of the flight? It just seems useless, a waste of time, money, and energy."

"Those planes are laboratories . . . decisive information can be gotten from visual observation."

"This just underlines everything I've said. We can't exist together here, Steve. It will never work."

"I don't want an argument, Keith. I'll check you later this afternoon."

"We have to share responsibility. I'm not taking it on the nose because you're out flying around."

"It won't exactly be Palisades Park out there. Just you make sure they lift those floodgates. That's the important thing now."

* * *

An hour later they boarded the four-engine Hercules hurricane hunter, and the ship lifted off into the calm, crystal skies southeast of Miami. In the large cockpit there were eight people: the pilot, copilot, flight engineer, flight meteorologist, Billy, Steve, Denise, and John Baxter.

"Mrs. Hansen, how do you feel about this little trip?" Billy asked.

"My juices are flowing. You've probably been up before."

"No, as a matter of fact, I've never been in a hurricane."

"I'm sorry about Dr. Ballantine's death," Denise said after a pause. "Were you close to him?"

"We all were."

The skies remained clear for a time, but as they closed in on the Puerto Rican coast, large banks of gray clouds began to pile up on the horizon and the pilot adjusted his throttles to climb high over the storm; the first observation would look right down into Claudine's snoot, the eye. It became chilly in the cockpit. There was silence.

"Look at that off the right wing!" Steve suddenly yelled. "God, what an organization!"

The plane banked to the right; they were over the swirling clouds of Claudine and below them was the eye, a full sixty miles in diameter. Running away from the still center was the wall cloud and finally bushy, spiraling rain bands. From the top of the funnel, hot air was being pumped up and out with as much kinetic energy as that of an atomic bomb exploding every moment.

"She's the biggest goddamned thing I've ever seen!" the flight meteorologist said.

"Let's find that nine hundred millibar line," the pilot ordered. "I don't like fooling around in something like this." He eased off his thrust levers; the plane began to slowly descend.

"What happens next?" Denise asked the flight meteorologist.

"We'll peel off to an altitude where we can pick up a nine hundred millibar level. Once we have that, we'll fly into the core using weather radar. At the same time we'll start dropping sondes recording instruments. They'll tell us the surface pressure, temperature, and wind speed and, then, we'll have a clear picture of the storm."

"Is this the only way to do it?" Denise asked.

"Sure is . . . what ship would be out in this stuff? The more we learn about the anatomy of the hurricane, the more we can accurately forecast its possible movement. We can also tell if she's deepening and at what rate."

The plane banked lower and lower as the thrust of the prop-jet eased to a low, melodic hum and they flew away from the solid walls of boiling black clouds; some twenty minutes later, the Hercules banked again and they began to probe for the nine hundred millibar line.

"More altitude," came the request from the edgy technicians monitoring the crowded instruments in the rear hollow of the aircraft.

"Take her up another five hundred," came the order.

The thrust levers were pushed forward; the aircraft climbed and finally settled down at 9,100 feet, the large mass of towering angry clouds coming closer and closer, spilling over each other, forming, unforming, reforming, as the vicious vertical air thrust and pumped. The plane started bouncing slightly and when the distance to the swirling monster had closed, the Hercules began to shake.

"Hope she's stressed for this," John yelled.

"She is," Steve answered with authority.

"We'll penetrate the rough air at maneuvering speed," the pilot said.

"Are you scared, Billy?" Denise asked.

"Of course . . . aren't you?"

"I don't know," Denise laughed nervously. "I've always looked at life as if it were going to end any minute anyhow, and I've had plenty of those minutes."

"I bet you have," Billy said, digging her nails into the arms of the seat.

Suddenly the first soft tails of the outer band of clouds slid by and it became darker and darker in the cockpit; the rain started hitting the plane's outer shell like marbles. It was impossible to see out the windshield, but the two pilots kept their eyes notched on the instruments, which began to rattle first, then vibrate, so that the numbers became a whitish blur, impossible to read.

The whole plane started to shudder. It was forced up in the violent air, then down, then a hard gust of air cut in underneath the left wing raising it with a flick as if the whole ship were nothing but a balsa-wood model out on a gusty autumn afternoon. Directional control seemed to be lost. The stomachs and hearts of all in the plane heaved this way and that, and sweat broke out on all of them as everything began to whirl and tremble in the hell in the air.

"Do you guys know what you're doing, Steve?" John yelled. "I've got eight thousand hours in the book and I've never felt anything like this!"

"We have it," the pilot said coolly, jostling his hands over the skating controls.

There was a sudden swoosh of air. The plane danced upward for a moment, hung there like a bird stopped in flight, and shook violently; there was a crack somewhere.

"What's that, Steve?" Billy asked.

"Nothing," he said. "Just the wing spar flexing."

"I can't believe you're so cool. Doesn't anything physical ever bother you? It's disgusting!"

They were trapped in an accelerating blast of fast rising air and the air speed needle wound up, along with the radar altimeter.

"Shit, I'm losing it!" the pilot cried.

"Just let her take care of herself," Steve shouted.

Their stomachs were pressed far down into their guts from the negative gravitational forces, and it became colder and darker as they were being hurled up into the higher, thinner altitudes. Suddenly with faces flushed and hearts beating wildly, as if this was the transport to eternity, they were flung out of Claudine sideways into the clear, cold environment of 41,000 feet.

The whole episode might have taken one minute, or five, or just seconds. Everyone's mind and senses were knocked out; the instruments could not read or handle the rapidity of their ascent through the darkness of the hurricane. There was no way of knowing exactly what had happened except that no reconnaissance plane in the history of big storm probing, which dated back to the forties, had ever been sucked into and thrown out of a gigantic storm like this before. Claudine had succinctly closed her clouds to intruders.

"Let's get the hell out of here!" the pilot said. "This is one storm we can't take!"

"What was the wind measurement back there?" Steve said into his mike. "Did you clock it?"

"We have a surface wind of ʟwo hundred and twenty sustained

. . . central pressure of about twenty-six point ten, but the gauges just broke."

"I think that's about the lowest pressure ever recorded," the meteorologist said.

Then there was silence as they all regained their breath and the Hercules turned in an arc heading back toward Homestead. Billy had wrapped her arms tightly around Steve's neck during the ordeal, but Denise sat stolidly straight.

Steve picked up the mike and asked to be patched through to the hurricane center.

"Claudine's deepened, Keith. Very bad. That premature evacuation you suggested—I think we should order it."

"Jesus, what a responsibility," Keith said. "I wish . . ."

"I know. I wish Lou were here to give the order, too."

"How did Billy take it?"

"Very well. She was fine. And, Keith, you son of a bitch, we did learn something. She's much worse than we expected!"

"That's one for you."

Even over the radio Steve could hear a softening in Keith's attitude about the hurricane probe. "See you in about three hours, Keith. Wait for me at the center, will you?"

At the same time the Hercules was being hurled in and out of Claudine, Maggie in her chauffeur-driven vintage Rolls glided into the arched driveway leading to Cynthia Baxter's home.

"Cynthia, darling, how are you?"

"Fine. How pleasant of you to stop by," Cynthia said.

"I can only stay a minute."

They settled in the tiled loggia before a tea service hastily rolled out by Cynthia's maid who had been with her for all of her fifteen years in Palm Beach.

"I *am* sorry to come unannounced, Cynthia, but I was passing by on my way to the Ocean Club and I just had to tell you what I had heard. Everybody's talking about it and I'm rather proud of you and Jayson."

"Why?"

"Well, first of all, I know that Jayson convinced Philip that those pictures should be taken at his party. Jayson understands a *lot* of our local problems."

"Yes, he's a dear man."

"But that night, Cynthia dear, I couldn't help but notice that you still had not completely . . . shall we say . . . absolved Denise? Then, I heard you were out together Sunday night for dinner at Capriccio's. Five people called me to report that you two were laughing and smiling like old times. I'm so proud of you, Cynthia. That's the nifty P.B. spirit . . . make up and forget."

Cynthia was really very pleased that Maggie had come to see her, though her feelings toward Denise remained unchanged. Still, her voice was tinged with softness when she replied to Maggie's compliment. "Thank you, Maggie. That's most gracious. Denise has had problems with her career and being married to that man. . . ."

"Isn't he frightful?"

"The more I get to know Denise, the more I like her, despite what happened. It was only an accident. I can't say that John didn't have something to do with it. He likes her, no doubt about it. Right now the two of them are flying into that hurricane with Dr. Mitchell. You remember him? He was here at Philip's party."

"Oh, yes, the tall, thin man." Maggie nodded.

"Right. Well, I always say that water will seek its own level. I've just wiped the slate clean. If John and Denise see their future together, I'm not going to stand in their way. She's a most interesting and attractive woman. Some people say I'm too socially oriented here in P.B. That might be true . . . I adore people and parties, but Maggie, one thing I'm not is a possessive, jealous woman. I think I still love John, we've been together a long time, but *c'est la vie*. . . ."

Maggie leaned over and kissed Cynthia. "You have what it takes, Cynthia. Even Nicole said so. She adores Denise too, you know."

After the Queen left, Cynthia went upstairs and called Jayson.

"Are you drinking or not?"

"I am *not*. You told me to have one drink and I did."

"When was that?"

"For breakfast this morning at the Everglades."

"Are you cold sober?"

"Yes. Come on over and see."

"I think I will."

Cynthia got into her bronze Silver Shadow and drove down South Ocean toward Jayson's house—Mizner to Mizner. She had decided to dress for Jayson and she wore a flame-colored tunic and all her jewelry. Shortly afterward, she turned into the House of Usher, a pet nickname for Jayson's collapsing rubble.

Cynthia rang the doorbell and Jayson, in a frayed but clean old Brooks Brothers shirt, thrust open the door.

"Hello, hello, how's me Lady Love! Hello, hello, how's me Lady Love!" Jayson sang to the tune of an English patter song.

He jumped about the Indian-carpeted hallway in an abandoned flight, bowing and marching and imitating a combination of Rex Harrison and Sir Harry Lauder.

"Jayson, darling, I adore you! You're lazy, polite, and you have great flair and style."

"Goodness, didn't know I was all those things."

"And so much more," she said, coming up and kicking him playfully.

His expression changed and he straightened suddenly and she could see that he had not been drinking. His eyes were limpid and innocent, an old nun's who had never drunk anything and gone to bed in perfect peace after a ring through the rosary ending at 8:45 P.M.

"Cynthia, why have you changed so? I've known you for fifteen years and you were always one person and now you're somebody else."

"Just because we made love?"

"No, no. I thought you were going into a permanent funk after the *Patna* scene, but instead you emerged a new female. You laugh now, even at Palm Beach, you carry on with Denise and come over here and please an old man. What happened, Cynthia?"

"Jayson, I guess I suddenly looked around me and said, 'What the hell have I been doing all these years?' The planning, the scraping, the goody-good girl . . . making peace with all those people I didn't like. Do you know what the *Patna* scene was to me?"

"No, actually. What was it?"

"It kicked my tail out of a long uphill struggle that I really was having trouble with. Now I love everybody."

"You're beautiful, Cynthia."

"Not anymore."

"Stop it! Every time I see you, your face is better. Can't even tell anymore. Well, now, where shall it be? The bedroom? The pool? The bar? The tennis court? The kitchen? Where, tell me."

"You name it," Cynthia replied, and added with mock coyness, "Guess what's on my mind?"

"Would you like to see my old Harvard pictures, faded as they are, on my walls? Would you be intrigued to know that I rowed for Harvard in the eights?"

"Delighted. And would you be intrigued to know that I went to Foxcroft after parochial school when my parents couldn't afford it, and graduated from Tulane on a scholarship and have nineteen hours toward my master's?"

"In what?"

"Sociology."

"So that's what you're doing in Palm Beach. Secret graduate work."

"I could write the book."

They laughed and he whirled her into the bar and they made two tall vodka and tonics. Then they danced up the creaking stairs and down the dark hall to the last bedroom. They danced out of their clothes into the bed and went through their lovemaking as if it were a burst of yonder spirit. It wasn't real love or passion, but endearment.

When Cynthia finally left Jayson she felt twenty years younger. She drove swiftly past the B. & T., out Southern Boulevard, beyond the airport until the wide four-lane cement highway blended into a two-lane macadam road, Highway 441, which went far west into the Glades. The huge, red sun was sinking. The shadows became longer. Cynthia turned on the stereo in the Rolls, something she seldom did, and then she twisted up the volume knob and sang loudly to Lynn Anderson's "I Never Promised You a Rose Garden."

When the houses petered out, she found a small dirt road and turned in, not really knowing where she was going. She drove the car over bumps and ruts, deeper and deeper into the wild outback. She pulled over to the side of the dirt road by a cabbage palm and got out, making sure to take her purse with her. Cynthia walked through knee-high saw grass to a clump of hardwoods that grew out of the soft land on a bed of turf-covered limestone. Once within the shadow of the Florida hickories, she opened her purse, took out the small pistol, loaded the clip with bullets, and shoved it into the pistol, upside down the first time. Then she corrected it.

She took her handkerchief out and tied it to a low-hanging branch and stepped back. She pinched off five high, whining cracks from about twenty-five yards, imagining that the handkerchief was Denise's beautiful face. She missed with every round.

Cynthia loaded up and fired again; still the white handkerchief was not even rippled by the trajectory breeze of the bullets. Again. And again. Finally she moved closer to a position about ten yards from the handkerchief and repeated her firing.

One bullet did manage to penetrate the linen. She came up to inspect her hit and stared at the hole seeing the skull of Denise Hansen shattered and bleeding. Then she laughed at herself. She knew she could never kill Denise. But she was enjoying her new-found sense of power and she could always take up target shooting if her aim improved.

As Cynthia was squeezing off shots in the Glades, the accountant for the Palace Beach System, a partner with the firm of Reinhart, Spencer & Co. in Miami, walked into Philip Guest's office carrying a load of ledgers. Mr. Benjamin, a studious little man who had once been an amateur flyweight boxer, had come at the request of the chairman to go over the expenditures thus far on the Regency Walk project. Philip had canceled the construction and he was about to be asked by his board what they had spent to date.

"Do you have the figures, Mr. Benjamin?"

"I do, sir."

"What are they?"

"Considering materials ordered . . . those already on the site . . . the hotel is down seven hundred and eighty thousand dollars."

Philip was stunned and he leaned back in his large leather chair and stared at the solemn man before him.

"I had no idea it was that much."

"There's something else that has shown up, sir," Mr. Benjamin said with a slight cough. "One of our associates discovered it. We first looked at the building material orders; then we compared them to the delivered receipts. They didn't agree. Materials for the Regency Walk project were ordered, but not delivered. We called the suppliers and they said there must be some mistake, but they couldn't discuss it until they went over their complete files. As a matter of review, we looked into the El Lugar project and St. Paul's Island, and the same pattern was repeated. In both cases, building supplies were ordered as per specifications, but some of the bulk supplies, such as precast cement slabs, I beams, roof joists, were never delivered."

"How much have we been shorted?"

"From what we can tell at first glance, about eight hundred and fifty thousand dollars on all three projects."

"My God," Philip said softly. "What do you think has been going on?"

The accountant continued as if he hadn't heard Philip's question, "Of course, it could be a housekeeping error; perhaps the construction foreman didn't file the delivery confirmations. That sometimes happens."

"But on this level?"

"It would be rare, sir, for it to be merely an oversight."

"It's a kickback!" Philip said forcefully.

"I didn't want to use that word, sir."

Philip got up and marched around the room, finally ending up at the bar.

"Do you drink, Mr. Benjamin?"

"I do not, sir, but thank you."

Philip poured out a tall Scotch and soda, something he seldom did during the working day, and returned to his seat.

"Do you have any theories about this?" the chairman said.

"Well, ah . . ." the accountant hemmed and hawed.

"Come on, Mr. Benjamin. You must have an idea of what happened."

"You understand, sir, our firm doesn't theorize."

"Then, tell me off the record. What do you think?"

"I think someone has deliberately shorted the building materials and then gone back to the suppliers for a rebate."

"And who would that be?"

"A person who knew about architecture and how to build around the shortages so they wouldn't be noticed."

"Mr. Hansen!"

"Perhaps."

"If Mr. Hansen were involved, do you feel that someone else knew also, for instance, Mr. Baxter?"

"I can't answer that, sir."

"These are very, very serious allegations, Mr. Benjamin."

"They are not my allegations, sir. All I'm telling you is what we discovered. We might never have realized this if you hadn't asked for an audit of the Regency Walk."

"How can we be sure that your theory's right? Do you have any suggestions?"

"Before we approach the suppliers, I think we should make certain that the materials are not in the present structures. If we say we have no delivery slips, they'll just say the materials were paid for and dumped on the site. They'll most probably come up with some sort of evidentiary proof, such as a signed shipping manifest. But that won't prove anything."

"I quite agree."

"Our recommendation would be to hire an independent architect and simply see if the I beams are in position as indicated on the plans. If so, the mistake was a clerical one; if they are not, then you know that the construction was shorted."

Philip didn't say anything. He sat there looking at the ceiling thinking he could not cope with another crisis. What else could happen to the Palace Beach? He picked up the phone and dialed the number of McKinsey, Hamilton & Smith.

"Joe, can you give me some off-the-cuff information?"

"Sure thing," the lawyer said.

"Under Florida law, what's the penalty for building a structure not to the plans as submitted to the building commissioner?"

The lawyer said he'd have to look it up and when he returned to the phone, he read the statute from the Florida State Penal Code.

"Thanks, Joe, glad I caught you," Philip said.

He put down the phone and turned to the accountant. "It's a misdemeanor in this state, punishable by ten thousand dollars' fine and/or up to a year in prison. We'll hire an independent architect tomorrow and take a ride over to El Lugar. Are you available, Mr. Benjamin?"

"I can make my time available, sir."

"I think I know who's behind this. Mr. Hansen and, much to my regret, my president. Of course, that's why John pushed through these projects. He was in it up to his neck with Mel—and that crazy business with Mrs. Hansen fits, too, because no one ever filed a complaint. They talked about it but no one made a move. They couldn't!"

Philip was anguished. What a fool he had been to try for a peaceful alliance between people who were fraudulent, even criminal. He wondered how far it extended: to Cynthia, to Denise, to the hurricane people? Were they all involved in a massive conspiracy that was designed to run down the entire coast of Florida?

CHAPTER

28

DENISE HELD IT BACK AS LONG AS SHE COULD, BUT WHEN SHE SWUNG
her feet to the apron at Homestead Air Force Base, she knew she
was going to be sick. She put her hand to her mouth and ran into
the ladies' room where Billy helped her.

"Can't blame her. I don't feel so good myself," Steve told John
Baxter.

"That was some experience, Steve, and I think that'll hold me for
a while, though I've got an hour's flight back to Palm Beach." He
shook Steve's hand and walked over to the tie-down area where he
preflighted his old 1962 Apache and waited for Denise to come from
the ladies' room inside the Operations Building of the base. She
approached the plane slowly, looking very pale.

"Denise, I think you've had enough flying for today. You might
be sick again. I'll call a cab for you."

"I want to go with you, John. Besides, a cab'll cost you a fortune."

"No, please, I insist. It's the least I can do."

"OK." She nodded her head and John watched her walk away toward the Operations Building.

He was too exhausted to file a flight plan, something he had never omitted before, but the flight into the hurricane had taken a lot out of him and it was only a short distance to Palm Beach. He obtained tower clearance and fed in the power. As the plane lifted off and climbed out, John saw far off his left wing the last of the refulgent sunset; then the gray stratus bands took over and darkness fell quickly. Below and as far as he could look north, billions of tiny lights appeared on the Gold Coast with sparkling clarity. It was as if some great hand had sprinkled bushels of glowing crystals upon the flat, canal-dug land.

The motors hummed on. The air at four thousand was still and cool and John was glad to be back in his own plane on a calm night. As he passed Lauderdale, Pompano Beach, Boca Raton, he thought about the morning's experience and the swaggering giant storm. He banked left over the Glades so as not to interfere with incoming traffic and the lights below him became scarcer. The flight passed over the pitch-black swamp and as he was adjusting his frequency dial to Palm Beach approach control, John's eyes crossed the instrument panel in a cursory way; in the glow of an aileron night light, he saw the white needle of his oil-temperature gauge resting on the upper pin. He thought that there must be something wrong with the gauge—a common occurrence in older planes—since everything else, the sound of the right engine, its manifold pressure and cylinder head temperature, seemed to be within limits. He knew he would be down in just a minute, too; he could see the green, rotating beacon of the airport off to the east.

Suddenly a rich red glow appeared, lapping out of the right cowling.

The fire was blown back along the trailing edge of the wing and it swiftly engulfed the wing. John was a cool, precise man, not given to uncertain action in an emergency; he cut the fuel switches on the right engine and he pushed the plane's nose down hoping that the rush of air over the wing and engine would blow out the gasoline fire. The plane struggled and he knew he had to make a quick decision:

the airport or the swamp? The cockpit was warming up; it would be impossible to make it back to the field, so he cut all gas switches and the master switch, and the other engine died as the air swished over the silenced plane.

It was as black as an unmanned coal mine.

He swore. How could this happen after surviving Claudine? He eased the controls forward to keep up his air speed and saw before him a cluster of squat palms. On an emergency landing he knew the wings should take the shock first and the forward impact speed of the fuselage would then be substantially reduced.

It worked. The wings were sheared off by the wheels-up landing and the Apache spun crazily in the mire of the trees. When it came to a halt, the fire was out and John opened the door, but his foot was trapped in the tangle of the partially collapsed fire wall. Frantically he tried to escape, twisting his foot this way and that. He grimaced with pain and felt the warm trickle of blood run over his ankle. John reached for the radio and twisted the dials, but it was dead.

Looking up, John saw that the thick palm leaves had covered what was left of the plane and then the stark realization: He could not summon help, the radio was dead; the trees were shielding his position and, worse, he had not filed a flight plan. No one knew where he was!

The following morning at nine o'clock Philip Guest was in his office awaiting the arrival of Mr. Benjamin. He received a phone call.

"This is Butler Aviation, Mr. Guest. I think you have a plane overdue. Mr. Baxter's car has been here all night. We called Homestead and they told us that he took off from there at six-fifty last night headed for West Palm."

"Did you check to see if the plane is anywhere else on the field?"
"Yes, sir."
"Was a flight plan filed?"
"No, it wasn't."
"That's unusual. Did Mr. Baxter radio trouble of any kind?"
"No, sir."
"If there were trouble, wouldn't he have radioed?"

"That would be the first thing he'd do. Mr. Baxter has eight thousand hours. He certainly knows his stuff."

"Has there been any report of a plane crash?"

"No, sir. We investigated that. The plane merely disappeared, and it's a damned big area, Mr. Guest. We don't know if he flew over the water or the swamp."

"All right. I think you should start an air and sea rescue search immediately. Let me know what you find out."

Philip hung up and he wondered about the Bermuda Triangle, then quickly another thought invaded his mind and he asked the accountant, who had arrived in his office for the flight to El Lugar while he was on the phone.

"Did John Baxter know about your audit of the books?"

"Yes, sir."

"Who told him?"

"You said we could have the cooperation of everyone. I came up here . . . let's see . . . four days ago and asked his secretary to give me the files on all the recent construction projects."

"Why didn't John release them to you?"

"He wasn't here. They said he had gone to El Lugar."

"On a Sunday? What was he doing there then?"

"I don't know, but yesterday morning I called him and told him that we had the complete files."

"Was he surprised?"

"I think he was."

"And did you mention the shortages?"

"Yes, sir. I asked him about the deliveries and he said he knew nothing about them. He sounded upset. Our conversation was very brief." The accountant paused, then said, "Was there something wrong with that? He was the man closest to the projects."

"No, there was nothing wrong with what you did. It all comes into focus now. I'm going to tell you something, Mr. Benjamin, but please understand it is in the strictest confidence."

"Of course, sir."

"I hired Mel Hansen, our architect, on John's say-so, and we rushed into construction on two projects that happened to turn out OK. Then the idea of the Regency Walk condos came up. I was

((229))

opposed to Mel Hansen from the beginning, I don't like his style, but John kept sticking up for the man. Moreover, John never researched the impact of Hansen's setback proposal. Now he's disappeared—that was Butler Aviation on the phone just now. The company plane was well looked after and John was an excellent pilot."

"What are you saying, Mr. Guest?" the accountant asked anxiously.

"I have a feeling, only a feeling, that John knew about the shortages and the bribe, Mr. Benjamin, and I believe he killed himself!"

The accountant was obviously stunned, but he said nothing as Philip picked up the phone and dialed.

"I want to speak to Steve Mitchell, please. Philip Guest calling."

When Steve got on the phone, Philip made a perfunctory inquiry about the storm and then he said, "I understand that John Baxter flew into Claudine with you yesterday?"

"Yes, we had a brief look. Why?"

"John's Apache is overdue, Dr. Mitchell."

"What!"

"It never landed at West Palm last night. Was he alone?"

"Yes," Steve said slowly. "He flew down with Mrs. Hansen, but she was kind of shaken up by the hurricane probe and John told her to go back by taxi."

"Did he seem to be in a strange mood, Dr. Mitchell, or did he appear to be under any pressure?"

"No, I don't think so. He didn't act any stranger than anyone else would have after flying into a hurricane."

Following that conversation, Philip called Cynthia and broke the news. As he suspected, she hadn't been notified and was of course very disturbed when Philip told her the circumstances of John's disappearance. She had simply assumed, the night before, when her husband hadn't returned home, that he and Denise had gone off someplace together again. But now, as she vaguely heard what Philip was saying, her thoughts raced madly along the path of possibilities.

"We are conducting an all-out search, Cynthia, but I think we have to face the fact that something could have gone wrong . . . with the plane, perhaps . . ." His voice trailed off, and then he said, "Has John been depressed lately or different in any way?"

"Well, John hasn't been himself for a long time. I think that's understandable," she said, trying to keep her voice steady.

There was a pause and Philip said, "Did you know he was with Mrs. Hansen yesterday?"

"Yes . . . yes . . . he asked me to go along, but I told him to take Denise. She likes that sort of thing more than I do."

Cynthia put down the phone slowly. At first she could not believe what Philip had told her. John was too good a pilot and surely they would find the plane. But as late afternoon dragged around, she felt a terrible loneliness. Sobbing, she mounted the stairs of the big Mizner house to their bedroom with a Scotch, and she looked at the pictures on the walls, hundreds of them in small black frames. Suddenly, she couldn't keep back the fears that swept over her and she began to wail as she saw their life in Palm Beach along the walls of their room. Was it for nothing? She knew that she loved John with all her heart. He was a dear, faithful man who had made one giant mistake, because of two people who had come to Palm Beach to snatch everything they could out of the resort. But maybe, Cynthia thought, she had failed him. Now it was too late. She wept for about an hour, padding about the vacant halls calling John's name, telling him how much she loved him.

Later, somehow, Cynthia found herself in the Rolls. She was driving out to the airport to the headquarters of the Civilian Air Patrol which was conducting the search. The big Florida afterglow had lengthened the shadows as the small single-engine planes returned to the field after winding their way back and forth across the desolate Glades.

"Did you find anything?" she asked one of the pilots. "I'm Mrs. Baxter."

"No, ma'am. I'm sorry. We've been searching all day, but there's nothing."

She returned to the small operational office and talked with other pilots who were gathered about the large grid showing the watery prairie that ran for miles to the west of Palm Beach.

"Hello, Cynthia."

She spun around and saw Denise who was approaching from behind. Her reddened eyes and sallow complexion made it obvious to Cynthia that she too had been devastated.

"Is there any word?"

"No . . . not yet."

There was an awkward pause and then Cynthia said, "Do you know what could have happened, Denise?"

"No, he just got into his plane and flew north. I watched him take off. I was airsick and had to come back by cab."

The two women continued to stand there staring at each other, and Denise who had placed so many hopes in John Baxter suddenly was overcome with what she had done to Cynthia. She came forward and took Cynthia in her arms. "I'm sorry," she whispered. "I really am."

Then, suddenly feeling herself out of control, Denise rushed off, away from Cynthia and from the airport. She drove her Mercedes crazily out toward State Road 80. She turned right instead of left though and drove into the Glades, exhausting her tears and hoping that she would find a stunned man walking along the dark, deserted highway—John Baxter.

Philip had not told Cynthia about the possibility of John's being involved in Mel's plans; he was not sure of the situation until much later that day when he and Mr. Benjamin and an independent architect flew over to El Lugar and made an inspection tour.

"There's supposed to be five I beams across the span of the main lounge," the architect said, after pushing a screwdriver up through the luminescent ceiling, "but there are only three. Further, the specifications call for the loggia tile to extend from the bar outside onto the veranda. Notice, Mr. Guest, that it stops at the bar. The exterior is simply cemented. There must be fifteen thousand dollars' worth of tile missing."

Philip Guest did not need any more proof and he felt sick. He could have expected such things from Mel Hansen, but not from John Baxter, the man he had admired and trusted all these years.

The wrangle of whether to open the floodgates or not was still unresolved and at the funeral of Lou Ballantine, Steve said, "The Glade growers have gone to Washington, Keith. The pressure is on. Peterson called me at home early this morning. The lawyers for Commerce and Agriculture say that if we flood the margin lands before a hurricane hits, the farmers could sue the government for up to five million dollars in compensatory losses . . . maybe more."

"That is grim."

"I've been thinking of something and I wish you'd consider it. What do you think about seeding Claudine?"

Keith drew back angrily. "You know how I feel about that, Steve!"

"But we may be forced to. If we can't open the gates and if she blasts through here, we'll be up against a tough situation."

"In that case we'll order a premature evacuation."

"You know as well as I do that will only be helpful in the Florida Keys. Do me a favor. Think about it."

"I already have. No seeding," Keith said as he took Billy's arm and walked toward his Porsche.

"Lou wouldn't have objected," Steve called.

Keith did not answer.

He and Billy drove away from the funeral in silence. Then Billy said, "I've never understood weather modifications."

"It's simple. You dump silver iodide into the clouds. That causes a premature rainfall. In a hurricane, the more rain you can get out of a cloud, the more the pressure comes up. In theory, the wind is supposed to die down then."

"Does it work?"

"A few hurricanes have been seeded. There's some evidence that the winds can be cut back a little, but there're risks."

"Why?"

"Tropical storms are necessary for crop production. Japan depends upon cyclones for one third of its rainfall. The growers in Georgia and Alabama need the tropical storm. Tampering with weather upsets the natural cycle. I think it's dangerous because we don't know the full impact of seeding."

"If we have the storm of the century on the way, we should use every device we have, shouldn't we?"

"And what would happen if it went the other way? Maybe the silver iodide would increase the winds. It's that chancy. We just don't know enough."

When they reached Coral Gables, Keith turned suddenly and said, "I feel as if I need a drink."

((233))

"That's not you—early in the day."

"I'm not me. I don't know . . . guess Lou's death got to me on top of everything else."

On their way to the Cattle Barn, a dark bar near the University of Miami, Keith picked up a local Miami paper trimmed with large, black headlines:

FLORIDA BRACES FOR SUPER HURRICANE!

"That should make Steve happy," Keith said.

"Keith, I don't think that's fair," Billy replied.

When they were seated in the booth listlessly pushing the ice cubes around in their Bloody Marys, Billy, who had stood up well under the strain of the past few days' shattering events, lifted her eyes and studied Keith's face. What had been clear brown eyes were now sunken and lifeless, and his face, once young and perfectly sculptured, seemed edged with traces of fatigue and age.

"What's really the matter?" she asked. "Is it Lou?"

"I respected him. He was old-fashioned, but he saw both sides."

"Steve bothers you, doesn't he?"

"Yes, but it's more than that. When I first came out of MIT I was sure I had the expertise and technology to solve the hurricane mystery, and I think I did some good work . . . employed extremely sophisticated methods."

"Of course you did, Keith. Even Steve admits that."

"But now all of a sudden everything's collapsed. Now we have a doldrum hurricane coming down on us. Why? I've searched all my data and inputs, and I feel terribly frustrated and inadequate because I can't get a fix on Claudine; how did it happen so quickly? Maybe Steve does have some innate sense about these storms that I don't have. He certainly moves around in a mystical way. I can't grasp it."

"Do you think believing and working on his theory of surface heating has given him a leg up?"

"I don't know. When you told me about that idiotic voyage . . . taking temperature readings all over the place, I ridiculed it."

"So did I. Wasn't scientific."

"Scientific. That's a joke! I'm an atmospheric scientist but I can't answer scientific questions. Yesterday I sent a message out to the reconnaissance plane asking them to feed us surface temperature around the areas where Claudine was organized. The water temperature is up but the direct link to hurricane formation doesn't quite jell. Inputs seem to contradict the position of the easterly wave."

"Then you're not completely discounting Steve anymore?"

"I never did. It's just that our personalities and methods clash. He's so sure of himself. I used to be, but I'm not now."

"Let me tell you something about Steve, Keith. He's still not over the loss of his wife. It's unnatural to mourn so long, but he blames himself for what happened to her. I know he does. I think he'd like to get on with living, but he's not as secure as you think. In his mind he has to find an answer to what happened up at Pass Christian. He knows he's not going to find it right now so he spends his energies trying to warn people what to expect. And he's very sincere about it."

"Do you really think he knew Claudine was coming, Billy? What did he know that we didn't?"

"He knew *nothing*. All this is a coincidence."

Keith took a big gulp of his drink and looked out over the bar.

"Do you love him, Billy? I saw you the other night, you know, in Palm Beach."

"Oh, Keith, I don't know what I feel about him. He's very different from anyone I've ever known. I don't completely understand him either, but once in a while he loosens up like he did at the party, and all of a sudden he's a new guy, very charming, fun to be with . . . and definitely not haunted."

"I'm beginning to believe it's an advantage to be haunted in the hurricane business!" Keith said savagely, downing the last of his drink.

"Hey, you're souring up."

"I've got things to be sour about. Lou's dead and he was the only one who understood what I was doing."

"And now you're out there without support?" Billy asked, with understanding.

"Yes. With no support," Keith answered. "Not even from you."

"Why does this business depend upon such a delicate framework of personalities and politics? Why can't we just go ahead and do our work like the rest of the world?"

"Because we never know as much as we think we do, and when we're foiled by these storms, everyone grasps at straws and different opinions."

"The pressure's not worth it sometimes. I know we're dealing with people's lives, but this business is too heavy, really. No one smiles. I haven't seen you smile in weeks."

"I'm surprised at you, Billy. You flew into a hurricane and almost got yourself knocked out. You should understand better than anybody. Was it heavy up there or not?"

"Yes, very. You should have been with us, Keith. What a ride!"

His eyes fell to the empty glass and he ordered another round of drinks and sat staring at the slowly revolving Bahamian fan.

"Steve asked me to go, but he knew I didn't have the guts for that kind of thing. I'm a numbers man, or I used to be."

"I don't blame you. I'd never fly into something like that again. The only reason I did . . ."

"To be near Steve," he interrupted.

"No, Keith, I just wanted to experience it firsthand." She laughed suddenly and laid her hand on Keith's arm. "You know it's funny. We run around trying desperately to understand what's going on with hurricanes and then there's that guy Mel Hansen . . ."

Keith didn't let her finish her thought, but said, "That scheming little bastard!"

"It's so ironic," Billy said, "a raw promoter like that who doesn't know anything about flood control puts us onto something. In all the years I've studied the Palm Beach basin, I didn't have the slightest idea that the flood-control system was weak and the saw grass was sick. If it weren't for Hansen's proposal, we would never have discovered it. How would we know about the canals, if it weren't for him?"

"It is a paradox. Just shows how inadequate we are."

"Come on, Keith, out of this funk. Be bright."

"Do you know what could happen here?" he said, studying her eyes.

"Unfortunately, I do."

"I've never had such a feeling of helplessness."

"All we can do is warn people."

"They won't listen! They never listen."

Then they both grew silent thinking about the great storm massed on their doorstep.

29

AN EXTENSIVE AIR-SEA SEARCH WAS CARRIED OUT THAT WEEK; JOHN'S plane was not spotted as it rested deep in the overgrown palm canopy of the Glades. Mel Hansen phoned a few people and asked what the real chances were of finding John Baxter; the Civilian Air Patrol and the Coast Guard told him that with each passing hour the odds were going against them.

"He probably went down at sea," the Coast Guard said. "And it would be impossible to exist long in those waters. Full of sharks."

Denise called Nicole, her only true friend in the resort, and Nicole came over to the *Patna* to find Denise in tears.

"I loved him, Nicole," she said.

Mel realized what a loss John Baxter would be, for he figured that Philip Guest would probably fire him now, but he had no idea what the chairman had discovered when he was called to the Palace Beach executive offices Friday morning. He walked in shaking his head. "Poor John. They say it's almost hopeless."

"It was hopeless from the beginning, I think. Now, Mr. Hansen, your time has come," the chairman said with a stony voice. "I'll get right to the point. We turned up some building shortages on all three of your projects. You've cheated us out of almost eight hundred thousand dollars, maybe more."

Mel drew back and he did not appear surprised, nor did he flinch. "I deny it," Mel said smoothly.

"Mr. Hansen, I think you overestimate our naïveté. We came across the shortage on a routine audit of the Regency Walk project. Then our accountants started looking into El Lugar and St. Paul's. The same pattern showed up. We hired an architect and found that half the I beams at El Lugar were missing, along with a dozen other materials in the specifications. Don't lie anymore, Mr. Hansen. It's too late!"

"Philip, I want to cooperate," he said, arranging a smile on his puffy lips. "I have a lot to tell you, but first I must consult my counsel."

"I understand. Go into John's office. There's a private line there. You won't be disturbed."

Mel seated himself at John's desk and picked up the phone. "Hello, Glen? Mel. When are you supposed to see the state attorney?"

"Tomorrow."

"Have you spoken to anyone about all this?"

"No, my lawyer told me not to."

Mel's mind worked in lightning strokes and it did not fail him now. "What has Daniels told the prosecutor?" he asked Markum.

"Only that I gave him an envelope containing five thousand dollars."

"And what did the building commissioner say?"

"Son of a bitch denied it, according to what I heard from another source on the board."

"Good, good. Now, you listen and try to pack this into your dumb head. John Baxter is missing and we're sure now that he'll never be found."

"Yeah, I heard about him on the TV. Too bad!"

"All right. He's dead, so we can use him. You say that it was Baxter who gave you the money, not the building commissioner, and you didn't know a damned thing about what was in the envelope. You thought it was . . . oh . . . a press release or something. That bastard, Guest, has discovered that we shorted on the building materials."

"How?"

"By audit. It'll only be a short time before he finds out that we sold the land to him. The guy is smart. I'm going to say that you and I were approached by Baxter to go short on the materials and hand out the money to Daniels."

"Are you mentioning my name?"

"Yes. It's already out in the open, but I think I can bargain with Guest. He's up to his ass with the bribe and building beyond the setback line. This would break his back . . . he'll fall in line. The last thing he wants is to find out that his beloved late president was a con man. That would topple the hotel."

"You're fucking smart, Mel. I gotta hand it to you."

"Don't say anything until I call you."

Mel returned to Philip's office and said, "My lawyer has advised me to cooperate to the fullest."

"Why have you retained an attorney? You must have anticipated our discovery."

"No, nothing to do with it, Philip. But I do have something to tell you. I was indirectly involved in the bribe. I'm a business associate of Glen Markum who handed the money to Daniels. I wanted to know where I stood."

"That's reasonable, I suppose. Now, Mr. Hansen, why don't you start at the very beginning and tell me everything."

Mel paused, collecting his thoughts and neatly putting the glossy touches on another of his massive lies.

"Some of this you know. I came to Palm Beach at the insistence of my wife. She made it clear to me that she didn't really love me, that Palm Beach was a spot to catch a rich guy. I just didn't have the style or money that she wanted, and Denise was fairly well finished in the film business when I met her. She had developed a terrible reputation in Paris, screwing herself into one picture after another. We made a deal. If I married her and set up practice here so she could operate, she'd split with me after she found her silver spoon. I'd get a finder's fee of fifteen percent of her income. All this was reduced to a premarital agreement. Originally, I was planning to take a job with a firm in West Palm Beach. I had no ambitions about a future with the Palace Beach. I didn't even know the hotel existed. Neither of us had ever been here before. All we knew was that Palm Beach's population was rich. At any rate, I met John Baxter soon after we arrived. I showed him the drawings and set designs I'd completed in the movie business, and he told me that he had been looking for an imaginative architect who could work on developmental projects for the Palace Beach."

"Yes, I remember. John was looking for someone about then. Go on, Mel."

Mel gloated. It was the first time the chairman had ever called him by his first name. Philip was beginning to believe him.

"He hired me and we worked very closely on the El Lugar project and St. Paul's Island. Then I found out quite by accident that John was very interested in my wife. I think they had been seeing each other on the QT for some time. Anyway, I confronted him with it and he confessed that he would like to leave Cynthia for Denise if things could be worked out. He certainly lived big enough. I thought he was the one, so I told him of my marital situation. Turned out he didn't have the real big money and since I was a part of the deal, I wasn't going to release her to a man like that. I had a financial stake in the outcome. Then John came back to me a couple of days later with a plan that he said would make us both rich and solve our problems. He suggested we buy up some cheap land and sell it back to the Palace Beach at a profit. Nobody need know who was behind it. That's where Glen Markum came in—he was a front man. Everything went off as planned."

Mel paused to light a cigarette; Philip politely pushed an ashtray toward him, then folded his hands and waited for Mel to continue. Mel could see him falling for the story. "I guess old John had been bitten by the bug then because he came to me again and said, 'Aren't there certain ways we can optimize the structures?' I knew what he meant . . . we would build to a set of 'special' plans. Well, I went along for a variety of reasons. I wanted to get out from under Denise. I needed the money because I had piled up a lot of debts running that damned yacht. But, you know, Philip, I really felt that those two resorts would pay off for the Palace Beach."

"They have. You were right."

"And that night aboard the *Patna*—there was no rape."

"I didn't think so."

"Denise needs new kicks all the time, that's the actress in her. That night she was fantasizing a rape and John played it out for her."

"Why didn't you say that to the police?"

"It was already too sticky. When John suggested the Regency Walk project, I objected. I had had enough of these schemes, but he said if I didn't go along he would bring certain things to your attention, not merely the shorting of materials, but the land deals."

"These are rather incredible allegations, Mel. I've known John Baxter for many years and I have trusted him for all that time."

"I know, I know," the squatty little man said earnestly. "But every bit of it is true, I swear. John started seeing my wife openly then. He took her to El Lugar several times in the Apache. A lineman there that I knew when we were building the place told me that Denise had paid him to record the times they showed up. Call him and ask him. Name's Haney."

"No, that won't be necessary." Philip, though cool, was obviously disconcerted. His discomfort showed through to Mel Hansen, who was feeling more sure of himself by the minute.

"Then John came over to the *Patna* one morning and said that he heard there was certain resistance to my setback proposal. He was, naturally, concerned because he didn't want the Regency Walk held up."

"I see. His concern had nothing to do with whatever ecological benefit might accrue from the seawall?"

"Oh, no, that only came out after Dr. Van Betzig arrived and those hurricane people jumped in with both feet."

"Are they involved in all this?"

Mel paused thoughtfully. "That Mitchell might be. I overheard him and John talking several times, and you remember how quiet John was during the meeting last week."

"I recall. But Dr. Mitchell spoke out against the proposal."

"Only after the bribe was revealed in the papers. He liked John; they were both pilots. Where do you think John was coming from

((242))

yesterday? Mitchell invited him and my wife on the hurricane re-connaissance plane!" Mel said triumphantly.

"Yes, I know that. So you feel he paid off Dr. Mitchell?"

Mel nodded.

"What about the bribe?"

"John asked me to set it up with Daniels. He said he was the most widely read real-estate editor in South Florida, and John furnished the dough. That's how upset he was over the criticism we were getting."

"Then why was the building commissioner named by Daniels?"

"Only because we wanted to protect the Palace Beach. And, one more thing, John threatened me with termination if I ever opened my mouth."

With that daring statement, Mel shot a quick glance at Philip to see how his story was going down. The chairman's face was once again impassive and he just kept asking questions in that controlled voice.

"John was comfortably off. What was his motivation?"

"My wife, of course. She wanted John Baxter and a lot of money, and she'd never admit this, but she set out to destroy Cynthia."

"She just about succeeded."

"I know. It was cruel."

Mel fell silent and stared at the blue carpet and tried to remember if he had left anything out. "John was very upset," he said finally. "I could see the strain coming on, but it was all his doing."

"Mel," the chairman said, "you've told me this for a purpose."

"I have, but, believe me, I was trapped by Baxter and I wanted to unload Denise. Once she got that close to her mark, she was hell to live with."

"Then what did John see in her?"

"You kidding? After seventeen years of marriage to the same woman? Sex! Denise was absolutely fantastic in that department, but she never wanted to put out for me."

Philip winced. "Well, Mel, this is quite a story. You should have come to me in the beginning, but of course you realize that now. What can I do for you at this point?"

Mel got to his feet and strode around the room. "I want to get off free. If all this comes out, I could lose my license and go to jail. If I tell what I know, it will further embarrass the hotel. If I don't talk, no one will ever know that John Baxter was involved."

"He might have another version of this," Philip said, toying with a gold pencil.

Mel leaned across his desk. "He might, but we'll never know, will we? Because he's dead. We're practical men. We can both benefit by his death."

Philip Guest held back his rage. Hansen had gone too far. The chairman's face did not reflect what he was thinking and he just stared at Mel Hansen, wondering how much of what the man had said was true.

"Blackmail is despicable, but you and your wife seem to be experts at using this device to ruin people."

"That's unfair."

"It's a fact. Everything you say is circumstantial."

Mel's mind went back to a memo John Baxter had written him just after the Regency Walk plans were submitted to John, and he said, "I have evidence."

"What?"

"I'll be right back."

Mel walked down the hall to his office, pulled out the memo from his files, reread it, returned to the chairman's office, and handed the paper to him.

To: MEL HANSEN
From: JOHN BAXTER

I have reviewed your submitted plans for the Regency Walk project. I approve of your design solutions and hereby have instructed our attorneys to prepare the necessary construction agreements. I hope we can use the same methods of building optimization that I suggested in the St. Paul's and El Lugar projects as they seem to have given us fine structures while employing certain cost-cutting features that have been beneficial.

"This is ambiguous at best," Philip said, handing the paper back to Mel.

"The word *optimization* to an architect means one thing. He also says that he suggested cost-cutting methods for St. Paul's and El Lugar. That's hard evidence."

"It could mean quite a few things. Mel, you've said a lot. I have quite a bit to think about. I'll be back to you."

"Tomorrow is the deadline. Glen Markum is giving a deposition to the state attorney."

Philip said nothing more. He only nodded his head as Mel Hansen, now very sure of himself, walked out of the office.

JOHN WAS PREPARED TO DIE.

He heard the planes overhead, but there was nothing he could do. He had been able to reach the emergency pack in back of the rear seat of the plane and had dragged it out. He could exist for a while on canned water and K rations. He knew he could saw himself out of the messed controls and firewall if he could only get as far as the shelf in the rear seat where there was a life preserver, life raft, and ditty bag containing tools and a hacksaw.

That was all he needed, but it remained a million miles away.

Realizing that he was going to die, he wrote a letter to Cynthia on the back of a sectional chart.

Friday, August 26, 1977
Somewhere in the Glades
West of Palm Beach International Airport

My darling Cynthia,

When you get this, I will be dead.

It is a sadly inappropriate time for me to express my lasting love for you, but it's also a moment of final desperation and I want you to know what happened. The plane crashed on the way home from Miami. As will be learned when they find this wreck, the right engine caught fire and I could not make it back to the field, even though the lights were in view. Such is the wilderness in which we live. My foot is trapped in the controls and I cannot escape, but I am not afraid. I think of you and the fulfillment and great happiness you brought me. My darling, the last few months of my life did not reflect my standards and everything that went before.

You know I did not rape Denise that night. She was willing and I was drunk, but I did go to El Lugar with her twice. The first time it was because she threatened me with the rape case, and Philip was, indeed, provoked and told me to cool everything. I made love to her; she demanded it, but it was meaningless.

The second time was last Sunday; we fished and I remember you had dinner with her and noticed how terribly injured she was. She's a scorpion, but a game little bitch and put up a long, three-hour fight against a big blue marlin, which she lost to a shark in the end. We went back to the cottage and made love and, in all fairness, it was not at her urging that time.

I took her on the flight into the hurricane because you didn't care to go and I admit that she is sexy and exciting, but with ethics and values that are not ours. You are asking: Was he going to leave me for Denise? Would he ever have told me these things? I would never leave you and as I sit here alone, with death so near, I realize more than ever what a rich life we had together and that Denise was only a passing symbol of my temporary recklessness. I was drawn in but it was my fault, and after our second time at El Lugar, I was planning to come to you with the truth.

My dear, take care of yourself and know that I died thinking of you. Please don't feel that what I did was a rejection of you; it was a sudden weakness in myself, and I shall always love you for what you have been and for what you are. You made my life worth living.

> *Good-bye, my dearest,*
> *Your loving husband, John.*

That Friday an extraordinary thing happened.

The Keys had been evacuated the afternoon before and it went well. Claudine had passed over the Keys, causing extensive property damage, but only one death and a few injuries had been reported. The track was forecasted to move across Florida Bay and crash ashore in the unpopulated region around Cape Sable where it was assumed she would diminish after hitting land.

Florida, from Key West to the Hillsborough Inlet twenty-nine miles south of Palm Beach, had been under a hurricane warning, and the watch continued to Punta Gorda on the west coast and northward to St. Augustine on the east coast with gale warnings extending to Savannah.

The civil defense had been mobilized in five Florida counties, and they stood ready for an emergency although no local statements had been circulated because the center had not issued a landfall prediction.

There were some moderately high seas around Palm Beach and the surfers were out that day. It rained off and on. When it appeared that the storm was no longer threatening the east coast of Florida, Keith ordered the hurricane warnings reduced to a watch. He extended warnings up the west coast all the way to Apalachicola.

At two o'clock Friday, when the Gold Coast was taken off the hurricane warning and the blood-red flags came down, the reporters went back to their offices and wrote their stories. Two of the accounts appeared on the seven o'clock news from the Miami TV stations and one was carried as a front-page item in the *Post*, the evening paper with the highest circulation in Florida:

**HURRICANE MOVES AWAY FROM SOUTH FLORIDA.
GOLD COAST SPARED AS CLAUDINE PASSES
TOWARD GULF SOUTH OF ISLAMORADA.**

The story went on to say that the hurricane had shrunk in size, which it had, and that the residents of the Gold Coast were in no danger.

There were very few people in Palm Beach who had taken the warning seriously anyway, with the exception of a group of elderly men and women living in a local retirement hotel. They had made private arrangements to evacuate the island in case the hurricane pushed up the coast. Again, the cavalier attitude was reinforced by the insignificant-looking waves. It stopped raining around noon and the sun came out in Palm Beach. The hurricane was far to the south and it has been proved that people in a warning or watch area are apt to believe that the storm is not going to strike them.

That Friday the Ocean Club in Palm Beach had scheduled their senior tennis tournament, a popular annual affair of mixed doubles for people over sixty, in which the winners awarded expensive prizes from Cartier to the losers. There was some doubt in the morning whether the courts would be dry enough for playing that afternoon, but the heat burst through around twelve o'clock and lapped up the dampness.

The news spread about Palm Beach in microseconds: Maggie Dunsmore had changed her mind and was entering the tournament. It had been three years since she had played and the appearance of an eighty-one-year-old woman on the courts in competitive action brought out a cheering crowd.

Denise attended and she sat beside Cynthia and Jayson. The three of them were solemn; each was suffering privately and differently from the effects of Baxter's disappearance.

"Have you heard anything?" Denise whispered to Cynthia.

"No. They're still looking."

"Oh God, it's so awful," Denise said.

Cynthia nodded stiffly without answering.

Maggie came out on the court for the mixed doubles; she only lost two games in the round robin and at four o'clock it was all over. She received a large cup and a ring of applause from the packed stands. Afterward she went up to Cynthia.

"Courage, my dear. We mustn't lose hope."

"He's gone," Cynthia said. "I know it, but thank you, Maggie."

The old lady patted her hand. "It would be a great loss to the town. John has always contributed so much."

Then Cynthia walked with Denise toward the parking lot and Philip Guest hurried toward her as she was getting into the Rolls.

"Cynthia, I'd like to speak with you alone for a few minutes, if I may."

"Come on back to the house, Philip."

They sat by the pool sipping gin and tonics. Cynthia noticed how heavily lined and strained Philip's face was; she knew he had given up hope, too.

"Cynthia, I think you must realize how very deeply I feel your loss."

She nodded. "My life's over."

"No, it's not, and that's not what John would want you to say."
He paused. "Something has come to my attention. I'm not sure you're
ready for this, but you have to know."

"There's nothing that can hurt me anymore, Philip."

He began to tell her then about Mel's "confession" and his threat
to implicate John and himself in the bribery scandal.

Cynthia sat perfectly still and didn't react at all to what he said.
When he finished, she lit a cigarette and said calmly, "Was there
any point at which you believed him, Philip?"

"Cynthia, the thought had crossed my mind initially . . . I won't
lie to you, but . . ."

"You would let Mel destroy the reputation of a fine man who's
gone and who can't defend himself? Philip, how could you?"

"Cynthia, I know how you feel." He put his arms around her and
held her as she began to sob. "It's all right . . . everything's going
to be all right."

He patted her gently. "Hansen's ruthless, he's an unscrupulous
man, but I'll do everything in my power to prevent him from tar-
nishing John's memory. You must pull yourself together and help
me. He covers himself cleverly. I think up to a point he might be
able to convince people. He showed me a memo from John that
could support his allegations. This affair, or whatever, that John
had with Denise is not entirely made up, and I know you realize
that or I wouldn't mention it. But that's going to be damaging."

She straightened up and dried her eyes and reached for another
cigarette.

"Well, he's a fool if he thinks I'll let him get away with this!"

Philip looked at her tentatively, not sure what she meant.

"I'm fine now, Philip. You run along and I'll talk to you in the
morning. Thanks very much for telling me."

Ten minutes after he left, Cynthia got into her car and drove
toward the arms store to buy fifteen boxes of ammunition. She'd
decided that she had been targeting the wrong Hansen.

There was a weak ridge of high pressure over Florida that day,
but the pressure dissipated and a low, or vacuum, filled in. Instead
of continuing on her projected westerly track, Claudine was now

swung northward by the upper steering currents, and that evening she stalled sixty miles to the south of Lake Okeechobee.

"That lake has to be emptied!" Billy Haughton declared. "The levee will break. Claudine is dumping rain at the rate of eleven inches an hour. The system will never take it!"

"You're right," Keith replied, "but Dr. Peterson says we can't open the floodgates until the hurricane is actually there."

"It'll be far too late then," Steve said.

"We're under orders from Commerce, Steve, we can't . . ."

"Call 'em."

A call was placed to the Secretary.

"We think Claudine will move up through central Florida."

"How positive are you?"

"We're certain."

"When it hits, the gates will be opened, not before," the Secretary said with the authority of his position behind him.

"If we don't drain the lake immediately, sir, we'll have a disaster out there just like we did in 1928. We can't worry about the farmers anymore. They're going to lose their seedlings anyhow."

The Secretary was unmoved and ten minutes after the disheartening phone call, a hurricane reconnaissance plane reported to the center over the patched communications network.

"We're seeing winds of two hundred in Claudine."

"Oh, Christ, are you sure?" Keith said into the mike.

"Yes, sir! We got five drops; four reliable ones. She's packing a helluva lot of power."

"We'll go back on a hurricane warning for both coasts, from Key West to St. Augustine, and extend the watch to Norfolk," Steve said. "You agree, Keith?"

"I do. What about evacuation?"

"We can't get into it yet because we don't know the exact track."

Each of them knew what they were up against. There was the threat of a dam burst out in the Glades, which would kill thousands in the central part of the state. And there was no high ground. Where would the people go? It would be worse than 1928: When Lake Okeechobee originally burst its banks, the middle part of Florida was relatively unpopulated and still two thousand died!

Now the rich margin lands in and around Belle Glade and Clewiston had a population of over sixty-five thousand.

As the rains fell out of Claudine, she shrank in size, all in a matter of hours. That should have been a good sign, for it usually signaled that the hurricane had reached the decay portion of her life. But it didn't happen that way. She tightened and the little bitch began to hairpin back over the Glades toward the east. Her winds, however, dropped to about a hundred miles an hour, a measurement taken with confidence since three airports confirmed it: Naples on Florida's west coast, Immokalee, a strip located in the central part of Big Cypress Swamp, which Claudine's eye had passed over, and the Clewiston Airport just south of Lake Okeechobee.

The hurricane center was not taking chances with Claudine, for she could go anyplace at this point, so that evening they placed the Florida east coast back on a hurricane alert.

What had gone wrong? The civil defense people looked outside when they received the call at eight-fifteen that night. There were a few clouds, high scattered cirrus, hurricane telltales, but through the clouds the haloed moon could be seen. There was no rain and little wind.

No one took the new warnings on TV and radio seriously. People were waiting.

"She's going out to sea," Keith announced, as they studied the new APT.

"No, it's a loop," Steve said, ". . . I think."

Claudine had backtracked, a not totally unique trick of storms, and she retraced her course down through central Florida and out to sea again. There she began to strengthen once more. Hurricane hunter planes reported that her winds were now back up to one hundred eighty, and once south of the Keys, the erratic storm took a turn northward.

The local statement was issued at ten minutes after ten, and everyone at the center agreed with the contents. Claudine was forecasted to hit Miami at eleven o'clock the next morning and to reach Pompano Beach that evening.

"I'm going home to grab some sleep," Steve told Keith.

"Go ahead. Relieve me at eight in the morning."

Even though Claudine had curved away from the big lake, she had dumped over twenty-one inches of rain into Okeechobee and Steve realized that the levee must be at capacity, and he worried about the next sequence of events. Claudine was strengthening over the sea and as she worked up the coast, more rain would fall upon the lake. Far too much!

He rushed home and found a dummy hand grenade, which he had brought back from Vietnam with the pin placed back into the detonator core. He put on a pair of Levi's, made a mask from a pillowcase, quickly cutting out two round holes for eyes and a hole to breathe through. He then drove very swiftly out Kendall Road toward the new Tamiami Airport. The field had been closed down because of the hurricane. He rolled out his Helio Courier, a short takeoff and landing plane (STOL), and he took off with no one seeing him. He poked the ship's nose toward the big lake.

Hoover Levee was built in the early thirties and it wrapped around the south and western ends of Lake Okeechobee; the levee was twenty-six feet wide on the brow and ran down to the lake on an inclination angle of fourteen degrees. Steve, who had an excellent memory, almost a photographic one, remembered the layout. There were high barbed-wire fences about every 280-foot interval on the levee top, and to the south side near Clewiston there was a manned control building from which the floodgates were operated remotely via a computer and electrical signal system that controlled the hydraulic lifting mechanisms.

During World War II when there were constant sabotage frights, the whole building had become a fortress. It was surrounded by a high fence and a nine-foot wall, plus a security station at the entrance from the lower road. No one had ever broken into the control station. On this night it was manned by two men: One was in the security station; the other was a hydraulic engineer who sat at the large control panel within the building. The door to the building was not locked because the security man often came back to have coffee with the controller on duty.

Steve, an expert in short precision landings, had gone up to the levee before and looked at the fence layout, and he had often thought of landing his plane on the top of the levee just for a challenge. It was wide enough, but the fences shortened the pinched space to 280 feet or thereabouts, tight even for a STOL plane pushed by a skilled pilot.

The rain and wind had begun and the Helio Courier flew low so as to avoid the approach radar at West Palm Beach Airport. Steve recognized the lights of Belle Glade, the largest town in the margin lands, and past it there was an immense blackness: Lake Okeechobee. He saw the levee lights; they had been installed to prevent break-ins, but they also provided landing illumination.

Steve cut his power, so he wouldn't alarm the controller, but there was such a thickness of cinderblock and cement around the little fortress that the man inside could hardly have heard anything anyway, even a low-flying jet. Steve made one pass at the building and the levee beyond; he pumped in his power, set his flaps, and slowly the STOL aircraft wiggled its way along the levee, shuddering on the edge of a stall. Once over the last fence he clipped the power and the single-engine plane lay on its highly sprung gear, squatting on the levee like an overstuffed pelican halts once it's settled in the water.

The position of the plane was thirty feet from the rear fence. Steve pushed the craft down to the barrier, turned it around for his takeoff, which would be short because the wind was now gusting thirty from the northeast, almost in a direct line with the levee. He placed the pillowcase over his head, grabbed the grenade, and walked toward the flood-control building.

Steve quietly swung back the door, locked it behind him, and moved into an anteroom whose walls were crowded with photos taken when the levee was under construction. The blue-shirted engineer was seated before his maze of dials and switches, and Steve, having taken off his shoes, tiptoed forward, clutching the mock grenade in his hand. In a quick movement he placed his forearm around the man's neck and shoved the grenade right under his eyes.

"Know what this is?" he said gruffly in a Florida "cracker" twang.

"A grenade," the man gasped.

"You see the pin?"

"No, sir."

"Know anything about grenades?"

"Yes, sir."

"The pin's been pulled. I have my hand over the trigger release."

"How did you get in here?"

"I murdered the guard."

"What do you want? I don't have any money."

"I don't care about that. Open the gates."

"Why?"

"Because I said so."

"I can't. The order has to come from Jacksonville."

"You want to die?" Steve asked, tightening his grasp.

"Of course not."

"Then open 'em . . . all of 'em."

The engineer made his decision quickly. "All right, but I don't understand. We might be opening them tomorrow anyhow 'cause of the hurricane."

"Maybe I'm a landowner . . . maybe I want to sue the government."

"I don't get you," the engineer said.

"Open them before I release the trigger. I've already murdered one man."

The engineer ran his trembling hands over the dials; he flicked switches, pressed buttons, turned on the hydraulic reserve pump, and cranked back the three massive handles that would start the process.

In three sections of the levee thick steel floodgates opened and water gushed through. It was two o'clock in the morning and no one saw the raging outflow from the high lake.

"How far do you want it to drop?" the engineer stuttered.

"What's maximum?"

"Nine feet, but that would flood the farmlands."

"That's what I want. How long will it take?"

"Two hours."

"Then I'll wait."

The lake water tumbled and fumed and rushed out along the skinny canals. An hour later the banks were overtopped. Millions and millions of tons of water inundated the farmlands and the Glades, and by three-twenty that morning the deluge had extended along the Boynton and Palm Beach canals pouring into the receptive Lake Worth.

It was not totally unnoticed. Three bridge attendants put calls in to the night man at the flood-control district to tell him that the water was rising along the Intracoastal and it wasn't even raining. Steve answered the phone, saying not to worry; it was a test. But the forced Okeechobee release began to evoke alarm. Highway 441 was suddenly flooded and another call came into the control room at Hoover.

"Tell them that the hurricane rains west of the lake are causing the flood. Say everything's fine at the levee," Steve instructed.

The sweating engineer did just that and everyone who phoned appeared satisfied. At ten minutes after four the flow was out of the lake. Steve warned the engineer not to move and left. He climbed the levee to his plane, wound it up and with the brakes set, he pushed in full takeoff power. When the little ship was shaking, he snapped off the brakes; the tail lifted and because of the early hurricane wind he was off well before the fence. He pulled into a high climb, dipped down again for air speed and as the dials inched up, he yanked back on the yoke. The Helio Courier was flying, and he headed for home.

By five minutes of six Steve was back in his apartment and he fell into an easy sleep. He was delighted with himself.

CHAPTER

31

EVEN THOUGH AN ESTIMATED 27 BILLION TONS OF WATER RUSHED OUT of Lake Okeechobee that night, it was only at 6:00 A.M. when the engineer was relieved by the day man that the incident was discovered. By that time the lake was down to nine feet and the floodgates had been closed, as FBI, state, and local law enforcement units rushed to the scene.

After a preliminary investigation it was thought that the intruder had come by boat, but how could he have scaled the fourteen feet of slime-covered levee? No one had thought of a plane landing on the levee top; it was just too short, and none of them knew about STOL aircraft. The idea of a helicopter was discussed and rejected since no helicopter operations were noted that night by the eight charter companies in the South Florida area.

Lake Worth was up two and a half feet; the inland waterway in the Fort Lauderdale area, one and a half feet, and Claudine's rain had started.

As the steel-gray dawn pushed through the Glades, John Baxter awoke from one nightmare to another: The Apache was surrounded by rising water that entered the cockpit and rose up to about his waist. He thought initially that it must have something to do with the hard and unusual rainfall. At any rate, he was drenched and scared now. He desperately tried to extricate himself from the wreckage but could not, and he figured that he would be drowned, which he thought would be just as well since it would be quick.

By eight o'clock that morning the canal water had sprung the weak banks; thousands of acres of farmland and machinery were flooded. And more was coming as Claudine's wall clouds were already dumping rain, at the rate of nine inches an hour, into the lake.

At nine o'clock the Army engineers in Jacksonville ordered the gates open.

"Open? We just closed them," the controller said. "They've been open all night."

"Who ordered you to do that?" the captain barked into the phone.

"A live hand grenade."

"A what?" he said, and when he was told the story he added, "Goddamn," in a tone that contained fury and amazement at the same time.

There was a conference going on in Lou's old office just about the time of the Army's interchange with the controller. Marc Peterson had taken over Lou's desk. He considered himself in temporary control, although he was a climatologist by training and an administrator by practice. Regardless of who was who, and what authority came down through the codes of the Department of Commerce, there was not one of the 144 employees of the hurricane center, from the man who swept the halls and filled the water bottles to the communication teletypists, who did not sense the import of what was happening that Saturday morning. Claudine's wind was already beating upon the fifth floor of the hurricane center as the emergency conference began.

Marc Peterson opened the meeting. "The purpose of this meeting is to form a course of action, while there's still time. Let's get an update. What is the current forecast?"

Keith answered. "Claudine will move up the Florida coast during the rest of the day."

"Is everybody in the forecasting section satisfied of that?"

There was a uniformity of nods, and Steve said, "We do not see an imminent deviation of the track, the upper air progs tell us that."

Marc looked around the group. "Last night a masked person broke into the control station at Okeechobee and forced the engineer to open the gates. Does anyone here know anything about that?"

There was silence.

"All right, what are the consequences of that drainage, Steve?"

"Well, at Miami we see little impact because the canals don't reach that area. Up around Boca and Pompano, we've had reports that the bridge escape routes are standing just seven inches under flooding. This could increase as we get the full runoff from Claudine's rains. Within four to six hours, we think escape will be impossible over the bridges."

"Dr. Haughton, do you agree?"

"Yes, sir."

"OK, let's move north. What's the situation?"

"Palm Beach and Manalapan are going critical. The lake is shallow there; it has very little release to the ocean," Billy said.

"What are your surge forecasts?"

"Eleven feet at Palm Beach . . . fourteen at Boca . . . nine at Pompano. We just got new SPLASH readouts, but they could be invalidated, depending upon the exact landfall."

"And what are Claudine's winds?"

"One hundred and eighty sustained," Steve answered.

"Do we have any disagreement on the facts so far?"

They shook their heads.

"Well, for once the center agrees with the center," Marc said. "Now, what do we do next?"

"I suggest that we seed Claudine," Steve said. "Try to knock off the wind field as much as possible."

"I disagree!" Keith said. "Too risky."

"Ummm . . . so do I," Marc added.

Steve stood. "We have to use desperate measures. If we can cut down the wind by twenty miles an hour, we'll save people's lives. What's the argument?"

"We'll come back to that. What else, Steve?"

"I believe we should order an immediate evacuation from Pompano to the Jupiter Inlet . . . that's just north of Palm Beach. There's only about five hours left. If the dunes are overtopped and the water from the lake converges with the waves, we'll have a disaster."

"You think it can be averted?"

"Yes," Steve said, "but only if we move for total evacuation right now while there's time. Secondly, there's nothing more we can do here, and I suggest that a team visit each of the radio and TV stations and the civil defense headquarters for Dade, Broward, and Palm Beach counties. We must impress upon them the importance of obeying our orders. At the moment they're lackadaisical—the sun is shining in Fort Lauderdale and the civil defense and media people are sluggish. Remember, we took down the flags and now we're putting them up again. Our forecasting credibility is at a low point. Also, we have two hundred twenty tide and wind gauges in the warehouse. This would be a unique opportunity to set up a lab in the Palm Beach basin, which has already been studied. We could learn a lot from what is about to happen."

"Good, Steve," the administrator said. "Go ahead and—" He stopped almost in midsentence. "What is about to happen?"

"I'm afraid there's going to be great loss of lives because too many things are coming together simultaneously, none of them under our control. I just talked to the police chief of Miami Beach. We ordered evacuation, but they're having trouble. People aren't leaving. The waves are low there; the rain is light and many residents think they're getting the tail end of a storm, rather than the front part. Last night they were told they were safe and suddenly they're not. They don't know what to believe."

"That's about it," Keith said. "Too much has gone wrong."

By nine-thirty, the teams were organized and nine available specialists loaded the tide gauges and left for Palm Beach.

In the meantime, Steve, Keith, and Billy tried to compose a stiff, frightening evacuation release, a joint statement that really marked the only time the three of them had ever agreed upon anything.

Keith said, "The text is great, but who the hell is going to believe us? We're the people who told them that the danger was over."

"You're right," Steve sighed, trying to hold back a yawn. He was tired, and there seemed to be a period of letdown. "All this is wheel spinning." He looked thoughtful for a moment, then picked up the phone, determination in the set of his jaw. "Operator, this is Steve Mitchell. Would you put me through to the President of the United States. Tell them it's a priority call."

"I'll try," she said.

Billy and Keith stared at him in disbelief.

Three minutes later they reached the White House switchboard.

"This is Dr. Mitchell, director of the National Hurricane Center, Miami. I'd like to speak to the President."

"The President is not in the White House today."

"Could you get him for me? It's an emergency."

"Give me your number and we'll try to reach the President. We'll call you back directly."

"My God, you've got balls!" Keith said.

They sat in silence. Then the phone rang. A man came on and said, "Dr. Mitchell, please stand by for the President." And then he was on the line. "What's the problem, Dr. Mitchell . . . that hurricane?"

"Yes, Mr. President. There's a crisis developing in South Florida. Yesterday we had a hurricane warning up for Claudine. She went across the Keys and stalled south of Lake Okeechobee. We had forecasted her to move up through central Florida, but she fooled us. The storm hairpinned, retraced her course. She's now curving around and we expect a landfall somewhere north of Pompano Beach."

"Have you ordered an evacuation, Dr. Mitchell?"

"Yes, sir, but people are not responding because Claudine appears to be so small. They're not frightened."

"Small?"

"Yes, sir. She's shrunk to about forty miles across."

"Why is this small hurricane so dangerous, Doctor?"

"Well, sir, size has nothing to do with intensity. We've just had an aerial drop. Claudine's winds are up over two hundred, but she's so puny, the sun could be out in Miami and all hell breaking loose in Palm Beach. But we at the hurricane center are well aware that Claudine's a very, very deceptive storm. And we've got to get that message across."

"What can I do, Dr. Mitchell?" the President asked.

"Sir, if you could make a quick tape and send it down here over the network lines, I think we could, perhaps, avoid a high death toll. We'll be glad to compose the text and get it on the wire to you."

"I'm in the middle of important foreign policy discussions, Dr. Mitchell, and this is a state problem. The governor should read your message."

"Mr. President, this is a vital matter. It involves a great many lives and we believe a presidential message would carry more weight. Minutes count, sir."

"It's that serious?"

"Yes, sir."

"Well, you compose your copy, wire it to the presidential desk. Put the code 'Ajax Three' on top . . . that means it's a priority message for the cable people and it'll go right to me. I'll call your governor and clear this. If he disapproves in the slightest, all bets are off. In the meantime, I'll see that our video tape unit is alerted. Since it's Saturday, I don't know how many we can round up." There was a momentary pause, then the President asked, "Was this cleared through civil defense?"

"Of course, sir."

"Fine, then I'll see what we can do."

Steve put down the phone with a smug smile and turned to Keith and Billy. "My father told me . . . always go to the top."

"Jesus!" Keith said.

Steve picked up the phone again and called Keesler Air Force Base and was put through to operations. "This is Mitchell, National Hurricane Center. How fast can we get into a seeding program?"

Keith clamped his hand over Steve's wrist. "Oh, no . . . you're going too far."

"Take your hand off me or you'll end up at the dentist."

Keith backed away seeing the hard determination packed into Steve's eyes.

"I'll get Peterson!"

"Go ahead." Then, Steve spoke into the phone again. "I want this baby seeded like hell . . . drop in all the silver iodide you've got."

Several minutes later Marc Peterson rushed into the war room.

"What the hell do you mean . . . calling the President! You have to go through me and then the Secretary and then the Presidential Assistant."

"I forgot."

"I don't like this a bit, Mitchell! I just got a call from the Secretary . . . I hope your résumé is up to date because he is very angry. *He* wanted to call the President."

"Tell him I'll let him do it next time."

Forty minutes later the President sat in the Oval Office before a camera. The announcer said,

"Ladies and gentlemen, the President of the United States."

The President began speaking, "This is an urgent message for the citizens of South Florida. I have been informed by officials at the National Hurricane Center in Coral Gables that the state is now undergoing an extreme threat from hurricane Claudine. This is a small hurricane; however, the National Hurricane Center emphasizes that it is extremely dangerous. Her winds have been clocked at over two hundred miles an hour. Beach residents, even those of you in high-rises, are *not* safe from the forces of Claudine's extreme winds. By the authority vested in my office, I am ordering all beach residents and those in low-lying areas from Pompano Beach northward to the Jupiter Inlet to evacuate immediately. Stay tuned to your local radio and television stations for instructions on where to go. You should not panic. You will be entirely safe if you follow instructions in an orderly manner. When the hurricane passes, you may return to your homes. The Red Cross, civil defense, and other appropriate bodies are standing by to assist you. I am also ordering all those in mobile homes to evacuate. Even a properly anchored mobile home cannot take wind speeds of Claudine's force. I am counting on all our Florida people to prepare for this hurricane emergency as you have done so magnificently in the past. I shall keep in close contact with your local civil defense officials and, again,

I repeat, there is time for an orderly and proper evacuation. Please do not panic. Thank you."

The tape was reproduced and sent out over the lines to six area TV stations, but in desperately trying to solve one problem, others were created.

Saturday morning was the worst time of the week to air an emergency message. Few people heard the appeal, but the civil defense of the involved counties were incensed anyway: Why had the President ordered an evacuation without consultation and advice from those who had previously planned the routing of an emergency exodus?

"You've got us all into a hell of a lot of trouble," Marc told Steve. "The Red Cross and the civil defense have been caught completely off guard."

"Don't tell *me* about local authority. I saw it up at Pass Christian. They didn't tell us what to do until it was too late."

"But you're calling for half the coast to be evacuated. We don't even have a forecast on this storm."

Steve went to the window, looked at the bright, sun-flecked clouds, and he turned around and slapped his hands on his hips.

"Don't you see!" he steamed. "We just can't get ahold of this one. She started in a strange place; she increased in size; she tightened, she swings this way and that, shrinks, hairpins, stops . . . starts . . . blows her top off!"

"Are you saying there's never been a hurricane like Claudine?"

"No. We've had hairpin turns in storms but, Dr. Peterson, you're an atmospheric scientist. . . ."

"Not in hurricanes."

"But you know that tracking a hurricane is the most difficult job we have. Face it. Our accuracy rate goes way down with a fickle storm."

"But what about the upper air currents? They steer these hurricanes. Surely if we predict the currents, then we'll have the storm track figured out."

"In many cases we can do that. Claudine is so powerful, we can't tell the upper air currents from the hurricane itself. The winds overlap. Are the upper air steering currents affecting Claudine, or has Claudine taken over the steering currents? Tell me what's going on."

"How the hell do I know? But evacuating the entire coast . . ."

"We have to. What would happen if we just said, 'Get out of Pompano Beach' and Claudine hit Jupiter? Thousands would be killed."

Finally Marc Peterson got Steve's message. "All right, I'm convinced, but the Secretary isn't."

"He doesn't know our situation. I think you do."

"I'm beginning to," the administrator said as he slumped down in a chair, exhausting a long, frustrated breath.

"Steve, could I talk to you alone for a few minutes?" Billy said as she saw him in the hall.

"Sure, meet you in the office. Let me tell the operator where I am."

He entered the fourth-floor research office a few minutes later and saw the bar set up. "What's this? We're not supposed to drink in here."

"I was sober when I went up in the reconnaissance plane and I decided that was my trouble. Now, I've become a hurricane philosopher."

"And you're dispensing booze along with your wisdom?"

"Steve, everyone's walking around with long, long faces as if we were the ones who ordered the hurricane. We're doing everything we possibly can. Keith's trapped in a nightmare. Do me a favor, don't lean on him too heavily. His numbers suddenly don't tell him anything."

"Maybe they never did."

"Enough, Steve, please. The spat is over. There's too much at stake. If it's any comfort, I'm kind of shaking inside myself."

"Well," he sighed, "I don't know what else to do."

"You've already done it."

"What do you mean?"

She crossed to him, kissed him lightly on the cheek, and whispered in his ear, "How did you pull it off?"

"What are you talking about?"

She moved to the bar, still smiling, and poured two drinks. "Here

. . . you need this," she said, handing him a vodka.

"Guess I do."

"I know you opened the floodgates last night. You were the masked man, the Lone Ranger. But how in the world did you do it? The papers say no one knows how the guy busted in."

"I didn't do anything."

"Of course you did. You might act a little loony sometimes when it comes to hurricanes, but nobody could ever say you don't have guts. Steve, you could have been killed last night! I think it's very funny, though . . . you in a pillowcase mask. I laughed like hell when I read about it . . . the director of the hurricane center playing the Lone Ranger. Why didn't you take me? I'm mad."

Steve started grinning then, thinking back to the previous night— jamming a dummy hand grenade in front of the petrified controller. He wondered how he had mustered all that wild audacity. Then he told her about landing the plane on the levee brow and she couldn't stop laughing.

"It's an Entebbe raid!" she howled, doubling up in giggles and a little giddy from the drinks. "It's glorious, Steve."

"Someone had to do it."

"I love you for cutting through all the government bullshit. Hey, I could have been Tonto! I really missed a big scene. But I guess I should go over to Winn-Dixie and buy some Betty Crocker cakes to practice up on . . . with the files . . . so I can bring them to you in the slammer."

"No one saw me."

"You landed a plane on the levee and no one saw you? Impossible. I bet they get you. That goon, Peterson, is on your tail . . . they'll figure it out. How many people knew about the dangerous flood level? Then you have one of those short landing planes . . . oh, my dear, they'll put you in the federal poke, but I'll come and see you because I love you."

He snapped his head around. "What did you say?"

"I said I love you. You're nutty but very brave."

"You must be getting gassed."

"A little, but I know what I'm saying."

He came to her quickly from across the room and tilted her chin up and looked into her eyes. "Never take advantage of a lady when she's drinking . . . I'm going to sober you up and then hold you to that."

"Promise?" she said lightly. "OK . . . I'll close the bar and we'll go back to work." She paused. "I'm scared, Steve."

"So am I."

"Look at that wind! And now the sun's coming out."

"I know, dammit! Why doesn't it stay in? That would help convince people a little."

"Did you ever think about the billions of dollars spent on hurricane research and detection? Even the radar in there costs two million dollars. Yet this storm is going all over the place and we don't even know why."

"Someday . . ."

"Yeah, someday," she said ruefully. "OK, funny one, on to Palm Beach. We can at least set up our gauges."

They had already called Philip Guest and made arrangements to be based at the Palace Beach. When they arrived the chairman quickly took Steve, Billy, and Keith into his office.

"What's all this about an evacuation? Did you hear the President's message this morning?"

"Yeah, I wrote it," Steve said.

"But why? Look out the window . . . the sun's shining."

"That hurricane could swing over here in a minute," Keith said.

"But no one agrees with you."

"Who's no one?"

"Well, the Palm Beach County Civil Defense has terminated the evacuation. People are coming back."

"On whose authority?" Steve blasted.

"Authority of the state civil defense."

"And they're going over the heads of the governor and the President? The President called Tallahassee," Steve said.

"But he spoke to the lieutenant governor. The governor is in Europe. Besides, if it's so bad, shouldn't you people be in Coral Gables?"

"We've already done everything we can do there," Steve said. "We're going to set out several hundred tide gauges along the coast to see if we can't learn something from this baby."

Keith, who had been studying the chairman, felt that something unexpressed was bothering him. "You seem to be upset, Mr. Guest. Is there a problem we can help you with?"

"I'm afraid not, Dr. Landon. It's the hotel. Running everything myself. With John gone, it all falls on me. People don't know whether to check in or check out and to make matters worse, we're hosting the Home Ball tonight."

"I suggest you cancel the ball, in fact, we just about insist that you cancel it."

"It means quite a bit of summer revenue to us."

"Mr. Guest," Billy spoke up, "this beautiful day could suddenly turn into a horror scene. Claudine is very small but she's a killer!"

While they were talking, Steve went to the phone and dialed the local civil defense. He described the characteristics of the crazy storm and ended by saying, "As co-director of the hurricane center, I'm ordering an evacuation."

"You don't have the authority and neither does the President. All you can do is give us forecasts. We decide what to do. That's the routine, Mitchell. We're geared to that and you know it. Even your local man at the airport isn't forecasting a flood situation. Look at the water mark in the lake . . . it's gone down six inches in the last hour."

"But it could come up again!"

Colonel Murray slammed down the phone and turned to his assistant. "That Mitchell is crackers!"

"Steve, what about the ball?" Philip was asking.

"I'd forget about the ball tonight."

"Perhaps we should wait just a bit and see what happens."

"It might be too late then. In fact, I'm sure it will be too late then!"

Neither Philip Guest nor anyone else outside the team from the hurricane center understood.

The hurricane team spent the rest of the afternoon setting up tide gauges around Palm Beach and Lake Worth, and as they worked, furiously pounding in guy wires, clouds began to lace the sun. They developed quickly, steadily, and Steve called the center. Claudine had snooped around Andros Island and the weird midget was now hankering to get at the Florida coast. She seemed to be on a final course, but there was no direct path back to her target.

On that Saturday there were about 8,900 residents in Palm Beach and about 1,100 visitors staying at the various hotels, including the Palace Beach. Only 146 people packed up and left after hearing the President on radio and TV. One was Lee Olsen, who lived two streets from the Palm Beach Inlet. Being a woman of intelligence, she was cautious and she said to herself: "Why would the President issue such an order if the situation weren't dangerous?" Lee called the Ramada Inn in West Palm Beach and booked a room, packed an overnight bag, arranged for the dog, and grabbed her red mink coat. She drove easily out of Palm Beach to the inn, only eight miles away.

CHAPTER

32

THE PELICANS, SEA GULLS, SNOOTS, AND SNIPES, ALL RESIDENTS OF THE Palm Beach coastal water, got out that morning, for they had an easy way of exiting: They flew inland. At 11:00 A.M. that Saturday thousands of seabirds were settling in the water holes and around the fairways of the Loxahatchee Country Club. The golfers complained to the club manager and the greenskeeper came out with a shotgun and put a few blasts over the birds' heads.

Claudine meandered around Andros Island in the Bahamas most of that day, trying to decide where to go next, and her winds were so powerful and barbaric that they simply blew the local birds, the Bahamian swallow, honeycreeper, the slender white cattle egret, over to the shores around Palm Beach County. There were thousands of terrified island birds walking around the Florida beach that morning.

The fish off Palm Beach were less fortunate than the birds, for some of them could not swim to safety. The weak surface swimmers, the smaller fish, were cut off, although escape for the pelagic fish—the deep, powerful swimmers, blues, dolphins, sharks, marlin—was simple: They merely dived deeper in the water.

Pushed before any great hurricane are vast areas of weed and bottom sediment stirred up by the rolling swells that scrape the seabed. The water of a landfalling hurricane is murky and the surface fish, deprived of oxygen, are weakened as they try to escape. Only the mullet can survive murky water.

The exhausted reef dwellers—the angelfish, parrot fish, and butterfly fish—struggled in and out of the bouncing weeds. And the sharks, always greedy, came in by the thousands to feed. The whole shore along the north end of Palm Beach was being cut by dorsal fins that Saturday and by late afternoon even the surfers who had been enjoying Claudine's forewaves came in.

"Look at all those fish," Cynthia said to Jayson as they walked along the beach at five o'clock watching the mounting waves. "Isn't that extraordinary?"

"I wonder why they're there, Cynthia? Do you think they know something that we don't know?"

"Come on, Jayson. Don't get profound. Did I tell you I booked rooms for us at the Palace Beach tonight? We're going to have a good time. The Home Ball and the hurricane party!" Then she sighed, "Oh, if only John were here." Jayson took her hand in his and they continued their walk down the beach.

Fifteen miles to the west the flood waters draining out of Lake Okeechobee streamed across the margin lands and the sloughs of the Glades. The rising water began to seep higher and higher into John Baxter's plane; it mounted up to his waist, his chest and was reaching for his armpits as he arched his back, thrusting his head upward to gulp the last bit of air.

But as the mucky water rose to kill him, it brought a way of escape, for the tool bag that had been stowed behind the far seat of the Apache, always in sight but never in reach of the trapped man, floated free and bobbed on the lapping water closer and closer to John's position. Finally he was able to grab it. He dug his hands into the pouch and took out a well-oiled hacksaw. Drawing in a large breath, he ducked his head into the blackness of the water and began to saw his leg free of the tangled wreckage. He worked in furious bursts. He knew it would only be a matter of minutes before the inundation would reach the overhead and his diminishing breathing space would be cut off. Then Claudine's rains began. The time between life and death was narrowing; he made a final assault and then there was a wiggle.

The firewall was loosening. With his breath bursting in his lungs, John Baxter made a few quick slashes with the saw and he wrenched out his bleeding thigh with his last particle of strength. He was free.

He lifted his bloody leg and pushed his 189-pound body against the door of the Apache; it opened and he reached in for the life raft as his feet began to sink in the mire. He jerked himself free of the suction, snapped the two pull cords of the raft; it inflated and he crawled onto it and collapsed.

PART THREE

DEATH

Death is like thunder in two particulars:
we are alarmed at the sound of it, and it
is formidable only from that which preceded
it.

COLTON

CHAPTER

33

THE FIRST VICTIMS OF CLAUDINE WERE SEAMEN. THOUGH THE STORM
had stripped the low marshy table of western Andros Island, the
area was unpopulated and the lady was such a puny bitch that she
could not be felt with any noticeable wind regime measurements
more than thirty miles from her eye. No one died on the island,
although there were injuries and extensive property and crop damage, but as soon as Claudine pushed out to sea, westward toward her
Florida landfall, she found her first victim: a small container vessel,
the *Bahama Dawn*, which plowed daily between the port of West
Palm Beach and Nassau with refrigerated consignments.

The captain of the vessel had received a marine forecast that morning that warned of Claudine; however, at 3:00 P.M., the time of
their scheduled departure from Nassau, the barometer read 29.2
steady—nothing to worry about—and the wind was only blowing
thirty knots. These tolerances were well within the operating range

of the *Bahama Dawn,* and, too, they had been advised that the storm was small and going south, which was the opposite direction of their course.

The steering currents guiding Claudine were delicate, however; at four o'clock the hurricane shifted to a more northerly direction and she picked up speed. The captain of the *Bahama Dawn* was now steaming into the core without knowing it. The glass slipped quickly; the waves, seething white walls of water, climbed to twenty feet, thirty feet, forty feet as the tumult of the wind squealed. He came about, putting his stern to the great oscillating waves, and he was being knocked, lifted, tossed, pitched, rolled by the uproar that had pounced down upon the vessel. It was hard to tell which way the wind was blowing; the blasts of foam came from every direction and the hissing waves had no pattern or regular course.

As the flopping, dying vessel was lodged in one meadow of gray-white lather, her stern started to broach for some reason, and when the next avalanche of water, whose skin was being peeled off by the two-hundred-mile-an-hour wind, overtook the listless little freighter, it merely swallowed the ship.

It went up, over, and down.

All that was left was a little oil on the spastic, milky surface and some deck litter. From beginning to end, the slaughter took six seconds.

The Rolls-Royces with their passengers of the elegantly dressed rich were arriving at the Palace Beach as Steve stopped by the hotel for a brief respite before returning to the hurricane center. Billy and Keith were going to finish setting out the gauges and scientific equipment, and then they, too, would be on their way back. There was a big meeting going on in Philip Guest's office where Maggie, Denise, and Nicole had gathered to discuss alternative arrangements for the ball should the hurricane hit.

"Forget the ball," Steve told Philip. "Why are you letting people into the hotel?"

"These ladies are running it. I told them the risks."

"Mrs. Dunsmore," Steve said, turning to her, "don't you realize what's going on out there?"

"Yes, but Philip said the walls of the Palace Beach can stand anything. We can always go upstairs; in fact, we've prepared the small ballroom on the fourth floor, just in case."

"Hurricanes can be killers, Mrs. Dunsmore! You're a smart woman, can't you persuade everyone to give up this foolish idea?"

Philip Guest saw the grim determination in Steve's face. "Well, ah . . . maybe Dr. Mitchell's right, Maggie. I'm calling off the ball," he said.

"You can't!" Denise cried out.

"It's our choice," Maggie said, "though perhaps Dr. Mitchell ought to be listened to."

"It's my hotel," Philip Guest said. "John Baxter would never have allowed this."

"How important can a party possibly be?" Steve said. "You people would risk death just to dance and be seen? You're all crazy!"

"Dr. Mitchell, look at this place. How could it be destroyed? The walls are five feet thick," Maggie said. "I know . . . Mrs. Stotesbury saw it being built and she told me."

The Queen sat calmly in a large chair sipping brandy and upon her head was a small diamond tiara. Nicole and Denise were stylishly dressed in St. Laurent peasant gowns set off by perfect hairdos and they, too, were studded with diamonds, which in Denise's case were borrowed from Nicole Bouchart.

"Mrs. Bouchart, let me ask you something," Steve said suddenly. "Where is your husband?"

"Why, he's home, of course."

"Is he being evacuated?"

"No."

"Why not?"

"Because he's too old. Lawrence doesn't go anywhere."

"Then why aren't you there with him instead of here?" Steve asked.

"I really don't think that's any of your business," she said stiffly, "but, as a matter of fact, he doesn't recognize me half the time and, besides, I can't leave now. It's raining."

"Where is Mel Hansen?" Steve asked, looking around the group.

"He's down at Glen Markum's. They're having a hurricane-watching party, but he'll be up later," Denise said.

"All right, everybody. The ball is off," Philip said. "I believe Dr.

Mitchell is right. I don't know what will happen, but I'm not taking chances."

"But where do we go? We're hardly dressed to slosh through a storm, Philip." Before the chairman could answer he was told there was a call for the hurricane people.

"Dr. Mitchell is here. . . . Just a moment," Philip said, handing the phone to Steve. "It's for you."

"Steve, this is Marc. We just got a new track: Claudine's straightened out. She's on a direct course toward the Florida mainland!"

"What's the landfall?"

"If she stays on track she'll hit Manalapan just south of Palm Beach between ten and twelve tonight."

"I'm coming right back. But do this now, please. Go to the communications room and tell them to get this on the wire right away to the civil defense headquarters of Broward, Palm Beach, Martin, and St. Lucie counties. They can set up the format, but here's the language . . . got a pencil . . . OK. 'Emergency message for four-county area. Hurricane Claudine now forecast to landfall between Fort Lauderdale and the Jupiter Inlet sometime after nine tonight. Winds are exceeding two hundred thirty miles per hour. Tides forecasted to rise thirty feet in landfall areas. Effect immediate evacuation.' "

"But that's not true. The winds are only two hundred and the SPLASH program says tides won't exceed twenty feet."

"Forget the program. Lie your head off! I'll be there as fast as I can make it."

Steve hung up the phone and quickly informed Philip Guest of the latest developments.

"Get a message down to Dr. Landon and Dr. Haughton—they should be around Mar-a-Lago right now—tell them what's happened. I'll keep in contact with them through you."

Philip nodded briskly as Steve raced out of the room.

This time the Palm Beach County Civil Defense took the warning seriously: It was on the official wire; the wind was rising and the sun was covered with a strange halo.

As Steve sped across the north bridge in Palm Beach behind a sheriff's car that would escort him back to Coral Gables, he saw the lapping waters of Lake Worth. A long stream of cars was moving over the bridge, but only thirty minutes after Steve left Palm Beach, the roads leading out of the town were blocked by the rising lake water. The rain had started to fall and the wind rose as Claudine made her way toward the Florida coast. She had settled down now and there was no deviation in her track. Those who were forced to abandon their cars at the bridges went back to the three refugee centers in Palm Beach that had been set up the day before by the Red Cross: Bethesda-by-the-Sea Church, St. Edward's Church, and the public school. There was no panic or alarm. People moved easily to the shelters and many others on the island who had never considered evacuation simply relaxed with their drinks and called their friends on the phone.

Billy and Keith arrived tired and dirty at the Palace Beach in response to Philip Guest's urgent summons and went directly to the chairman's office where, incredibly, the ladies still sat arguing about the ball. Philip was on the phone with the police.

Their message was terse: "The bridge roads are under. We can't get off the island."

Philip turned to the others, after hearing the news. "We're not getting out of here now . . . that was the police. The roads are cut off."

Billy felt a hard knot curl up in her stomach.

"Now we can go on with the ball." Maggie beamed. "It'll be a different affair, but we'll improvise."

Keith said to Billy in a low, snarly voice, "These pampered babes are so cuckoo . . . they don't even want to be helped."

"Shouldn't we go to the disaster shelters?" Philip asked Keith anxiously.

"I don't know. No one place right now is safer than another. I guess we should stay here."

"What's going to happen, Dr. Landon?" Philip asked.

"I think the island will be overtopped . . . flooded. There's a possibility of using small boats, but right now. Not later. By the time the storm hits, the lake will be such a raging ocean nothing will be able to operate. What's the highest building around here?"

"Century Towers," Philip said without hesitation.

"That's where Mel is," Denise cried.

"Let's talk to him."

Philip picked up the phone and a moment later he had Mel on the line. "Mel, this is Philip Guest. We're calling from the Palace Beach. We have to make some decisions. Keith Landon is here and he wants to talk with you."

Keith asked Mel about the conditions around the forty-story condominium.

"This building is overdesigned. We have our own electrical generator," Mel said, half drunk and in excellent humor, thinking that Philip was going to give in to his blackmail scheme.

"What's the grade level?" Keith asked.

"Twenty-seven feet," Mel answered.

"I think we ought to try for higher ground while we can still get down the coast road. Can you take more people down there? We can't get off the island."

"Sure, Doc, come on down. It's safe here. Tell Philip to bring some of that special Palace Beach blend. There's a nice party room on the penthouse floor. It'll hold four hundred easy."

Maggie said, "Denise, you're the head of this ball. Make an announcement."

"No, no, Maggie. Let Philip do it. Everybody knows him."

The small orchestra playing in the ballroom hushed as Philip entered, and made the announcement, saying that it would be dangerous to remain in the hotel, and he suggested that everyone evacuate down to Century Towers.

There were a few boos as the waiters hurried to and from the bars, and some people got up and left. The clamor of the hurricane wind was not heard through the massive facade and people felt secure at the flowered tables in the main ballroom.

"How could this hotel go?" Jayson asked Cynthia.

"I don't think it would. My God, that would be the end of Palm Beach."

Steve arrived at the hurricane center at six-twenty that evening after having raced down I-95 at over a hundred miles an hour behind his squealing escort. As soon as he entered the war room, he called Billy and Keith back at the Palace Beach. They told him that the roads off the island were already under.

"Where are you going?" Steve asked.

"Down to Century Towers. They have higher ground there."

Just as he put down the phone, Marc Peterson rushed into the room.

"I want to talk to you . . . outside!" he said with a hard voice.

In the hall a flushed-faced Marc turned to Steve. "Where's Keith?"

"Still in Palm Beach. I'm taking over temporarily."

"You've been fired by the Secretary for lying to the President. And someone saw your plane land on the levee last night. They checked the number out with the FAA. The United States Attorney is preparing an indictment."

"In the middle of a hurricane he's preparing an indictment? Beautiful!" Steve howled.

"You're a madman!"

"Let's forget all this. Is everything out on the wires?"

"Yes."

"All right. Now, let's work this storm."

Marc eyed Steve's determined face for a moment, and then he nodded. "OK."

As the two reentered the war room, one of the specialists rushed toward them.

"Dr. Mitchell, we've just had a confirmed drop. The winds are now up to two hundred and thirty!"

"I'm not surprised. OK. Run another SPLASH program and get the warnings up as far as Savannah and Apalachicola in Florida. We don't know what this fucking storm will do. Move it!"

Ten minutes later the results of the SPLASH program came over the wire from the Maryland computer.

"Twenty-nine feet!" someone said.

Suddenly Steve thought about Billy and Keith on the higher floors of Century Towers and he grabbed the phone.

The line was dead.

"Marc, I have to leave. There's nothing more I can do here anyway," Steve said as he yanked at his raincoat.

"What . . . where are you going?"

"Does it matter? I'm fired, remember?" Steve smiled.

"But I need you," the administrator cried out.

"And we need Keith and Billy. They're in for a hell of a time up there and they don't know it. Call Homestead. Tell 'em to get the

((281))

biggest chopper they've got over to the football field right away."

"Wait, what about *here*?" Peterson yelled out in desperation.

"Grimes's a good man. Just do what he says. I'll give him a set of alternate instructions."

"You can't do this. I'm ordering you to stay!"

"Sorry, Marc. I've been fired, and besides, I'm a criminal. You know the Commerce Department doesn't want criminals working for them."

Marc was still sputtering when Steve waved and ran out of the room.

The scene that greeted Billy and Keith and the Palace Beach group as they came from the entrance of the hotel was strangely ironic: Squads of local photographers were taking pictures of the most elegant evacuation ever carried out. Lines of beautifully coiffed, jeweled, and gowned women were making their way from the baroque doors of the great hotel toward their Rolls-Royces. Chauffeurs were opening and slamming doors and the shined motor cars slowly pulled away, easing through the rain puddles and around coconuts that had fallen to the center of the palm-lined driveway.

The pressure of the approaching hurricane had increased. The rain was now slashing sideways due to the mounting wind friction; millions of birds clogged the air and they squeaked and squealed as if calling out a direful message, and the air itself was loaded with spinning palm fronds and pebbles and sand and shells. High above, illuminated in the blaze of lights protecting the Palace Beach from intruders, could be seen the inky edges of the racing nimbus clouds whipping in from the northeast.

There was dread, but no panic.

Philip Guest was worrying about his hotel's reputation being ruined if Mel Hansen told his story to the state attorney. Nicole Bouchart drove her white Bentley home thinking of what Steve Mitchell had said: Why wasn't she with her husband? She realized that she was not ready to die. Her life had been cunning and shabby. It would be impossible to make up for all the years she had left Lawrence alone, the world of lies and lusts in which she had existed; suddenly there was no one she could explain herself or her life to, and if she could, how would she say it: that she had been in the husband-hunting business and that she satisfied her uncontrollable desires any way she could?

She entered the house and felt it rattle under the push of the hurricane wind, and she went directly to her husband's room to speak to him, but he was gone.

"Mrs. Bouchart," the maid said, "the master was evacuated by policemen."

"Where did they take him?"

"St. Edward's Church, I think."

"Did . . . did he know what was happening?"

"His mind was very clear, madame."

Nicole packed a few jewels in a small bag, her income tax records, and she gazed from the window to see the waves from the lake mounting over the bulkhead, gushing in and out of her pool. It was the end. She knew it.

With her two maids, Nicole drove over to St. Edward's Church at three miles an hour; the streets had been turned into streams and they were bombarded with falling coconuts. She could not find her husband in the packed church and she got into the car again to drive down to Century Towers, but the Bentley's electrical system had failed.

Across the street Nicole saw crowds of soaked people moving into the old Paramount Theater, an elaborate Moorish fantasy out of the silent film era, and she entered the theater. They were showing an early John Wayne film to the evacuees. She sat down and started to cry.

CHAPTER

34

JUST AS NICOLE ENTERED THE PARAMOUNT THEATER, THE FIRST DEATH occurred in Palm Beach. It happened on Arabian Road two houses down from the residence of Lee Olsen who, at that moment, was enjoying a safe, dry dinner at the Ramada Inn. Water had over-topped the low, slanting beach on one side and the lake was fuming up and overflowing. Waves were already breaking and curling around the home of a woman whose son was a well-known Hollywood actor; she had evacuated to West Palm Beach that afternoon. Water crashed through the plate-glass windows of the deserted house. Heavy, mad seas boiled through it and, having no release, back to the ocean; they continued inland, flooding the first four streets of the island: East Inlet, Arabian, Caribbean, and Mediterranean Road. With the in-flow growing minute by minute, millions of small fish were tossed up onto the streets.

Schools of sharks who had wreaked their carnage devouring small fish at the beach were also swimming inland. The man-eaters could not penetrate the powerful combers and were unable to dive under the breakers; the bottom was just too close. The rising lake to the west was no salvation: It was freshwater, an alien aquatic world.

Mrs. Louise Hepplewhite, a forty-five-year-old widow, decided around six o'clock to escape by car with her four poodles. She did not get far; Claudine's rains had already flooded North Lake Way in front of the Sailfish Club and her car stalled there along with twenty-three others. She got out and moved through the mucky slop back toward Arabian Road to the north, thinking that she would be safer in her own home.

When she arrived there the convergence was well under way.

The ocean water was piling up against the lake water and the wind shrieked at speeds up to 160. Her strength was about gone as she looked at her darkened house—all the lights had failed in the town about twenty minutes before, at 5:42. Poles and trees were now being uprooted. A hail of seashells battered her face as she slowly pushed through the knee-high water to reach her already half-inundated home. Suddenly she felt the sharp-edged scales of a clamoring bluefish and the woman was petrified, thinking it was the nip of a shark. (Palm Beach residents knew their waters had one of the heaviest concentrations of sharks along the eastern seaboard because of the closeness of the Gulf Stream and the high concentration of game fish in the area.)

She ran screaming and fell over a submerged curbstone just to the side of a hearty clump of bayonet cactus. Her body plunged into the knifelike spears and several of the stiff lances penetrated her stomach. She could not free herself from the impaling and the water curled up around her and mercifully took her life as she let out a shrill cry. Her last.

The second death occurred just down the street: An elderly man who had chosen to remain at home went upstairs and stood before a great plate-glass window drinking his Scotch. The window shattered with such power and force that his neck was ripped open, and he died in a bloody puddle upon the white carpet.

The third and fourth people died on Mediterranean Road. They, too, had made their way back from the flooded area by the Sailfish Club: a mother and her eleven-year-old daughter.

The trapped sharks were thrashing about the flooded streets. A school of eight tigers, the largest about fourteen feet, had two enemies: the thundering combers bounding in from the sea and the fresh lake water that was rising to meet them. As the woman held her frightened daughter's hand, she felt a tug; the girl was snapped from her grasp and there was a splash and a shaking of the sharks' jaws. The screaming little girl was ripped away and then the mother felt the razor's edge as another tiger clamped its row of teeth about her thighs. She fought forward into the bloody mayhem. The movement of her feet was a new threat to the sharks and they acted out of a raw instinct for survival, killing the woman and her daughter.

The next person to go lived on Caribbean Road. He died from a heart attack, easily, swiftly, and cleanly.

Inch by inch the muddy brown water rose on the north end. The air was filled with flying palms and the old resort was being stripped of its fashionable houses and greenery. The dead fish swirled about in great masses and the chic, complacent people, those who had not escaped when they had time, began to die agonizing deaths one by one.

CHAPTER

35

ELEVEN MILES TO THE SOUTH THE ATMOSPHERE WAS ENTIRELY DIF-
ferent. The Century Towers people, of whom there were 190 in
residence that night, were enjoying nature's show: Stereos played,
people laughed and danced. The condominiums around them were
darkened by the central power failure, but Glen's apartment, like
many others, was alive with guests, and cold cuts had been set up
and the bar was well stocked.

Mel and Glen stood on the balcony bracing themselves against
the wind as they talked.

"Glen, old buddy," Mel said. "This is going to be one hell of a
night. Got an exciting hurricane to watch and when the Palace
Beach people get here, we'll take Guest aside for a little conference.
Our problem is solved: John Baxter sure died at the right moment!
Palm Beach has started to flood and people can't get off the island.
If our plan had been adopted, the lake wouldn't have come up so
high. It's the case in point."

At that time, five minutes after seven, Claudine had stalled again. She was positioned fourteen miles off the coast, and the full impact of her winds and rains had not been felt by those in Palm Beach or in Century Towers.

Forty floors below the Markums' condominium, Haddie Griswold, the manager of Century Towers and a former construction contractor from Texas hired by Mel and Glen when the complex was first conceived, took his poncho and an umbrella and walked outside to check on things. He bent and jerked his big body into the slashing onshore wind and sucked in the smell of flying salt being tossed up from the surface of the sea. His umbrella was yanked away from him in a matter of minutes by the shuffle of Claudine's winds. He was worried about the shade awnings, which were stretched on pipes to either side of the pro shop. When he reached the Century Towers tennis courts, not only had the awnings been ripped away, but the might of the hurricane wind had plucked the pipe stretchers as well. Haddie stood in the lee of the cinderblock pro shop and looked at a twisted mass of metal. He then tilted himself into the wind and started back the other way on the walk that ran beside the seawall.

Something caught his eye and he stopped, balancing himself against the press of the sodden air. The backfill that supported the seawall was gone—scoured by the combers. Each wave was overtopping the remains of the seawall. He remembered how he had advised Mel to lay heavier footings to support the bulkhead.

"Hell, no!" Mel said. "The tower footings go down forty feet to bedrock. The seawall is only a fixture."

It was less than a fixture now: The wall wasn't there anymore. As each wave crashed up the slope, which rose to the base of Century Towers, more and more sand was traveling to sea, looted by the powerful backwash. The lawn behind the seawall was now a series of deep gullies and Haddie moved closer. The base of the east building was under attack, for the cement slabs holding the pilings were now visible under the canopy of green lights, which lent a certain theatrical effect to the deathly onslaught.

Being a construction man all his life, Haddie was worried. He didn't exactly know what was happening, but he thought he had better inform Mel since he was the architect. Haddie had no way of knowing that Mel was an artist with outsized ideas rather than an architect with a sound structural background.

After shaking the water off himself and toweling his face, Haddie went up to the Markum apartment. It was bright, noisy, and gay. Haddie found Mel and took him aside.

"Mr. Hansen, there's a lot of erosion down by the seawall. In fact, the seawall isn't even there anymore."

"So what?" Mel said as he waved at someone across the room.

"I could see the cement slab and the tip of the piling system."

"Haddie, my boy," Mel said, wrapping his thick arm around the manager's damp shoulder, "this building's hurricane-proof! Our grade level is twenty-seven feet above sea level. Why do you think all the people from the Palace Beach are coming down to my building? Don't worry. Just go downstairs and welcome our refugees to warmth and safety and, Haddie, take a look at the plaque on the wall of the lobby. This is the building that won four architectural awards and they don't give those lollipops away for nothing."

Haddie left the apartment feeling better.

A stream of polished Rollses and other luxury cars crawled from the Palace Beach down South County Road, twisting in and out of the debris toward Century Towers. The roads were still passable. Massive flooding had not occurred except at the far north end where one hundred sixteen people were already dead. No one from the other part of the island knew it, as the phones were out and police cars could go no farther north than Palm Beach Country Club. The sea road was already being showered by huge, crashing waves, but the south end of the island, being higher ground, was not yet overtopped.

Cynthia and Jayson followed the long line in their Silver Shadow. They did not talk, for even in the tightly sealed Rolls, where the loudest noise according to the advertisements was the electric clock, the shriek and shrill of the rising wind made conversation impossible. Jayson looked over and in the dashboard lights he saw that Cynthia was crying.

"Cynthia, love, are you afraid?"

"Yes, I am, Jayson," she yelled over the hurricane roar. "I think things are going to be different after this. Could we go back to our houses for one last visit?"

"I don't know if we have time."

"Let's try."

Jayson, who didn't need to be persuaded, turned the car up El Vedado, inching through the mushy greenery toward South Ocean Boulevard. High-flying scud veiled the Rolls, but the high grade level had held back encroachment of the sea. Cynthia and Jayson ran up to the darkened Baxter house and once inside they went to the kitchen for a flashlight. They played it around the beautiful living room; all the props of a careful rise in Palm Beach were sitting there just the way they always had. But John Baxter was gone and both Cynthia and Jayson knew that the house would soon be picked up by the growing sea. Cynthia had to make up her mind quickly; she collected every picture of John she could find and she raced upstairs to gather her jewels, her will, and a bundle of stock certificates. Just as she returned, there was a large crash and spray of flying glass. A palm tree came through the window and with it, rain and a sharp blast of hurricane air.

"Hurry, Cynthia!" Jayson shouted.

"Yes, yes, I'm coming."

She picked up a scrapbook, her social history in Palm Beach, and she put it under her arm, then she stopped by the door, taking one last look at the room where she had given so many parties and tried so hard to inch her way up. The Persian rug, which they had bought on time payments eleven years before, was now covered with seaweed that had come in through the window. Cynthia took a few steps back into the room, her feet squishing on the soggy rug, and she tossed the scrapbook into the growing pile of flotsam.

"Let's get out of here!" Jayson yelled over the thunder of the storm.

They ran to the car and drove south on the flooding beach road. Jayson turned into his driveway. "I have to get a few things. You wait in the car."

"Jayson, look at your house!" she shrieked.

In the headlights they saw that the facade was partly collapsed. For years people had been telling Jayson to reinforce the ancient

Mizner walls, but he couldn't afford it and now the wind had started to take away the rancid old place.

"Don't ·go in there, Jayson . . . please!" Cynthia pleaded.

But he went anyhow. He pushed open the old Spanish door and entered the hall. All the trapped smells met him and he gagged. Jayson stepped over the living-room wreckage and as he reached for a couple of pictures of himself in polo days and a picture of his mother and father, there was a crack far above him, then a second crack.

The beams swayed and suddenly the barrel tiles and joists and rotted roof rafters gave way, spraying first a veil of old dust down on Jayson's threadbare tuxedo. He started to run, but a heavy oak beam caught him on the head, knocking him on his back and pinning him to the soggy floor in the decaying room. Cynthia heard the crash above the hurricane pandemonium; she rushed inside to see her old friend trapped under the beam as more and more litter started to rain down.

"Oh, God, Jayson," she cried.

"Go, Cynthia, get out of here!"

Then he waved a kiss toward her.

She knelt down and embraced him.

"Anybody in there?" a policeman yelled from the door. "I saw the car lights."

"Mr. Kendall's trapped. Help me get him out."

"There's not much time, Mrs. Baxter," the exhausted officer said as he shook the water off his raincoat.

"Please . . . you have to help!" Cynthia screamed.

The policeman came over and tried to lift the beam. It would not move.

"It's no use."

"Call the fire department!"

"Phones are out and so is my radio."

"We can't leave him here," Cynthia pleaded.

"Go ahead, Cynthia darling. It was over for me a long time ago. And you've made me very happy in my last days."

"No, Jayson . . . no," she sobbed. They frantically tried to yank the beam away; there was another crack from above and the rest of the roof came down upon Jayson, burying him as he let out his final scream. The officer jerked Cynthia away just in time and took her outside, and as she looked back to say good-bye to Jayson, there was a thundering roar and the entire house collapsed. The once proud palace, a mark of Palm Beach status, was now a wet and malodorous mound of rubble.

"You had a narrow escape," the officer said. "We'd better move out of here."

"Are the roads still open to Century Towers?"

"Yes," he yelled, "but the water's moving up fast. If you want to make it, drive like hell!"

The officer got in his car and turned north.

Cynthia got in the Rolls, then she took her gun from her purse, opened the window, and threw it out.

"I'm sorry, John. I went crazy . . . please forgive me."

She started the car and drove south, crying for John, for Jayson, for anyone.

36

CENTURY TOWERS STOOD OUT LIKE A HUGE BRILLIANT BEACON ON A
black, howling plain. Only Century Towers had its own generating
equipment and it was, indeed, a welcoming fort to Philip Guest and
the others from the Palace Beach when they turned up the driveway,
still unlittered as the huge twin towers had held back the blasts of
the wind.

The complex, as Mel had reassured Haddie, seemed strong, solid,
and safe.

Sixty monied partygoers left their cars in the oval and ran for the
front door and ten minutes later they were in the roof ballroom, a
glass-enclosed structure, now shielded by drawn hurricane shutters.
The Home Ball had simply moved down to South Palm Beach and
Maggie declared, "It's our tradition to continue."

Part of the orchestra arrived along with food and liquor snatched
up from the Palace Beach at the last moment and the festivities
went on.

Keith, Billy, and Philip Guest went directly to the Markum apartment. It was in a different world, far removed from the horror outside, and their hurricane-watching party was in full swing. About thirty people, some with candles and cameras, had pushed into the apartment; others had brought whiskey and some of the guests stood on the outside terrace in raincoats and hats watching the madness far below.

Mel had drunk quite a bit and he was very friendly toward Philip Guest; he thought he had the chairman trapped and he figured he would get the word in as soon as possible before things became too hectic.

High above in the dark skies south of the Towers there was mounting panic as the Air Force chopper thudded through unleashed winds that swirled at greater speeds than her turning blades.

Claudine tore at the machine.

The helicopter, being far less stable and lighter than the hurricane hunter plane, was jolted around as if she were tissue paper. When they reached Pompano Beach, the howling winds slammed the chopper about so that the confused pilots suddenly found themselves looking south instead of north. "I don't know if we can hold this," the captain yelled back at Steve. "We're exceeding our design capability."

"Like hell you are," Steve answered.

"How would you know?"

"I have a degree in aeronautical engineering. Just don't overcontrol the stick."

"That's all right for you to say."

"Want me to take it?" Steve yelled.

"I suppose you're rated?"

"I can fly them."

"Wonderful."

The chopper, rattling and bobbing, managed to reach the parking lot of Century Towers. Steve jumped out, but as he did, a sharp-edged gust measuring 210 miles per hour blasted around the northeast corner of the east building and scurried under the belly of the chopper. It lifted the light craft in the air before the desperate pilots could apply thrust to the turbine. They cut the switches instead and the unsupported craft came down with a crash. The kerosine tanks burst into flames and Steve rushed back to drag out the stunned pilots.

They ran to the overhang of the building as Haddie bolted out. "Christ, what's happened?" he said.

"A little mishap," Steve answered.

"Man, you're looking at four million dollars go up," one of the pilots screamed at Steve. "I hope to hell you've got a good reason for making this trip!"

"There's going to be the devil to pay!" the other cried.

"I'm already in trouble . . . it doesn't make any difference now," Steve said as they watched the chopper turn into a pile of whirling ashes.

"We'll never get the fire department!" Haddie yelled above the peal of the wind.

"Don't need it," Steve said, pointing to the thick sheets of rain pouring down on what was left of the helicopter.

As Steve took the elevator upstairs, he was unaware of what Haddie had discovered near the seawall. Steve thought that the danger would come from exploding glass, not from the rape of the sand clutching the pilings far beneath him.

"How did you get here?" Billy exclaimed as Steve entered the thumping apartment.

"In a helicopter that was. Listen, I think we should move these people off the top floors. Too much exposed glass."

"Keith mentioned that."

"How many are in the building?"

"I don't know, but Mrs. Dunsmore and her group are in the penthouse."

"Claudine's packing winds up to two hundred and thirty and she's on a direct track to Manalapan."

"That means Palm Beach is in the worst quadrant!"

"Exactly. I'm going upstairs to talk to the partygoers. See if you can find Keith—I may need some reinforcements."

When the wind reached 210, Glen and Gloria Markum came back in from the balcony.

"Isn't this exciting, Gloria?" Glen asked.

"Oh, yes . . . so wild down there and so cozy and safe in here."

"One thing about a high-rise," Glen said to his wife, "the water will never get up this far."

Denise was talking to Gloria Markum when she saw the tearful Cynthia Baxter enter the apartment. She rushed over to her. "Are you all right? What's the matter?"

"Jayson was crushed to death, Denise!"

"Oh God. Jayson, too." Denise was shocked. "What happened?"

"His house collapsed. Oh, Denise, it was terrible."

"Here, have a drink," Denise said.

She led Cynthia to the couch just as Glen Markum was taking Mel Hansen and Philip Guest back to the study for a conference.

"I never thought I'd be trying to escape a hurricane in your apartment," the chairman said, looking as if he had already fought the storm.

"It's safe here," Mel said. "Now I told Mr. Markum about our little offer. Have you reached a decision?"

"I have."

"And?"

"Mr. Hansen and Mr. Markum, I wouldn't in a million years consider making up a story like that. If you wish to accuse John Baxter of bribery, go ahead, but I'll reveal all the details of our meeting to the proper authorities."

"Who'd believe anything you said?" Glen scoffed. "You don't have John Baxter."

"But I do have a tape. Do you think I would listen to you without recording the conversation?"

"So, you have a tape. It's not admissible in court," Mel said smugly.

"That's true, but it will carry some weight. You people have caused me a lot of trouble and your wife—well, I won't even say it. I'm going to tell the state attorney the whole thing!"

Philip left the study and when he reached the living room he was told that Jayson Kendall was dead.

"I'm sorry, Cynthia. He was a good man . . . too bad he had that booze problem, like so many in Palm Beach."

"I think he was licking it in the end," she said.

Philip Guest glanced hard at Denise, then he left the Markum apartment and took the elevator upstairs to the roof party room. Steve was standing in front of the people talking.

"I'm sorry, but I don't think this building is safe. The hurricane will hit here in a matter of hours. Please, all of you, go downstairs."

There were a few oohs and ahs.

Philip said, "Are we really in danger here?"

"I don't think we can afford to take the chance that I might be wrong, Mr. Guest."

Keith nodded his head. "I agree with Steve. There's going to be a lot of pressure on this structure."

"Listen, everybody," Philip yelled. "The hurricane people believe we should leave now."

Some started to go, but others who were very drunk by this time decided to wait.

"They're fools!" Steve said.

His memory raced back to Camille and the nightmare seemed to be taking place all over again.

"We can't drag them out," Billy said. "But I think we should talk to as many as we can around the building. How much time do we have?"

"I don't know," Steve said, "but let's get going."

The wind was screaming at 215 miles an hour as they hurried downstairs, and the large plate-glass windows began to rattle and wobble in the Markum apartment. But there were no cracks yet. The lights had flickered twice, but remained on, and the party grew noisier, the music louder. They were all instant friends.

Far below the scouring action continued. More and more of the cement piles were exposed; the storm surge had not reached the base of Century Towers, but the sand under the structure was beginning to disappear. Eleven feet of piling were now exposed and the sand around the rest of the thirty feet to the limestone bedrock was being quickly transported back out to sea. To the uninitiated eye, it looked like a massive water-filled bomb cavity.

The piling cluster on the northeast side of Century Towers began to move; it was just an inch or so, but a pattern of swings was now in motion. There was a twofold action: The downward load was not being supported and there was an increasing lateral wind pressure against the building. High up on the thirtieth floor, a crack started by the elevator, though no one was there to see it.

Tons of water poured out of the broken canals and Lake Worth started filling up; there was no release because the waves had begun to overtop the central and south ends of Palm Beach, and the wild raging currents rushed down the street covering the island from the sea to the lake. Claudine's vicious wall cloud burst ashore to the south; convergence occurred within the basin; the situation in Palm Beach now was almost identical to the one that had destroyed Pass Christian, but on a much larger scale. The backwater gushing out of Lake Okeechobee combined with the furious seawater, and waves eighteen feet high were slowly undermining the entire town.

In the south end water flowed down to the lake like a frenzied waterfall. Gradually, the rampaging hurricane water began to eat away at the old Mizner houses; windows shattered, roof tiles were ripped off. When the 230-mile-an-hour wind reached under the eaves, complete roofs came down, then facades. With the houses, a whole way of life was collapsing.

The first large building to succumb was the Palace Beach. Being so close to the sea, the currents and waves ate under the structure so that it simply hung over the water like a cantilevered Medici palace. It poised for quite a time; only a few people were inside—eight guests and twenty-five in help, who were scurrying about to save what they could. Then the roar started; gaping cracks sliced up and down the thick building, windows broke, great pilasters crumbled, chandeliers fell. There was a thunder of marble falling upon marble, and finally as screaming people made their way out, the venerable hotel, the landmark of Palm Beach for almost fifty years, started its sickening slide into the mad sea.

All that was left by nine o'clock was the front facade plucked of windows. It looked like the set of a great movie spectacular that had gone broke during production.

Fourteen miles to the west John Baxter was still fighting for his life. He had wrapped his bleeding leg in bandages from the first-aid kit, and he was being dragged out of the Glades along the rushing surge of canal water bubbling down to the lake. The small life raft was spinning crazily in the white water and he paddled furiously, trying not to collide with the cactus and trees that poked above the surface. He realized that if one pierced the rubber, and he was forced to swim, he would never make it. He could hardly breathe in the salt-infested hurricane air. He only wanted one thing: to find Cynthia. He called her name over and over, but only the grotesque wind answered him.

Seven miles northeast of John Baxter's desperate fight for life, Lee Olsen was asleep in the snug, dry Ramada Inn. It had not been flooded and not one window had blown in.

The entire north end of the finger island was inundated by a raging sand-filled cataract. The hurricane-watching parties had become less gay, but little sense of panic prevailed. No one had told anyone that the water would rise over the first floor; believing themselves safe, most of the residents who remained on the island—those who elected to stay and those who were cut off—simply went upstairs with their candles, canned food, and booze. The only radio station in Palm Beach, WPBR-AM, with studios directly on the beach, had been knocked out of service, but WJNO across the lake in West Palm Beach continued to reassure its listeners that the hurricane, while powerful, was small in size and would soon pass.

Claudine's potency was demonstrated by the collapse of the station's antenna along with nine others in the county and, finally, no radio stations were heard. The upstairs hurricane-watching parties in the north end continued; there was some flying glass but the surge had only risen nine feet: The storm had not yet come ashore at Manalapan.

But far out to sea a tidal wave, or a rogue, was making up. It was composed from the fury of the wind that had whipped the water in different directions at once.

The wave built. First to fourteen feet, but as it galloped along, more water was collected and the rogue grew to twenty feet, then thirty feet, rare but not unknown, in a highly developed hurricane.

The barbaric watery wall rushed toward the north end of Palm Beach, enlarging to forty feet, finally about fifty. It hit the beach with a death-shattering roar. Those watching the upheaval from their windows saw something awesome and white coming down upon them. The monstrous avalanche crashed down on the houses, ripping them off their foundations, sweeping everything—furniture, food, bodies, objets d'art and all the other Palm Beach props—into a great twisting mass of water. This torrent of humanity and artifacts was hurled toward the lake as more and more houses were swept before it, until that part of the north end from East Inlet to Queens Lane was stripped. Only two people out of 340 survived the weltering wave.

But two miles south of this slaughter, the rich and the confident piled out of their Rolls-Royces and quietly entered the disaster shelters. Not one of them knew what had happened on the far end of the island. It might have been the most exclusive disaster setup in the history of such establishments. Parked this way and that around Bethesda-by-the-Sea were squads of Rolls-Royces, Maseratis, Jaguars, and Mercedes; and inside, the Reverend Doctor Alkin led the people in prayer, while someone played the pump organ since the electricity had been cut off from the main organ.

"We place our lives in your hands, Dear Lord," the rector was screaming over the shrill of the wind, when the doors burst open and a man ran hysterically up the aisle.

"The Palace Beach . . . it's gone. The waves got it! The street out front is beginnin' to flood up."

All at once the panic began. The millionaires poured out of the church, not wishing to risk a possible departure, even in this station so close to God.

The street was already covered with a sickening lather of rushing water carrying dead fish and parts of once proud hedges, their flowers closed and dead. Some people climbed into their cars to make the final ride, but the elegant cars shorted out; others pushed along the slop on foot toward Worth Avenue where the highest buildings in the resort stood. All the "confident rich" started their frantic march toward the safety of the mink mile. Those in St. Edward's Church were saying Catholic prayers and they left about the same time as the Episcopalians, heading south toward Worth Avenue.

No structure in Palm Beach ever provided such an appropriate stage for the theatrical town as the old Paramount Theater built in 1927. Few in show business of any merit missed the P.B. Paramount: Chaplin, Hope, Jolson, Gershwin were just a few who played there.

This was to be the last night for the historic theater and its final scene far outdid anything that was shown on the silver screen or stage during the fifty years that the Moorish monstrosity stood. When the lights went out, the old projector carbons, showing a rerun of *Shampoo,* went black. But there were candles and Cokes and everybody sat around talking, including Nicole Bouchart. But at ninetwenty that night, surge had overtopped the beach at the ocean end of Sunrise Avenue. The slushing waves entered St. Edward's

Church first; however, the Paramount Theater was built on a higher foundation and it was a full twenty minutes before the 120 people in the Paramount realized that the water was gaining, and that St. Edward's was being abandoned as Bethesda had been some minutes before.

The first indication that the old theater was about to finish its life was a shaking. It was dark inside and no one could see that the rich golden decor of the roof was beginning to peel off. The rafters were giving way to the pressure of the wind, which had reached 190 miles per hour in the periodic gusts, placing about 130 pounds of pressure per square foot upon the building.

In the case of the Paramount the wind pressure was too much for the old wooden roof; sections were pared away like paper in a sudden flapping, shearing, and wrenching of ancient materials. Rafters were smashed and once the blasting wind gained entrance to the theater, it simply shot upward in a howling gust.

The entire roof exploded externally in a geyser of warm, pulverized plaster, and bits and pieces of wood whirled in the air. What shot up came down, and sixty-seven people were crushed to death in a haze of powdery, falling debris. Nicole Bouchart was sitting under some balcony supports that, fortunately, held. There were screams in the dark as a great cloud of granulated plaster veiled everything. Nicole scrambled on her hands and knees to reach the front door that was only an inch above the wind-whipped water. The walls of the theater were staggering violently as the wind eddies pushed in and out. Believing that the theater was about to collapse, Nicole ran through the mini-ocean on North County Road for the safety of St. Edward's Catholic Church.

Nicole entered and fought her way through knee-high sandy water; she looked up the darkened nave to see two candles burning on the altar, throwing a flickering glow over the crucifix. In the hollow of the flooded church she heard people praying softly. Her head cleared and her mouth and eyes and nose were free now of the ground plaster that had bombarded her just after the theater roof landed back inside the orchestra of the building. Nicole saw that there were people in the choir loft and she climbed the stairs to the group huddled at the far end; they had decided to remain in the church rather than push all the way to Worth Avenue through the surge.

She sat in a rear pew just behind the organ. Nicole prayed with the others; but she didn't know the words, so she made up her own.

38

THOSE COWERING IN THE PALM BEACH PUBLIC SCHOOL, WHICH WAS much closer to the overflowing lake, had a real reason to panic, for the water just bounded into the classrooms with sudden alacrity. People made their desperate move in one wild flight, bellowing, kicking, shoving, hitting, and helping others, in some cases.

"Don't panic!" a Red Cross worker shouted, trying to be heard above the whine of the wind and the screams below.

Eleven people were trampled to death by the door as the P.B.'ers made a reckless gallop for safety and they, too, thought of the high buildings on Worth Avenue.

The first group from the three disaster shelters, the two churches and the school, did reach safety on the mink mile; the historic avenue was under only two feet of water at the time. Those who had never been allowed in the Everglades Club, as members or guests, broke through the doors; they ran down the twisting baroque halls until they found the darkened bar and helped themselves after breaking open the battened liquor lockers.

"This is the Everglades Club! Members only! Besides, it's not open until November. We're painting," the manager cried.

Other people pushed up through the murky swill and rushed toward Gucci and Cartier and Saks, breaking into the show windows. It was a wild scene of sacking.

They had gone delightfully rabid and taxi drivers and gardeners and maids and millionaires were sloshing about with armfuls of Gucci loafers and Cartier jewels. The aberrant escapees had temporarily forgotten the hurricane and they continued to smash their way into art galleries, dress shops, gift shops and take whatever they could carry.

Everything broke down.

Cultured people turned into criminals and there was a sickening onrush of last-minute greed and insane joy.

But the water began to press upward and it brought the trapped man-eating sharks. Some were barely clinging to life in their fight to get back to the sea, as they thrashed up and down Worth Avenue; it was the widest street in town and the converging water was not that fuming or difficult to move through. The great tiger sharks and hammerheads, having to rest, their fins and gills on the edge of exhaustion, swam through the bare show windows of the fabled stores and they cruised slowly in the darkness between floating gowns and mannequins trying to regain the strength needed to make it back to pure saltwater.

Worth Avenue was clogged with as many as two thousand people pushing their way through the sand-laden surface of dead fish, birds, dogs, human bodies, wreckage, palm fronds, bits of food that had floated out of Taboo and the other restaurants along the once-glamorous street. The sharks, perhaps believing they were safe in their retail-store sanctuary, became alarmed by the invasion of so many people who were churning up the water.

They flashed out of the elegant emporiums with their jaws sprung open and, in a wild burst of delirium, they clamped their teeth into struggling thighs, yanking at the human flesh, flopping their tails as they went from one person to another.

A maniacal, barbarous stampede began. People fell screaming into the water. Some were trampled and they drowned.

The street turned red.

Then there came a second enemy from the sea: Great clusters of Portuguese man-of-war had been hurled inland. They wrapped their ugly, purple tentacles around flying arms and legs, delivering their extremely painful poisons. Nine Palm Beach people died in this manner.

All this was unknown to Steve, Billy, and Keith as they pleaded with the Markums' guests to leave. Maggie, who had come downstairs, said, "Dr. Mitchell, aren't you being a little too particular? Look how high we are!"

"That's not making you safe!" Keith yelled, but few people in the apartment were paying much attention so they left and went door-pounding, trying to get people to move to the lower floors.

This seemed to be contradictory: Most residents of Century Towers associated height with safety. They could not possibly believe that they were threatened. They had been told their building was the strongest condominium in South Florida—built on bedrock. They didn't realize their grade had been raised in order to secure a cheaper insurance rate.

The blackish pool at the base of Century Towers continued to enlarge like a water hole being flooded by some underground spring. But those who gazed down on the lighted ocean thought only how dramatic the hurricane was; they weren't frightened because the curling, battering waves were not even up to the tennis courts that faced the wrecked seawall.

The lights mounted on the building facade shining down on the insanity did not illuminate what was happening in the subterranean shadows of the foundation under the building, but more and more subsoil was being stolen by the onrush. The piling system on the northeast corner moved and yawed just about a foot. This upset the load pressure, which was transmitted throughout the building. It was not anything one could feel yet, but on the thirty-fourth floor cracks opened; one appeared in the concrete by the disposal chute next to the elevator bank. It began on the wall near the ceiling and quickly, like a flash of lightning, it danced its jagged path down to the floor, then across to the door leading to the hall. An almost identical crack started on the twenty-fifth floor in the utility room. Two other cracks began in the corridor outside the noisy party in 40-A, the Markums' unit, but the split in the concrete slab was under the carpet, not visible except for a slight bulge in the rug.

The party at the Markums' had grown gayer and livelier. Mel, standing near the window, noticed a small fissure no longer than five inches in one side of the glass wall-panel; he thought it was caused by the wind pressure. It was not. The man could not possibly have imagined what was happening forty stories below him right under their feet. They had purposely left the hurricane louvers open to see the sight below: Hurricane combers twisting, curling, crashing upon the beach, delivering thousands of tons of water in one whirling assault after another, were all seen from the air. The crowd stood two deep at the windows.

"Look at that one!" Maggie exclaimed.

"Beautiful, aren't they?" Denise said.

"Folks," Glen yelled, "I think we'd better close the storm shutters."

"Oh, no, it's great, Glen . . . wait a little bit," Mel answered.

"A couple of minutes more," someone called.

"No . . . no . . . let's not take chances," Glen said.

Mel went to help him. They slid open the glass door just enough to push through and a burst of wet air tongued into the living room with such speed and pressure that it seemed shot from a large power compressor.

"Close it quick!" Denise screamed, feeling the belt of the raw, clammy wind that turned the living room into a white fuzz. Cocktail napkins flew, small chunks of rye bread were flung about, and the flower vases toppled over.

Mel and Glen shut the door behind them and grabbed for the ends of the hurricane louvers, struggling to pull them across the rails. Mel felt the wind pressure edging him against the glass. He hadn't realized its strength or how much salt was in the hurricane air. His breaths came quicker; water began to enter his lungs and he felt the sodium in his windpipe. He strained and tugged. Denise saw what was happening and she shoved open the glass door. Another stream of air shot into the room, forcing the people back against the buffet table, now in shambles as the small sandwiches were tossed into the air.

Mel finally yanked one side across and Glen wrestled with the other shaking louver. The wind gusted to 240 miles an hour!

Its ungodly force smashed Mel into the plate glass and he was rocketed into the living room, headfirst, his feet lifted by the fierce blast of air. He started to yell and covered his face. Snagged in a crystal cobweb, he was surrounded by hundreds of slivers of glass that sliced his body as if it were paper.

Everyone let out the same howl as they staggered backward. Glasses, pillows, draperies, lamps, chairs, tables, forks, knives whirled through the air. The guests crouched on the floor covering their faces. More glass ruptured in an ear-shaking crack. Hundreds of ragged, razor-sharp bits shot into the Markum living room. Like darts, they sank into the flesh of the people. Then the torrents of side-driven rain burst through the draperies. Two more expansive glass windows exploded, a second and third eruption of crushed glass flew across the room, riddling the wet walls. The wind roared in and the water came. The whole apartment was laid bare to Claudine and, for all practical purposes, the people were in the storm.

Glen Markum was bleeding from arm and leg lacerations, but Mel rested unconscious in a pool of blood. Denise tried to call for a doctor, but the outside phone was dead. With Cynthia's help, she dragged Mel into the hall by the front door, and Gloria got them sheets to wrap his body to stop the bleeding.

Glen quickly deserted the living room and he limped over Mel and went to his office down the hall to see if it was still intact. It was. None of the windows was broken. He stood there looking out into the wild night asking himself how all this could happen. He was so shallow-brained that he did not worry about his physical or moral survival, only the effects that the hurricane would have on the setback proposal.

The hurricane was almost ashore now just to the south of Century Towers and the surface pressure had dropped to 26.10! A low vacuum was created outside the glass window and a reverse detonation occurred. Glass flew outward; the bits were suspended in the air for a microsecond. Some pieces fell, but the smaller fragments were hurled back into the opened room with extraordinary power.

Glen Markum was picked up and sailed through the window. His body fell forty floors and what remained of the shoe salesman turned millionaire was never found in the long search for bodies.

CHAPTER

39

GENERALLY THE LIGHTS KEPT BURNING IN CENTURY TOWERS AND THEY gave people an odd sort of comfort. In some of the apartments where the glass had blown in or out, the local wiring was ripped, but the lights remained on in all the public halls and stairwells. Steve, Billy, and Keith worked their way through the upper floors banging on doors to warn the occupants, and most started down the stairs to the lower floors. Many of them arrived in the lobby where they sat around chatting amiably. The Palm Beach crowd finally condescended to leave the roof ballroom, mumbling and grumbling as they moved downstairs.

The base of the Towers was five feet above the surge level. No water ever entered the front part of the building. The glass around the large marbled lobby was protected by an overhanging concrete

((310))

slab designed to keep the rain away, and before the large expanse of tinted windows were deep-rooted Australian pines, and these retarded the wind force. The windows in the lobby rattled, but not one of them broke throughout the horrifying hours when the wind went crazy.

"Steve, these cracks . . . they're all over the place!" Billy said.

"I saw them on the way down. What do you think is causing it?"

"The foundations are probably going."

"How?" Keith asked.

"We'd better have a look at the parking garages under here," Billy said.

The lights still burned as they made their way into the dim subterranean areas. The first level was unflooded and they continued down to the subbasement. Opening the door, they peered out upon a terrifying scene: The whole garage was inundated with spinning lather; waves were flowing in around the cars and beach matter was all over the place.

"That's it!" Billy yelled. "See that sand . . . it's coming in from the wave set. This place is going!"

"Let's pull 'em out of Markum's apartment!"

Cynthia, who had only a superficial arm injury, looked around the room. It was crisscrossed with bleeding people sitting on the wet rug. Maggie had a jagged piece of glass hanging out of her stomach; Mel, who had come to, was writhing with pain and screaming; Philip Guest and his wife were huddled together in a corner.

"Cynthia, we have to do something!" Denise said.

"We should have got the hell out when they told us."

"Well, we can't leave Maggie . . . all these people . . . now. Call downstairs. The house phones are still working."

Cynthia grabbed the intercom and Haddie answered.

"This is Mrs. Baxter up in forty-A. The windows are shattered and there are people injured here. Is there a doctor around?"

"There was one in the other building, but I think he left this morning. I'll try him."

"Oh . . . and wait a minute," Cynthia said. "There are cracks in the wall too."

"Mr. Hansen told me the building is strong as hell, Mrs. Baxter, and he ought to know. I wouldn't worry about it," Haddie said.

Philip Guest came across the room and knelt by Maggie who was lying on the rug bleeding.

The old lady looked up at him with eyes still bright and alert. "What's the answer, Philip?" she whispered.

"I'm not sure I ever understood the question, Maggie."

"Do you know my only regret?"

"How could you have regrets, Maggie? You're the Queen!" He laughed, trying to reassure the woman.

"Oh, nonsense. You don't think I ever took all that seriously? It was a huge joke that I enjoyed privately. But my regret is not to die in Palm Beach."

"You're not going to die, Maggie."

"Of course I am. I can feel it. All of you should get out while there's time. Take them away, Philip."

"We're not going to leave you, Maggie."

"Please, Philip."

"How do you feel, Maggie?" Cynthia asked, crouching by the woman she had handled so carefully through the ascension years in Palm Beach.

"Terrible. The only good thing is that it won't last long."

"We'll move her toward the elevator. They say it's still working," Denise said.

"Cynthia, darling," Maggie tried to grasp her hand. "I'm sorry that I took the *Patna* affair the wrong way. John was a fine man and I know you loved him."

"I still do, Maggie, more than ever."

"Where will . . . will . . . you go after this?" Maggie asked, her breath beginning to come in short, choking spasms.

"Back home," Cynthia answered. Then she thought about her house, and added, "There is no home anymore."

"I have a feeling there won't be a Palm Beach to go back to . . . but we had some fun there, didn't we? I wonder how dear Eva Stotesbury would have taken this . . . bravely, I'm sure. . . ."

Cynthia began to cry, seeing the color drain from the Queen's face.

"Someone said to me," Maggie whispered, "kind of kiddingly . . . that if anything ever happened to Palm Beach the whole world would suffer . . ." She smiled at the thought and turned her head and died.

"God, she was quite a gal," Philip said, dabbing at his eyes.

"Yes, and she died with Palm Beach," Cynthia said. "I guess it's only fitting."

Far down in the pit of erosion, the pilings on one system were beginning to sway, only a foot or two at first, but it was progressing. They swung steadily back and forth like a metronome; the foundation system could not take the down friction load and there were six thousand tons of cement pressing upon the naked pilings.

Two of them cracked.

The unequal load shot up through the building. The convulsion hit the corners first and branched out as cracks along the walls. The rugs suddenly ruffled up in the Markum apartment.

The elevator climbed smoothly and as they stopped at the fortieth floor Steve saw the bloodied victims being carried down the hall.

"You were right, Dr. Mitchell," Denise said. "The windows blew in on us . . . there're four people bleeding badly and Maggie Dunsmore is dead."

"I'm sorry," Steve said. "Well, get them into the elevators." He turned. "The rest of you . . . listen carefully . . . you must start down the stairs immediately."

"Steve, wait . . ." Keith said. "Let's try to pack as many in the elevators as possible. It'll be a lot faster."

"You may be right."

"But the stairs are probably safer," Billy said.

"All right, everyone," Steve yelled again. "Take your choice . . . stairs or elevators. You'll get down quicker in the elevator, but you could be trapped if the current goes off or if the building collapses."

"What's your choice?" Philip asked his wife.

"The elevator, I think, dear."

"I'm going in the elevator, too," Denise said. "Someone will have to help with the injured . . . we can't carry them down."

"I'll help," Cynthia said.

Gloria Markum was looking around for her husband. "You go ahead. . . . Please take my grandchildren with you. I have to find Glen." And she started back toward the apartment.

They lifted the bleeding people into the opened elevator. Most of the others chose the stairs and they marched down in single file as the whole building began to shake and rumble.

"God. I don't think there's time!" Billy said.

"How do you see it, Keith?" Steve asked. "Elevator or stairs?"

"One's about as bad as the other. The stairs, I think."

"I agree . . . more flexibility."

The center hub of Building "A" East had three elevator shafts: one for service, two for passengers, and as the swaying pilings began to wrench and pull at the structure's backbone, elevator rails and counterweights started a racking motion; the load distribution became unequal. The rails of the elevators pulled away from the poured concrete sides where they were anchored by a series of eleven-inch steel rods. The shuddering began first in the pulley house located on the roof. Finally, as more and more of the steel rods ripped out, the rails started to twist.

Mel, who was being carried to the elevator, began to groan from the pain pulsating deep inside him; the glass arrows had punctured his stomach. It took Philip Guest and two other men to hold him down as he reeled. The elevator door closed and Cynthia pressed the button. It started with a jerk and a shudder. The counterweight was loose above them and when the elevator moved a shearing sound pierced their ears. The cab began to shake as its weight tried to straighten out and push on through the twisted rails. Finally, it halted and the lights went out.

"Oh, my God!" a woman screamed.

"Don't panic!" Denise yelled. "We'll be all right . . . somebody give me a hand."

They helped her up to the ceiling and when she came through the top and lit a match, she saw a door about four feet above her.

"Get a man up here!" Denise cried. "I think we can open the door."

A teen-ager was boosted up through the escape hatch. Denise

looked up quickly as an iron fastening bolt suddenly dropped from above; then another fell crashing on top of the elevator.

"Stay inside!" she yelled to those in the cab.

As Denise pushed against the greased elevator cables, she felt the tremble in the rails; more cement chips fell around her and she was hailed upon by bolts jerked out of the upper elevator housing. At that moment the building started its torsional movement; the twisting action could now be felt in all the apartments above the twentieth floor. It started with the column on the far southeast side, the most exposed.

The swinging motion accelerated; it finally exceeded the bending movements of the cement pilings under the cap. The lower halves fell away, disappearing into the erosion pool; the upper parts hung to the cap for about thirty seconds like needles pushed into a cushion, but thousands of tons were pressing down from forty stories above and the cap fell slowly and vanished into the sandy pool.

Nothing was supporting the column now and it dropped four feet pulling each floor slab away from its anchor. In 32-B a man and his wife noticed the floor sink on the outer edge of the building. He grabbed her hand and they raced into the hall.

Cynthia, who had always suffered from claustrophobia, hoisted herself out of the elevator and the young man dropped through the hatch, thinking it was safer inside. The raining bolts had stopped and the two women who had connived against each other and hated each other stood on top of the cab holding onto the greasy cables in their blood-soaked ballgowns.

Suddenly the elevator fell about three feet. Cynthia slid off the side and her leg was caught between the edge of the cab and the inside rails. Denise placed her arms under Cynthia's and began yanking her up.

"Stay with it, baby . . . I'll get you out."

Cynthia was released with a jerk, but Denise lost her balance and tumbled into the space between the shaft rails and elevator cab.

The elevator let go again and dropped another six inches.

Denise's leg was crushed and she let out a deep howl and a string of curses.

"I've had it!" she cried. "Goddammit! I'm as good as dead!"

"No," Cynthia said. "You got me out. I'll do the same for you."

Cynthia could hear the bones cracking in Denise's legs, the razor-sharp shreds rubbing together, and she held her tightly in her arms.

"I want to tell you something," she whispered.

"Hell of a time . . ." Denise grunted, panting with pain.

"I bought a gun . . . I was crazy, I guess . . . thought I was going to shoot you."

"I'm sorry, Cynthia, for what I did to you. Don't blame you, but I thought Palm Beach was my last chance."

"Were you going to marry John?"

"I guess I was trying."

"I thought so. But look how trivial all our battles over men and social status suddenly became . . . the storm changed everything."

CHAPTER

40

MANY OF THE BUILDINGS IN PALM BEACH WERE REDUCED TO PILES OF
wet muck. The surging water grabbed the smaller houses; the
foundations of the larger structures were only weakened by the tide
pressure, but they were not sunk deeply enough and that set up the
next sequence. The storm came ashore at Manalapan as forecasted
at ten-forty that night, and as it did, an awesome black twister
sprang from the outer band of clouds, touching down just fifty yards
south of the Bath & Tennis Club. The whirling five-hundred-mile-
per-hour winds in the core of the vortex began an assault up the
finger island.

The crippled houses and buildings were no barrier to the rotary
tornado winds. The hellish vortex sprinted into Palm Beach, lifting
and spinning whatever was left. Roofs, palms, crushed facades of
houses went and when the deep roar of the tornado hit Worth

Avenue where most of the buildings still stood, the twister finished off what was started hours before.

The shops and galleries tucked away in twisting cul-de-sacs were jammed with refugees who watched horrified as one by one the old Mizner creations collapsed into piles of rubble and were covered over by the sewer of water below. The Everglades Club, where members had fought to preserve their exclusivity, began to rattle and crumble and within ten seconds the whole monument to grace and respectability was crunched and then atomized into a million small flying pieces. Saks Fifth Avenue went, then Bonwit's, Elizabeth Arden, and Gucci. Seventeen hundred bodies would be found later in the sand-covered wreckage of one of the most renowned streets in the world.

The twister worked north, demolishing what was left of the Palace Beach, Bethesda Church and the Royal Poinciana Shopping Center, but as the twister moved on it began to diminish.

Palm Beach was not only hit by Claudine's high-powered wind field but also inundated by a fast-moving surge that spun crazily this way and that, mounting extremely forceful water pressures. That was the set when the black tornado dropped down out of the outer rain band. The mammoth wind alley snatched the partly uprooted trees, and the maelstrom sucked and spun them into the air as if they had not been anchored to the ground at all. It was about the same for the buildings. Most of them were wobbling and shaking by the time the twister struck. The climax was a matter of basic mathematics: There just wasn't enough botanical or structural resistance to withstand the plundering tornado winds.

Nicole heard the guttural roar of the tornado above the storm's squeal. The twister grew louder as it neared, and she trembled, thinking that the hurricane had picked up force. Like everyone, Nicole did not have the slightest notion that a tornado was winding its way up Palm Beach. When the twister struck the church, the fine stained-glass windows, those donated by the Kennedys and the Hearsts, turned into hundreds of slivers. Bits of color-crinkled glass spun around in the nave.

The rancorous wind twisted upon itself and the church disintegrated into a chasm of fluttering debris. Everything flew: the roof, the walls, the altar; the pews went on an airy merry-go-round and when the twister moved on the shrapnel crashed into the black sea of the nave. A mound of writhing people from the choir loft hit the water-filled vestibule with a dull thump. There was an inextricable massing of flailing hands and legs and heads. The bodies of those who flopped below were denuded. The tornado wind came with such a stunning shock that it completely ripped off everyone's clothes, including tightly strapped brassieres.

Prayers for survival had hardly been answered. Nicole felt that was unfair. She had tried awkwardly to make an atonement, praying for less, not more. Still, the twister left as fast as it had arrived. The main section of the church was a lump of crushed stones; but the vestibule remained relatively untouched. Two walls stood, but they were wobbling. And Nicole who had an instinctive sense of self-preservation felt that they would collapse in a second. She had to get out.

Strangely enough, her trip down from the jumbled choir loft was in the shell of a pew. It not only cushioned her fourteen-foot fall, but it remained relatively intact and became an instant boat. Bleeding and naked, she found the rocky floor of the church and with all her might she pushed the pew through the tidewater free of the church. She looked around to see if others were doing the same thing; all the other pews had been splintered and in the dimness, she motioned to a couple of others to join her. They struggled out of the main arch whose doors had long since snapped away.

There was a crack. What was left of the church tumbled in. But Nicole was free somehow and they found her the next morning, unconscious, her bruised body draped over a pew, which had floated two miles; it was beached in a mass of tangled wreckage on the far side of Lake Worth in the City of West Palm Beach.

CLAUDINE'S SMALL, TIGHT EYE WAS CROSSING MANALAPAN FOUR MILES south of Century Towers. Her guttural 230-mile-an-hour winds twisted into the quadrant with such a booming shock that great, mountainous whorls of mad, hissing water leaped against the lower floors of the condominium. The watery blast shook the entire structure in a series of tremors. Glass on the northeast side of the building was pulverized by the siege, and a white cloud of finely ground plaster seeped out of the naked tower as if the condominium were veiled in lace, and the fifty-foot waves were totally atomized.

Far down on the exposed bedrock, denuded of sand, the northeast column moved off its cap—only about six inches, but the relocation upset the friction load. A shudder ran up through the building; fissures widened and those who had returned to their apartments after the elevators failed let out long, wailing cries. They felt the rumble under them and saw the rain of plaster, the grating of huge picture windows and, terrified, they raced for the halls.

The balcony of the Markum apartment, being the highest, snapped first. A crack five feet wide flashed across the wrecked room as the floor pulled away from the center hub of the building. The columns twisted and undulated. Concrete slabs collapsed in a slow, sickly manner; each floor came crashing down on the next, kitchens hit kitchens, bathtubs banged into bathtubs, and over this tumult rose the final, piteous shrieks of helpless people being dropped floor by floor with the soggy avalanche. The downfall was sluggish but deadly, as the victims were pommeled and smashed to bits.

Steve, Billy, and Keith were in the hall of the twenty-ninth floor when the northeast column gave way. They heard the throaty roar above them and then the plaster started spilling out of the expanding cracks.

"It's going!" Keith yelled.

"What'll we do!" Billy screamed out.

He didn't get a chance to answer: About that time they saw the wall at the far end of the corridor pull away, the depressed floor bending like a diving board. Then the carpet began to slide downward, dragging them toward the black hole at the end. The wind and rain shot in, drenching them.

"Climb up the rug . . . hurry!" Steve shouted.

There was a great rumbling of concrete, then a small explosion as the twenty-ninth floor was jerked away; the carpet twisted and Steve grabbed Keith's hand with lightning speed. Billy grasped Keith's belt and when the floor broke under them they were hurled back against the elevator shaft, which had remained intact.

"Get up on the ledge!" Steve screamed as he pulled Billy and Keith toward a small, jagged slab of concrete.

Horrified, they huddled together, seeing the relentless collapse of the building. A metal fire door was behind them and Steve yanked it open; he got on his knees and dragged the other two inside as the lights flickered and began to die out. Suddenly the remaining walls quivered and shook violently. They looked at each other with twitching faces.

"It's no use!" Billy cried.

The floor of the stairwell began to erupt. Another thundering sound shattered their ears; the slab above them let go and they were bombarded by a downpour of crushed concrete. Billy and Steve were dazed, but in the semidarkness Keith saw a fire hose coiled behind a glass case on the surviving wall. He pulled himself up the tilting floor and bashed in the glass. Keith quickly unrolled the thick hose, and Billy and Steve, who had come to their senses, wound the line around their waists. Then the whole floor was ripped out from under them and they frantically gripped the fire hose, their cord of life. The hose was slippery and wet and Keith's bloody hands couldn't hold it. He slid helplessly along the line until he seized the brass nozzle dangling at the end.

They were now exposed to the fury of the hurricane and the slashing wind began to swing them against the building; the salt-filled air choked their breathing and each time they crashed against the elevator shaft, more air was pounded out of their lungs. Keith was kicking at the end of the hose and he was getting the full force of the impact.

Steve inched down along the line, realizing that Keith could never hang on. He had almost reached Keith's flailing body and could see his terrified face when a hard-edged gust caught them. The hose swung far out into blackness and then like a stringy pendulum it came in again. Steve lurched wildly down the hose, hoping to cushion the collision, but the brass nozzle clanged against the wall, and Keith's knuckles were shattered. Screaming he let one hand go; Steve tried to grasp the free hand waving in the air and their fingers touched just as Keith's other hand slipped off the nozzle.

He tumbled end over end into the pulverized remains of Century Towers twenty-nine floors below!

Steve clung desperately to the fire hose, his mind numb; he could hear Billy screaming hysterically and his own eyes were burning with salt and tears. Finally Steve hauled himself up to Billy's position.

"Billy, can you hear me?" Steve shouted above the wind.

She nodded.

"Above . . . just above your head."

She looked up and saw the ledge of the twenty-ninth floor, which had not given way. Slowly, painfully they worked themselves up the slithery hose and finally they could grasp the jagged concrete and pull themselves up on the slab. Billy burst into heaving sobs and Steve held her tightly. They looked far below into the large, fuming heap of wreckage being washed by a froth of mountainous waves.

"He saved our lives," Steve said. "He was the only one who saw the fire hose."

Stunned and bleeding, they clung to each other. The torrential rain continued to beat down upon them, but the wind was already backing off. Claudine was so small that her fury diminished as quickly as it had arrived. But for Keith Landon, it was too late.

The east side of the elevator cab facing the direction of the collapse had already been separated from the guiding rails; the inside runners were twisted, meshed into the curled rails. The elevator shaft alley burst open. Three sides were pulled away by the thrust of the cave-in, but the west wall, the one that was supporting Steve and Billy, held, even though it was crisscrossed with deep cracks and the cement-sprayed cinderblocks were separating. The west side of the building, which had not been undermined by the beach surge, remained intact, and those who escaped to the lobby survived the night petrified and exhausted, but unscratched. Fifty-seven were escapees from the Palace Beach.

Above the stalled cab there were eleven cables stretching far up to the basic pulley system on the roof. The cab house had been stripped away; in fact, it had been the first to go. Inside was a massive I beam and the mighty yank of the tumbling floors wrenched the beam and bent it; it did not break, however, for it was well anchored into the thick cross sections of the surviving roof.

The pulleys and the cable network stayed with the central beam. When the building fell away, the cables that were holding the cab below eased up; the elevator dropped about a foot along the tangled rails, until the cable slack went taut and the cab shuddered to a bouncing halt.

Denise's leg, locked between the elevator and the remaining wall, was further contused and more of her bones were crushed together. She let out a terrible scream that outdid the hurricane roar.

"Help me, Cynthia! Get this over with! Choke me . . . do something, Cynthia. I can't stand it!"

"You'll be all right," Cynthia called. "Just try to hold on a little longer, Denise. Please. You'll be all right."

"Hell I will!"

The wind went. The hurricane pushed inland losing its force nimbly. Suddenly the bombardment of sound was reduced to a soft purr. The teen-age boy pushed open the hatch again and his bloodied head and hollow wide eyes were seen in the halo of his flashlight.

"Christ, we're hangin' up here!" he said.

"Everything blew away but us," Cynthia said.

"God! Are we going to get out?" he cried.

"Yes, of course we are," she answered, though there was great uncertainty in her voice. "What's happened in there?" Cynthia asked.

"The Guests and three others are alive. Mr. Hansen and two women are dead."

He shone his light down and looked back into the cab. Then he vomited.

Cynthia took the boy's flashlight and aimed it into the cab. Philip looked up at her with the sallow face of a dead man. He was holding his wife; she seemed to have a bad head injury. Those who were living stood ankle deep in a sea of blood and urine. Cynthia almost vomited herself.

"Cynthia, let me go," Denise begged. Two minutes later she slipped into unconsciousness. Cynthia cried for herself and for Denise, but she held an arm around the actress, keeping the weight of her body off the mangled leg.

CHAPTER

42

IT WAS A BLASPHEMOUS, FRIGHTENING DAWN. THE SUN ROSE MAGNIF-
icently in a large ball over a glorious emerald sea. The lacing of
white water had completely withdrawn, but the ocean was heavy
with large swells, the only reminders of the night's fury. As the
golden light flushed the grayness, more and more devastating sights
came into focus: Up along the shore toward Palm Beach all the
condominiums had collapsed. Eleven of them—what had been glittering answers to Gold Coast living—were nothing more than lumps
of sand-covered rubble. The only structure left standing was the
west end of Century Towers. As more light drifted in, its forty-story
view lengthened.

Where Palm Beach once stood there was a long, low mound of
washed-up sand. Flimsier materials, pulverized by Claudine and her
tornado, were carried across Lake Worth. What was Palm Beach
had come to an ugly end on the shores of the town Flagler intended

as the servants' quarters for the well-laundered class who lived across the lake. It was a paradox, some said, Palm Beach winding up as the garbage of West Palm Beach, the town many P.B. people had called the "Waste Paper Basket." In the bitter aftermath of the storm it became just that, filled with the bodies and possessions of those who had derided it.

"Cynthia, is that you up there?" Steve called.

"Yes," she yelled down to the ledge. "Denise's leg is crushed. Who's that with you?"

"Billy Haughton. Keith Landon fell off."

"I'm sorry. He was a nice young man. Steve, we're in terrible shape up here. I don't think Denise can stand it much longer. Can you get us out of here?"

"I'm sure going to try, but I don't know how this minute," Steve answered back.

They looked below and saw people streaming out of the lobby, staring up at them. In the west building of the Towers there was an amateur radio ham and he got a message through since Glen's diesel generators had continued to work throughout the night.

Steve peered down at the mountains of concrete jamming the receding swells. He wondered where Keith was and his eyes suddenly filled with tears.

"Keith saved our lives."

"I know," Billy said.

"Why did I treat him the way I did?"

"Steve, don't start blaming yourself. It was just a difference of outlook."

"I'm finished with hurricanes," Steve sighed. "I've been caught in two of these bitches."

"The first time was a coincidence. The second time you stuck your nose into it."

"I should never have suggested that we come up here. Peterson was right. We should have remained at the center."

"That all depends on what the equipment has to say, if it wasn't blown away."

"Well, guess I'll be in the poke long enough to think about it. But one thing, Billy."

"What?"

He looked deep into her eyes. "I buried Alice last night."

"For good?"

"Yes. It's over. I've been an ass, I know."

"You did what you thought was right, always, Steve."

"But dammit . . . wasn't I clumsy!"

As dawn came, John Baxter's brain reeled. During the night he had been rushed down into Lake Worth out of the mouth of a canal and at six o'clock in the morning he finally looked around and recognized the buildings of West Palm Beach, which had escaped most of the devastation. Then he peered farther . . . something was wrong.

Where was Palm Beach?

He was going crazy, he thought. The lake was perfectly calm and it was filled with floating bodies and debris. He took his small paddle and pushed across to what had been his home and his life, as Coast Guard cutters weaved up and down Lake Worth looking for survivors. There were none.

Palm Beach had returned to what it was just after the Ice Age, a shell-and-sand bar rising from the sea. A whole society, a tradition had been stripped by nature. John reached the other side of the lake where the Brazilian Docks had stood. He came upon the shore and saw a few arms and legs and Gucci loafers in the sand. Something caught his eye: a glitter. He reached down and picked up a heavy jeweled bracelet of twenty carats and he wondered which one of the dead swans it belonged to. Then he collapsed upon the beach and looked up into the warm sun.

"You all right?" a Coast Guard man yelled from a nearing picket-boat.

"As right as I can be . . . is everyone dead?"

"Just about. A few people escaped down to Century Towers . . . come on aboard."

John dragged himself into the small twenty-eight-foot boat and they sped down the lake and landed near Century Towers. Buzzards and rescue helicopters circled overhead.

Rescue teams could not risk cutting through the weakened wall to free those in the elevator. Billy and Steve were picked up first by slings and delivered to the parking lot of the building around ten o'clock that morning. Thousands of disaster units had entered Palm Beach, some by boat, others by helicopter, but there was little for them to do. Two people emerging from one of the Coast Guard helicopters landing near Century Towers were United States federal marshals. They accompanied Dr. Marc Peterson and the Secretary of Commerce who had flown down to the disaster area in the early morning hours.

Rescue teams with acetylene torches swung from the helicopters. Denise was given three transfusions at the site and rushed to the hospital. No one knew how she stood the pain and the loss of blood, but she did. John Baxter arrived in the crowded parking lot of Century Towers just before Cynthia was freed along with Philip and Laura Guest.

John hobbled toward his wife. She couldn't believe what she was seeing and neither could Philip who was coughing and stumbling.

"Darling," he said, clutching her.

"John . . . what . . . where did you come from?"

"My plane crashed, but I got out. It's a long story."

They were taken by helicopter to a nearby hospital and all the way they smiled at each other.

"Back from the dead," he said.

"Yes, we've both been jounced into the real world . . . so lucky." She closed her eyes and they kissed, then she opened them.

"Mel's dead, but Denise got out."

"I heard."

"John, you were never involved with the bribe?"

"Of course not."

"Philip will be glad to hear that, but I think he never lost faith in you. I love you, John, very much. We're back where we started so many years ago before I tore off in the wrong direction."

"Forget it. We're just beginning and I like new beginnings."

"As long as the slate's being washed off, I have two confessions to make," Cynthia said, grasping John's hand. "I made love to Jayson Kendall twice before he was killed."

"And I made love to Denise." John paused. "If it had to be anybody, I'm glad it was Jayson. How did he go?"

Cynthia told her husband about the collapse of his old Mizner house and then she said, "I'm not through confessing. I bought a gun and I was going to kill Denise . . . not really . . . I was so upset over the way she was taking you away from me, but I could never bring myself to do it and anyway, I couldn't hit a damned thing!"

"I know all about that," John said, smiling.

"What? How?"

"Well, it is a bit unusual to see a well-dressed lady drive up to a gun store in a Rolls and purchase a weapon. The salesman tracked the license plate number and he called me."

"He did?"

"Told me all about it."

"Why didn't you say something or stop me?"

"I didn't have to. I know you, Cynthia. You could never hurt anyone; it was just something you had to get off your chest. What Denise did to us was unconscionable."

"Well, there are several sides to her; she's got a lot of spunk."

"Don't tell me. I saw her take a fish one day off El Lugar in a way you wouldn't believe."

"That's what caused her injuries that Sunday night?"

"Yeah, she boated a real big one on a fifty-pound test line . . . unbelievable."

"Do you love her, John?" Cynthia asked slowly.

"No, darling, of course not. I was intrigued by all that sexiness and her tenacity."

"She saved my life up there, John."

"Then we owe her something."

"A kiss and a big boot in the pants!"

They grasped each other and embraced and for them it was a mending.

When Steve and Billy were landed by helicopter in the parking lot, the U.S. marshals came up to him and said, "Dr. Stephen Mitchell?"

"Yes."

"You're under arrest."

They took him away in handcuffs and placed him in another helicopter. Billy stood there thinking of the strange, ardent man, and she bit her tongue and felt the lump grow in her throat. She knew that she had loved him all along, and maybe she could have helped him when he needed it, but she also cried for another man, Keith Landon.

"What a goddamned business to be in!" she said to the medic who was assisting her into another chopper.

AFTERMATH

THE TRIAL OF THE UNITED STATES AGAINST STEPHEN MITCHELL ON a seventeen-count indictment was held at the Federal Courthouse in Miami. He was found guilty of defrauding the President of the United States and guilty on fourteen other counts specified in the federal indictment. His attorney made a passionate plea: It had been definitely established that his actions in opening the floodgates and pressing for a presidential announcement saved the lives of over ten thousand. The judge told the court he would reserve sentencing and the jurist was called by the President the next day who said that a pardon would be forthcoming. The judge was going to suspend the maximum thirty-year sentence anyhow.

Steve and Billy went back into the hurricane business and he was made director of the center. They were now linked into vital data: Their scientific collecting devices worked in the Palm Beach basin and several interesting new solutions to hurricane surge seemed to be emanating from the fresh informational base. Steve Mitchell and Billy were married and they took their honeymoon in the Caribbean aboard a fifty-three-foot Hatteras called the *Pleasure Pie*, but this time there were no technical instruments aboard.

Palm Beach was turned into a state park and recreational area and at one end there was a large monument honoring all those who died on the island. On the top was a statue of the founder, Henry Morrison Flagler, and below were etched the words:

IN HONOR OF 7,810 WHO DIED HERE ON AUGUST 27, 1977, IN WHAT WAS PALM BEACH, FLORIDA, A LEGENDARY TOWN THAT HELPED FULFILL A SMALL PORTION OF THE AMERICAN DREAM. THOSE WHO LIVED AND DIED HERE GAVE MUCH OF THEMSELVES TO THE NEEDS OF MANY OTHERS AND THEIR CONTRIBUTION SHALL LIVE ON AS LONG AS THE WORTH OF A PLACE AND ITS PEOPLE IS MEASURED BY THEIR GENEROSITY.

It was interesting to note that when the last testament of the respected and beloved libertarian, Queen Maggie Dunsmore, was probated, all of her eleven-acre estate by the sea, including her home which, in the end, wasn't there anymore, was awarded to the City of West Palm Beach as a recreation site, for rich and poor alike, and black and white.

John and Cynthia went back to New York and slowly the horrors of Palm Beach were erased as they began a new life. Denise's leg was amputated, but she recovered very well. Not too long after, she married an attorney in John's office. The two women became close friends and the sad past was forgotten. Each found firmer identities, along with Nicole Bouchart who went back to Belgium after her husband's death. Philip Guest continued with the remains of the Palace Beach System for a while, but he soon retired and returned to his original home in Boston. None of the Markums was ever found, but after the tragedy Dr. Van Betzig was discovered in St. Mary's Hospital in West Palm Beach where he had been taken with a concussion sustained while trying to flee his hotel in the early hours of the hurricane.

A congressional report of 450,000 words was laid upon the President's desk eighteen months later, but after all the public outcry and all the fact-finding summaries, the whole tragedy was reduced to some simple denominations that everyone understood, perhaps for the first time.

The worldwide network of meteorologists, especially the tropical storm specialists, shared their data and sophisticated instruments, and the warning systems through U.N. appropriations and research were fairly well unified. The specialists, with the exception of Steve Mitchell and a few others, had thought they knew quite a bit about cyclonic killers. It turned out that they knew far less than they thought. The international community of scientists studying tropical storms rejected the criticism, saying that their warning and detection systems were totally adequate as far as the state of research and technology allowed.

But one senator asked the obvious question: If the most that could be done was being done and the world's meteorologists had things in hand, why did 248 people die in Camille, 11,340 in the Palm Beach basin, and over 300,000 in Bangladesh?

There was no single answer except that the nature of tropical storms remains enigmatic. They are mysterious and fickle. But the frustration of tropical storm specialists, even if the secrets of their study were finally grasped, would painfully remain: Who believes the weatherman anyhow?

Few!

HURRICANE CLAUDINE

Meteorological Events: Hurricane Claudine started as a disturbance on August 17, 1977, in an area seventy-five miles east of
the Cape Verde Islands and was observed on Dakar and Praia
Airport weather radar. The disturbance became a depression
on August 20 as the track moved on a northwesterly course. On
August 21 Claudine was declared a hurricane with wind speeds
exceeding 115 miles per hour. Claudine passed north of Puerto
Rico, Hispaniola, and Cuba and made a landfall at Islamorada
in the Florida Keys. She continued up into a remote part of
the Big Cypress Swamp. On the evening of August 26, Claudine
stalled and turned on an easterly track. With diminished winds
the storm crossed the coast south of Miami and continued in an
arc across the western section of Andros, largest of the Bahama
Islands. On Saturday, August 27, Claudine's wind regime in-
tensified and the hurricane curved back toward the United
States mainland, crashing ashore at Manalapan at approximately
10:40 that evening. The hurricane continued into the Everglades
where it began to decay.

Statistical Abstract:

Lowest central pressure: 26.10 inches of mercury * (Observed by special meteorological recording station, Lake Worth, Florida.)

Wind regime: Sustained wind speed: 215 miles per hour †
Periodic gust, twenty seconds: 248 mph (Observed by special meteorological recording station, Rybovich & Sons Boat Works, West Palm Beach, Florida.)

Highest storm surge: 18.9 feet. Observed: Palm Beach Inlet

Lives lost: 11,340 (in landfall area)

Injuries: 23,189

Homes destroyed: 19,565

Homes with major damage: 31,750

Homes with minor damage: 48,211

Mobile homes destroyed: 4,940

Mobile homes with major damage: 3,276

Small businesses destroyed or with major damage: 1,962

* Lowest confirmed surface pressure reading, western hemisphere
† Highest confirmed wind regime, western hemisphere